COOKING LIGHT.
Cookbook 1989

COOKING LIGHT.
Cookbook 1989

Oxmoor
House.

Copyright 1988 by Oxmoor House, Inc.
Book Division of Southern Progress Corporation
P.O. Box 2463, Birmingham, Alabama 35201

Library of Congress Catalog Number: 87-061020
ISBN: 0-8487-0747-8
ISSN: 0884-2922

Manufactured in the United States of America
First Printing 1988

Executive Editor: Ann H. Harvey
Production Manager: Jerry Higdon
Associate Production Manager: Rick Litton
Art Director: Bob Nance

Cooking Light Cookbook® 1989

Editor: Janice L. Krahn
Associate Foods Editor: Cathy A. Wesler, R.D.
Copy Editor: Melinda E. West
Editorial Assistant: Pamela Whyte
Production Assistant: Theresa L. Beste
Test Kitchen Director: Julie Fisher
Test Kitchen Home Economists: Nancy C. Earhart, Christina A. Pieroni, Gayle Hays Sadler, Paula N. Saunders, Lisa G. Sisk, Jill Wills
Photographer: Jim Bathie
Photo Stylist: Kay E. Clarke
Designer: Faith Nance
Recipe and Menu Developers: Culinary Arts & Services, Betsy Fannin, M.S., R.D., Marilyn Wyrick Ingram, Jane Ingrassia Reinsel, Lisa Weiss,
Exercise Model: Karen M. Anderson

Consultants, University of Alabama School of Medicine in Birmingham:
Julius Linn, M.D.
Susan Brown, Assistant Editor
Charlotte Bragg, M.S., R.D.
Karen Counts, R.D.
Heidi Hataway, M.S., R.D.
Laura Dunnam, Exercise Physiologist
Angela Shorter, Exercise Specialist
Julie Sulentic, Exercise Physiologist

Cover: *Tuna Salad Niçoise (page 68)*.
Back cover: *Cheesy Squash Chowder (page 214)*.
Page ii: *Cranberry-Grape Sorbet (page 79)*.

To subscribe to *Cooking Light* magazine, write to *Cooking Light*, P.O. Box C-549, Birmingham, Alabama 35283.

Contents

Living Well Is The Best Reward

Welcome to *Cooking Light Cookbook 1989*. This all-new volume includes the latest breakthroughs in nutrition, including highlights from the all-important Surgeon General's report. The report underscores the need for Americans to understand the importance of eating more vegetables, fruits, and whole grain products. It also emphasizes the fat factor and its relationship to health and disease. The message sounds simple: eat less fat. The path may appear to be clear—avoid fried foods, use less fat and oil, and trim the extra fat off meat. However, there's more to the story.

Several years of research have given us a clearer picture on fat. Today, terms such as saturated and polyunsaturated have become household words. Now we know more about the type and amount of fat in the diet that contribute not only to heart disease, but also, as we have learned most recently, to certain types of cancer.

Use this book as you begin a lifetime of living well. Follow the fitness guides and embark on planning your own total fitness program. Statistics show that Americans are far from the fitness goals established by the U.S. Public Health Service. These objectives were scheduled to be reached by 1990, so now is the time for you to get going and bring your fitness level up to par.

Cooking Light Cookbook will assist you on your path towards achieving better health. Along with recipes, menus, a calorie-nutrient chart, and a weekly meal plan, you will find an abundance of information on fitness and nutrition and the role these play in bringing about a healthier lifestyle.

Living well in today's world means making the right food and fitness choices while maintaining a healthy balance between work and leisure time.

Update '89

America, You're Doing Better

You're exercising more; eating lighter, healthier foods; and smoking less. Clearly, these lifestyle changes are making significant contributions to the continuing decline in deaths from heart disease, strokes, and kidney problems.

Advances in technology have led Americans to expect the best that medicine can provide. As a result of recent medical research, drugs are now available that dissolve clots to prevent heart damage from heart attacks—and to the relief of many, there is now a vitamin A cream to help smooth wrinkled brows.

Today, we know that eating properly and exercising regularly contribute to better health. Making positive lifestyle changes based on this information can enhance the best that medicine can provide.

Surgeon General's Report

The compelling evidence that healthy eating means healthy living has led to the first-ever Surgeon General's report on nutrition and health. Although the Federal Government, through various agencies such as the U. S. Department of Agriculture, has made recommendations about healthy eating, this report is the first from the Surgeon General. It summarizes the scientific evidence related to nutrition and health, including information from studies on humans, animals, and large populations. The medical experts note that as Americans are eating better, diseases caused by diets deficient in nutrients have diminished and have been replaced by diseases of dietary excess and imbalance.

Fewer Fatty Foods

The Surgeon General warns that Americans must make changes in their eating habits, and of highest priority is reducing intake of foods high in fat. The report points out that because Americans eat so many fatty foods, they often have little room for foods high in complex carbohydrates and fiber, which are more conducive to good health. Reducing fat, especially saturated fat, reduces the number of deaths from today's top killers—coronary heart disease, diabetes, stroke, obesity, and perhaps even some types of cancer.

Reducing the amount of fat in the diet lowers blood cholesterol levels. In fact, studies have shown that for each 1 percent reduction in total blood cholesterol, the risk of developing heart disease drops by 2 percent. Eating less fat also keeps the calories reduced to help achieve or maintain normal body weight.

The Specifics

Eating a variety of foods ensures getting the wide array of vitamins and nutrients you need, and this recommendation has been supported by a broad spectrum of scientific evidence. Make sure these foods are generally low in calories, fat, saturated fat, cholesterol, and sodium.
●Although sodium does not cause blood pressure to rise in everyone, studies suggest that reducing sodium intake would be prudent and certainly harmless for most Americans.
●Because excess body weight is a risk factor for several chronic diseases, everyone should attempt to maintain a desirable body weight. Do this by reducing calorie intake and burning more calories through exercise.
●The Surgeon General's report makes specific recommendations for alcohol: no more than two drinks a day, if at all. Studies indicate a direct correlation between increased blood pressure and consuming more than two drinks. Alcohol can result in addiction, cause birth defects in children born to mothers who drink during pregnancy, and cause disrupted family functioning, suicides, and homicides. When combined with smoking, alcohol increases the risk of cancer of the mouth, larynx, and esophagus. There is some evidence, though less conclusive, that too much alcohol plays a role in the development of cancer of the liver, rectum, breast, and pancreas.

When More Is Better

The report underscores the need for Americans to understand the importance of eating more vegetables, fruits, and whole grain products. These are foods that are rich in complex carbohydrates and fiber but relatively low in calories.

In addition to these recommendations that can benefit everyone, the Surgeon General suggests that community water systems be fluoridated and that people vulnerable to cavities, especially children, limit intake of sugary foods. Consuming more foods and beverages high in calcium is recommended for adolescent girls and adult women; and for these groups as well as children, the importance of consuming foods high in iron is emphasized.

If the nation takes these recommendations to heart, better and healthier lives should be the result. The first step, however, is to examine the latest scientific evidence and put it into practice.

Focusing on Cholesterol

The most significant research during the past year revolved around cholesterol. Studies continue to confirm that lowering cholesterol levels in the blood lowers the risk of heart disease. Even bigger news is that controlling cholesterol can delay, and may reverse, the narrowing of blood vessels caused by cholesterol build-up. The message is clear: Lowering blood cholesterol levels will prevent heart disease and in some cases may reverse disease already present.

See How You Compare

The National Heart, Lung, and Blood Institute has announced that nearly half of all Americans have blood cholesterol levels that put them at an increased risk for heart disease. The thrust of Countdown, USA, the largest health screening of its kind, is that every adult should know his cholesterol level. According to a 32-state survey completed by the Centers for Disease Control, only 6 percent of the adults surveyed knew their cholesterol level. But more surprising was that less than half of the respondents had ever had their cholesterol level checked.

The desirable cholesterol level for adults is below 200 milligrams per deciliter (mg/dl). A cholesterol reading of 200 to 239 is borderline-high, and a reading above 240 places one in the high-risk category.

The National Cholesterol Education Program now in full swing notes that if the total cholesterol is above 240, a more comprehensive test to measure harmful low-density lipoprotein (LDL) cholesterol should be performed. Even if the total cholesterol level is in the moderate-risk category, this test may be advisable should other risk factors be present such as a family history of early coronary heart disease, high blood pressure, or diabetes.

Ideally, the level of the harmful LDL cholesterol should be below 130 and the level of the beneficial high-density lipoprotein (HDL) be as high as possible, at least more than 45.

If your level of undesirable LDL cholesterol is borderline-high (130 to 159), do not be discouraged. Following a cholesterol-lowering diet under medical supervision often corrects the problem. If your LDL remains high after six months on a low-cholesterol diet, your physician may recommend one of the new, more effective cholesterol-lowering drugs.

Adding Cold-Water Fish

Research continues on the effects of omega-3 fatty acids and their relation to heart disease. Omega-3s, an oil from fish, clearly lowers the levels of triglycerides, a fatty substance in the blood. This oil also lowers high cholesterol levels of those who have high triglyceride levels. Whether fish oils lower cholesterol levels in people with normal triglycerides is not yet clear.

Research indicates that omega-3s decrease the tendency of blood clots to form. In animal studies, they have been found to decrease the damage inside artery walls that allows cholesterol plaques to accumulate. Omega-3s also appear to block the body's chemical reaction that sustains inflammation. This may help explain their ability to provide slight relief for rheumatoid arthritis, although extremely large doses were

needed before any improvement was apparent.

The American Heart Association and the American Medical Association, among other concerned groups, warn that research on fish oils is still incomplete. The dosage necessary to produce beneficial effects has not been determined, and adverse reactions and long-term effects are not yet known. For now, get your fish oils from cold-water fish such as salmon, tuna, herring, mackerel, and lake trout rather than from supplements.

Getting the Right Fats

Saturated fats remain the main nutritional culprit, according to research. Studies confirm that the body uses saturated fats to manufacture cholesterol, and eating saturated fats increases total blood cholesterol, especially the harmful LDL variety. Substituting polyunsaturated fats for the saturated variety tends to decrease total blood cholesterol. However, some studies suggest that polyunsaturated fats lower levels of beneficial HDL cholesterol as well.

Preliminary studies indicate that monounsaturated fats, which include olive oil and canola (rapeseed) oil, may provide the desirable balance of lowering LDL cholesterol levels but not HDL levels. Further studies are needed, however, before specific recommendations to increase monounsaturated fats can be made. The story on fats, which ones you need and in what amounts, is far from complete.

Exercising Everywhere

Without doubt, more Americans are participating in the fitness boom. Cruise lines, airports, and hotels are offering fitness facilities for Americans on the go. And as scientists continue to learn more about how lifestyle influences the quality and length of life, more companies will add fitness programs, capitalizing on the idea that fit employees are more productive.

More information has emerged about weight-lifting, too. Many fitness centers now offer programs that combine regular aerobic exercise with strength training. According to recent studies, aerobic exercise can moderate the elevating effects on blood pressure caused by weight-lifting, providing that both exercise types are done in the same session.

Look for more emphasis on cross-training. Spas and fitness centers will encourage variety in the workout to overcome boredom and increase motivation.

Aerobic dancing has been refined to a low-impact, high-benefit activity. Even so, it remains primarily a woman's exercise choice. One survey of 500 men revealed that changing the term from "aerobic dancing" to "aerobic conditioning" would help get men involved in this heart-healthy exercise.

Exercising Moderately

Although aerobic activities clearly improve cardiovascular fitness, recent studies indicate that less vigorous activity also confers benefits, especially for people who have not exercised previously. The National Institute of Health claims any activity is better than none. Working in the garden, bowling, fishing, or playing golf reduces the risks of developing heart disease, not to mention that these activities can be fun.

Exercising moderately also reduces stress more than resting does, according to a study completed by the University of Wisconsin. Forty minutes of resting lowered blood pressure for only 20 minutes after the rest period, but 40 minutes of vigorous aerobic exercise lowered blood pressure for 2 to 3 hours.

Despite all we've learned, coro-

nary heart disease is still the leading cause of death in the U.S. today. Government statistics indicate that, for the nation as a whole, a sedentary lifestyle plays a stronger role in deaths related to heart disease than does smoking or high blood pressure. The Centers for Disease Control has concluded that the least active people are almost twice as likely to have heart disease as those who are most active. The remedy is simple: Get out and take a walk, work in the garden, or play a round of golf. Even better, engage in aerobic activities. These clearly improve cardiovascular endurance.

Yo-Yo Dieting

Research has shown that the yo-yo pattern of losing weight and regaining it later takes a toll on the body's weight reduction mechanism. Dieting causes the body's metabolism to slow as a starvation response to conserve fuel. Yo-yo dieters gain weight back more quickly and lose it more slowly the next time. Also, continually losing and regaining weight appears to increase the levels of fats in the blood and thereby heart disease risks, according to information from Northwestern University.

There is a remedy—a prudent diet with moderate calorie restriction combined with exercise. Exercise speeds up metabolism, thus burning more calories for energy, and keeps it elevated for up to 1½ hours after exercise. In addition, exercise builds muscle and decreases fat tissue. This is important because muscle burns more calories than fat tissue does.

Exercising for Weight Loss

In a Gallup survey of more than 1,000 adults, 45 percent said they

would use exercise to lose weight. And losing weight by exercising provides more cardiovascular benefits than losing weight just by dieting. However, swimming may not be a wise weight-loss choice. Regular exercise in cold water signals the body to store more fat for insulation against the cold.

Obesity is not always the result of eating too much food, according to scientists at the National Institute of Health. A person's weight reflects not only the amount eaten, but also how efficiently the body stores the calories. People who have previously been overweight require fewer calories to maintain weight than people who have always been slim. Because of this, the critical element to consider is exercise. Increased exercise is an important factor in helping to keep the body's metabolic rate at a higher level.

The fat-burning problem begins in infancy. Researchers in one study concluded that the best way to prevent obesity in infants is not to decrease their food intake, but to increase their activity levels.

Buying the Right Foods

Even though saturated fats remain the staple of snack foods and bakery products, the food industry is starting to respond to scientific evidence about health. A good example is beef labeling—the U.S. Department of Agriculture has renamed the leaner cuts "select" to emphasize that they are a better, healthier choice than "prime."

Including lean red meat—about 6 ounces a day—need not elevate cholesterol levels, according to a study in the British Medical Journal. After consuming a diet low in saturated fat, men with high blood cholesterol levels lowered their LDL levels by 11 percent. When the percentage of fat in the diet was reduced from 35 to 27 percent and fiber was added, their LDL cholesterol fell by 24 percent.

To satisfy a sweet tooth and help in the battle of the bulge, develop a taste for fresh fruits, crunchy vegetables, and dark, coarse whole grain bread. Avoid relying on products with noncaloric sweeteners, for these may not help in achieving weight loss goals. A study by the American Cancer Society showed that women who used noncaloric sweeteners were more likely to gain weight than non-users. Most likely, these women believed that using the sweeteners cut their calorie intake enough so that they could compensate by eating more.

Another type of substitute may soon be available, pending FDA approval. Simplesse, a product made from microparticles of egg whites and milk protein, is said to have the texture and taste of real fat. If the product is approved by the FDA, it will appear in place of fat in products such as ice cream, mayonnaise, and salad dressing. Heat destroys Simplesse, however, so it cannot be used for cooking or frying.

The FDA is also studying Olestra, another fat substitute. Olestra is a combination of sugar and oils that the body cannot absorb; therefore, it contributes no calories. According to reports, Olestra's taste and texture closely resemble that of fat. Because it is heat stable, it can be used in conjunction with other fats and oils for cooking, frying, and baking.

The FDA is studying both of these products before releasing them to the public. Nutritionists worry that people may fill up on fat-substituted foods such as ice cream and potato chips and not leave enough room for healthy food choices such as fruits and vegetables.

Fighting Back

If you get your highs from exercise instead of from alcohol, you will be better off in the long run. A Harvard study found that women who had one to two alcoholic beverages a day had a higher risk of developing breast cancer. However, if all of the risk factors are taken into consideration, alcohol increases the overall risks by only about one percent. A more recent study from the American Health Foundation found no conclusive evidence for any alcohol-breast cancer link, except for perhaps a weak link in very lean women.

A high-fat diet has also been suggested as a risk factor for developing breast cancer. But a Harvard study found that women who ate a low-fat diet (30 percent of total calories as fat) were no less likely to develop breast cancer than women who ate a high-fat diet. The study was conducted for only four years, so critics believe that a longer study of more people may be necessary. Another possibility is that it may be necessary to lower the fat to a spartan 20 percent before the risks are effectively reduced.

Citing funding problems, the National Cancer Institute (NCI) cancelled its Women's Health Trial, which was to evaluate whether a diet lower in fat might provide protection from breast cancer. Despite the cancellation, the NCI continues to recommend a varied diet low in fat and calories and high in fiber, and cites a variety of health reasons for doing so.

The benefits of eating certain foods continue to be confirmed through research. The water-soluble fiber in fruit, oats, and barley has been found to help lower blood cholesterol. Eating foods rich in vitamin C may inhibit development of cancer of the esophagus as well as cancer of the stomach. Now, researchers at the University of Alabama at Birmingham are studying the effects of folic acid found in spinach and other green leafy vegetables. Preliminary evidence indicates that folic acid supplements

may reverse precancerous changes in the cells lining the bronchial tubes and the cells in the cervix.

Scientists also are studying the B vitamin niacin, which may play an important part in repairing damage to cells caused by all cancers. In studies sponsored by the National Institute of Health, cells in a test tube that did not contain enough niacin were ten times more likely to be transformed into cancer cells than those exposed to niacin. In this setting, niacin appears to repair DNA damage that may signal cancerous transformation.

The average diet supplies the RDA of 20 mg daily, and important sources are tuna, chicken, and salmon. Because research has been confined to animal and in vitro (test tube) studies, results of studies on people are necessary before niacin's role in repairing cancer damage can be clearly defined.

Having Fun and Staying Healthy

Research continues into the effects of positive thinking and attitude and their role in health and disease. Some scientists have linked pleasure—laughter and the fun it includes—to prolonging life and fighting off illness. Experts at Stanford University Medical Center note that a good old-fashioned belly laugh can help strengthen the immune system, relieve stress, and even relieve pain.

The discovery of dopamine, one of the brain chemicals called neurotransmitters, led to this knowledge. The brain releases dopamine and you feel pleasure—it is that simple.

Watching funny movies makes you laugh, and laughter causes a drop in compounds that suppress the immune system. In fact, laughing may have a good effect on most of the body's major systems. So, laugh all the way to a good workout, and smile while you enjoy a healthy *Cooking Light* meal.

The Food and Fitness Connection

Medical research shows that healthy eating plays a large part in creating a healthy lifestyle. Throughout *Cooking Light* you will find nutritious eating plans that can be adapted easily into your lifestyle. Note, in particular, the pyramid plan featured on page 8. It demonstrates clearly the foods that should form the base of your meals, those that should be eaten in moderation, and those that should be added sparingly to your meals.

Many authorities believe that nutritious eating, regular exercise, cessation of smoking, and controlling stress will dramatically reduce the mortality rate of heart disease and cancer. Although the benefits of regular, moderate exercise have been well established, the lack of exercise has topped the list of heart disease risk factors for Americans as a whole. The U.S. Public Health Service cites studies showing that fewer than 20 percent of Americans get enough regular exercise to improve cardiovascular fitness. Use our exercise guidelines to assist you in planning your total fitness program and enjoy the health benefits while you have fun.

Getting started on the path to healthy eating and regular exercise need not be difficult. Look for culinary tips in the *Cooking Light* Kitchen and new products in the Marketplace that will make your progress easier. And try incorporating our behavior modification steps into your daily routine. This should allow you to accomplish positive lifestyle changes more easily.

Regular aerobic exercise and a balanced diet form a winning team as you strive towards the goal of being at your optimum health and fitness levels. Mushroom-Pecan Pita Sandwiches (page 184) are a wise food-energy choice.

Nutrition research continues to support the belief that balance, moderation, and variety are the keys for establishing healthy eating patterns. A nutritious diet calls for an emphasis on complex carbohydrates, while a moderate amount of protein and a limited amount of fat are recommended. This means that attention should be paid to the source of calories, not just to the number of them. Prudent eating can be fun. And indeed it should be, because many of today's leisure activities center around well-planned, beautifully-served food.

Getting the right balance in your meals may call for just a few simple adjustments. And balance is the key—you can enjoy almost any food as long as your meals provide all of the necessary nutrients. Knowledge is power. And knowing which foods to increase and which to cut back on gives you the power to eat with gusto while reaping the healthy benefits of a balanced diet.

BUILDING BLOCKS FOR GOOD HEALTH

Think of good eating as a pyramid plan. The pyramid allows you to incorporate the Basic Four Food Groups into your daily eating plan and provides information about the food your body needs for optimal health.

The foods that provide complex carbohydrates, the foundation for your meals, form the base of the pyramid. The blocks include bread and cereals, fruits and vegetables, and vegetable proteins. Half the calories you eat each day should come from these foods. The smallest area of the pyramid is the tip, which represents fats, sweets, and alcohol. In between are meats and milk. These vary in fat content and are listed accordingly.

Use the pyramid to put eating into perspective. Eat more of the low-fat foods at the base and you will reduce your risk of heart disease, cancer, and obesity. Eat moderate amounts of the foods in the center of the pyramid. Eat those at the top only sparingly. By adopting this plan, you are choosing a healthy approach to eating.

The pyramid plan allows you to include all of the nutrients needed to sustain life: carbohydrate, protein, fat, vitamins, minerals, and water. All foods are composed of these nutrients in varying amounts and are compiled into the Basic Four Food Groups according to their similarities in nutrient composition.

The first group, breads and cereals, also includes rice, pasta, and grains. This food group supplies most of our carbohydrate—the energy source the body uses most readily. Although most Americans think of these foods as being fattening, they actually contain, gram for gram, the same number of calories as protein and one-half the calories of fat. These foods don't necessarily add pounds to the body, especially if you leave off the rich, creamy sauces and butter.

Most breads, grains, and cereals are enriched with B vitamins (thiamin, riboflavin, and niacin) and iron. To ensure that you meet your needs, help yourself to four servings from this food group each day.

Complex carbohydrates—as supplied by whole grain breads and cereals, and other food groups

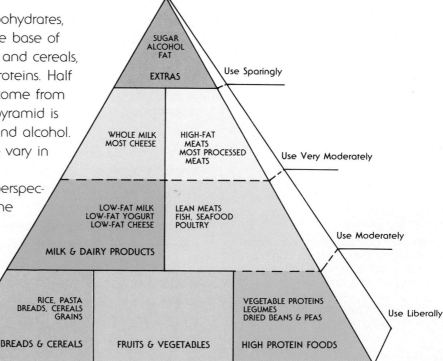

Adapted with permission from J. Pennington, *Journal of Nutrition Education* 13:53-55, 1981.

including fruits and vegetables and vegetable proteins—come with an added bonus: dietary fiber. This indigestible portion of plants is either water-soluble, which means it forms a gel in water, or is not affected by water and is classified as water-insoluble.

Water-soluble fibers, found in foods such as oats, barley, seeds, legumes, fruits, and vegetables, have a gel-like property that allows them to bind to substances in the intestine. This binding action may play a role in reducing blood cholesterol levels. It also slows glucose entry into the bloodstream, which may improve blood sugar control in people with diabetes. Insoluble fibers are roughage foods such as wheat bran, corn bran, whole grains, and nuts. This type of fiber helps food move through the digestive tract more quickly, possibly preventing a variety of digestive problems and protecting against some cancers, such as cancer of the colon.

The National Cancer Institute recommends eating 25 to 35 grams of fiber each day. Most Americans would need to double their present fiber intake to reach this goal. Raw fruits and vegetables and whole grain breads and cereals have more fiber than foods that have been peeled, cooked, pureed, or refined. For example, a medium apple has about 4.3 grams of fiber, ½ cup of applesauce contains 2.9 grams, and the same amount of apple juice has only 0.02 gram of fiber.

The second group, fruits and vegetables, should also be enjoyed in liberal amounts. They contain an abundance of vitamins and minerals as well as pectin. Found exclusively in this group, pectin is a water-soluble fiber that may help control blood cholesterol.

Surveys show that Americans are eating more fruits and vegetables, but attention needs to be given to the form of the food and the way it is prepared. So as you look at ways to improve your eating habits, try to choose 4 servings of fresh fruits and raw or steamed vegetables each day.

High-protein foods make up the third food group. Protein is vital for building bones and muscles; growing hair and nails; and making enzymes, hormones, and red blood cells. For most Americans, getting enough protein is not a problem; in fact, most probably consume more protein than is needed. Protein cannot be stored, however, so the amount the body does not use to repair tissue will either be used as energy or stored as fat.

You need no more than 3 ounces of protein—a portion about the size of a deck of playing cards—at any one meal. You need only two servings a day, for a total of 6 ounces of protein.

Legumes are a high-protein food and include tofu, dried peas and beans such as soybeans, lentils, split peas, and red and navy beans. Like meat, these plant foods are rich in protein and iron, but they are also similiar to whole grain foods because they provide complex carbohydrate, fiber, and generally, little fat. Nuts and peanut butter are also in this category, but they contain considerable amounts of fat. The fat is unsaturated, however, and is therefore less of a problem than the saturated fats found in many meats.

Although legumes can be a valuable protein source, a healthy diet based solely on them must rely on more than one source of plant protein. To improve the balance of amino acids, which are the protein building blocks, consume legumes along with grains or any cereal food. Examples are red beans balanced with rice, peanut butter on whole grain bread, and black-eyed peas served with cornbread.

Fish, shellfish, and skinned chicken and turkey are good low-fat choices. In addition to protein, most meats are rich sources of iron, zinc, and many of the B vitamins. Trimming all visible fat from meat lowers the amount of fat you consume. Some luncheon meats can be a low-fat choice as well. In the past they have been notoriously high in fat, but leaner choices are available today. If the label reads 3 grams of fat or less per ounce, the meat qualifies as lean.

High-fat meats are one of the major sources of fat, particularly saturated fat, in the American diet. In meats such as marbled steaks or in processed meats such as hot dogs, fat contributes more of the calories than protein does. These foods, as well as prime rib, bacon, and sausage, should be occasional foods, not regular features on your menu.

The fourth group, milk and dairy products, supplies protein, calcium, zinc, riboflavin, niacin, B_{12}, and thiamin. Today, most milk products are fortified with vitamins A and D, which increase calcium absorption from the intestine. By now, most Americans are aware that not getting enough calcium increases the risk of developing osteoporosis. An adult should consume at least 2 servings from this group a day; children, teenagers, and pregnant or lactating women have higher calcium needs, however, and may require up to 4 servings a day.

Be sure that you choose low-fat dairy products. The low-fat products retain all of the nutrients of whole-milk products but not the fat. For example, more than 50 percent of the calories in whole milk are from fat but only 2 percent of the calories in skim milk are from fat. A recent survey showed that Americans are conscious of the fat differences in milk, and the consumption of low-fat and skim milk has increased. But the attention to healthy eating should not stop there. Use low-fat or nonfat yogurt in place of high-fat products, such as sour cream, and use low-fat cheese for hard and processed cheeses.

The fifth or "other" group is in addition to the Basic Four and is the area from which you should choose foods most sparingly. The group includes sugars, alcohol, and fat.

The major health problem related to sugar is that it causes dental cavities. In addition, many people fill up on high-calorie sweets, neglecting the most nutritious choices. Because sugar and alcohol contain no nutrients other than calories, enjoy them sparingly.

You need only about a tablespoon of fat a day to transport fat-soluble vitamins and supply essential fatty acids for growth and tissue repair. Although many people have reduced their fat consumption, further efforts are necessary. High-fat cuts of meat have been traded for leaner cuts, but with the increased consumption of high-fat cheeses and salad dressings, total fat intake has remained about the same. To keep fat in perspective, it is placed at the tip of the pyramid, indicating that you need only a small amount compared with the needs for complex carbohydrates, the foundation blocks for nutritious meals.

Fats can be divided into three types according to their composition: saturated, monounsaturated, and polyunsaturated. They are made up of hydrogen atoms riding on a carbon chain. The more hydrogen attached to the chain, the more saturated the fat. Saturated fats, according to the American Heart Association, are responsible in large part for the high blood cholesterol levels of many Americans. Monounsaturated fats have fewer hydrogens than do saturated fats, and polyunsaturated fats have even less. But be alerted to a process called hydrogenation that is used to make oils into a more solid form, such as in vegetable shortening. This process transforms a polyunsaturated fat into a more saturated form, and in turn, eating too much increases your risk for developing heart disease.

Animal fats contain a high proportion of saturated fatty acids. Vegetable fats, however, contain primarily monosaturated and polyunsaturated fat, with the exception of coconut and palm oils. Both coconut and palm oil are vegetable oils but are more saturated than most animal fats. These oils have been used by food manufacturers in crackers, cookies, non-dairy creamers, and whipped toppings because they extend the shelf life of these products.

THE BEAUTY OF BALANCE

The beauty of building a balanced diet is that you don't have to worry about getting enough vitamins and minerals. They are in the foods you eat in sufficient amounts to meet most needs.

All nutrients work together to maintain good health. For example, adequate carbohydrate intake preserves protein for its main function of building and repairing tissues. Minerals help regulate heartbeats and nerve and muscle responses, and they help move oxygen from lungs to tissues throughout the body. Vitamin D helps get calcium into bones, and iron absorption is enhanced when you eat vitamin C-rich foods at the same meal. Vitamins work with carbohydrates to produce the energy you need to take your daily brisk walk or swim.

Cooking Light and eating properly are the keys to looking and feeling your best. Team the pyramid eating plan with your exercise prescription to increase your self-esteem, enhance your looks, and improve your health. You will get an added lift from the sense of well-being that accompanies taking control of your life.

Computing Nutrition

Your Daily Needs

To estimate your calorie requirement, multiply your current weight by 15 to get your estimated need. Remember this is only a rough guide because your calorie requirement will vary somewhat according to age, body size, and level of activity. If a change of weight is desired, either add or subtract 500 calories per day to allow for weight gain or loss of 1 pound a week. However, a diet of less than 1,200 calories a day is not recommended unless medically supervised. For additional information concerning your individual requirements, consult a registered dietitian (R.D.).

Implement the *Cooking Light* 50-20-30 guidelines (page 24) by calculating the amount of carbohydrate, protein, and fat for optimal health. Multiply your calorie requirement by the percentages 50, 20, and 30 to give the calories from each nutrient. Divide the carbohydrate and protein calories by 4 (4 calories per gram) and the fat by 9 (9 calories per gram) to find the grams of each nutrient needed.

For example, here's how to calculate the distribution of a 2,000-calorie diet:

50% carbohydrate = 1,000 calories ÷ 4 = 250 grams carbohydrate

20% protein = 400 calories ÷ 4 = 100 grams protein

30% fat = 600 calories ÷ 9 = 67 grams fat

Therefore, for a person eating 2,000 calories a day, 1,000 calories would meet the 50% carbohydrate guideline, while no more than 400 calories and 600 calories would be from protein and fat, respectively.

When planning your meals, refer to the daily amounts to help you make the most of the nutrient values that follow *Cooking Light* recipes. Although there is no RDA for sodium or cholesterol, suggested intake is listed below along with the RDA for iron and calcium.

Iron	18 mg
Calcium	800 mg
Sodium	1,100 to 3,300 mg
Cholesterol	less than 300 mg

Every Recipe Analyzed

Calories per serving and a nutrient breakdown accompany every recipe. The nutrients listed include grams of carbohydrate, protein, and fat along with milligrams of cholesterol, calcium, iron, and sodium.

Determining Calorie Percentages

Use *Cooking Light* nutrient breakdowns to calculate the percentage of calories contributed by carbohydrate, protein, and fat. Let's say you are looking at the recipe for Rich Oat Bran Bread (complete recipe on page 101), and you want to determine the percentage of fat in a serving (one ½-inch slice).

First, find the grams of fat per serving. This is calculated in the analysis to be 1.2 grams. To find the percentage of calories from fat, multiply grams of fat by 9 (the number of calories per gram of fat) to get fat calories per serving. Then divide this quantity by the total calories. You'll find that fat contributes 13 percent of the calories in one slice of Rich Oat Bran Bread.

To calculate the calories contributed by carbohydrate and

RICH OAT BRAN BREAD

PROTEIN 3.2 / FAT 1.2 / CARBOHYDRATE 17.4 / CHOLESTEROL 0 / IRON 0.8 / SODIUM 45 / CALCIUM 31

protein, multiply grams of carbohydrate or protein per serving by 4 (the number of calories per gram of carbohydrate or protein). Divide the quantity by total calories.

Menus and Menu Plans Meet 50-20-30 Guidelines

Each slice of Rich Oat Bran Bread meets the recommended percentages. more than 50 percent carbohydrate and no more than 20 percent protein or 30 percent fat. All recipes will not fall so neatly within the guidelines. The goal is to achieve the recommended balance of nutrients on a daily basis, taking into consideration three meals and a snack. Use "Healthy American Meals" (page 23) and "*Cooking Light* Menu Plans" (pages 242-243) to create meals that meet the 50-20-30 guidelines.

How the Recipes Are Analyzed

The recipes are developed for people who are interested in lowering their intake of calories, sodium, fat, and/or cholesterol to maintain healthy eating patterns. If you are following a medically prescribed diet, consult a registered dietitian to see how *Cooking Light* recipes can fit into your specific meal plan.

The calorie and nutrient breakdown of each of these recipes is derived from computer analysis, based primarily on information from the U.S. Department of Agriculture. The values are as accurate as possible and are based on certain assumptions:
• All nutrient breakdowns are listed per serving.
• All meats are trimmed of fat and skin before cooking.
• When a range is given for an ingredient (for example, 3 to 3½ cups flour), the lesser amount is calculated.
• Alcohol calories evaporate when heated, and this reduction is reflected in the calculations.
• When a marinade is used, only the amount used (not discarded) of the marinade is calculated.
• Garnishes and other optional ingredients are not calculated.
• No fruits and vegetables listed in the ingredients are peeled unless otherwise specified.

Exercise—The Perfect Partner

The fitness goals set by the U.S. Public Health Service apply to all age groups. The agency's goal by 1990 is that 90 percent of all young people from ages 10 to 17 will be regularly participating in physical activities that can be carried into adulthood. In addition, the health service hopes that at least 60 percent will be participating in daily school physical education programs.

More than 60 percent of adults between 18 and 65 and half of those over 65 will be engaging in regular physical exercise, if the government's objectives are carried out. Current statistics show that only 20 percent of all Americans exercise regularly, 40 percent exercise sporadically, and the remaining 40 percent not at all. Those figures are far from the 1990 goals—so it's time to get out and get going to bring our fitness level up to par.

EXERCISE—THE HEALTH AND BEAUTY AID

Exercise works wonders for the body. The most important benefit is improved heart and lung fitness. Building cardiovascular fitness helps by lowering the resting heart rate—your heart will be pumping more blood with fewer beats, therefore working less. In addition, exercise can lower your blood pressure at rest while building a more efficient body.

Impressive scientific evidence indicates that if you exercise properly on a regular basis, you will be less prone to heart attacks, strokes, and other life-threatening conditions than people who are sedentary. By combining exercise with the proper diet, you will improve cholesterol and other blood lipid levels.

If weight loss is your goal, exercise can lead to a reduction in body fat as well as strengthen bones and muscles. You may sleep better and find that you feel less stress. Studies have shown that exercise relieves mild depression and provides a general lift in spirits.

For many people, the "body beautiful" is reward enough for becoming fit. A toned and trim body can be yours with regular exercise. A fit body looks good, and looking good makes you feel good. Whatever your motivation, if you exercise, you will reap a multitude of benefits.

WHAT'S YOUR EXCUSE?	
Excuses	Solutions
Too busy	Make exercise a priority. Commit just 2 hours a week. Four 30-minute workouts leave you 166 hours—or 99% of the week—for everything else.
Don't have enough energy	Actually, exercise gives you more energy, both during exercise and afterwards. By reversing the fatigue cycle, you'll feel less sluggish and be filled with vitality.
Too involved with family	Exercise is a great way to spend time with your family. Make exercise a family affair and get fit together.
Feel awkward and uncoordinated	Most health clubs teach you to use their equipment and show you proper techniques. If you feel conspicuous, attend a club that caters to beginners, or use convenient home video tapes.
No place to work out	A special place isn't needed—just open your front door and start briskly walking your way to fitness. Or inquire about a mall walking club in your area.
Can't afford fancy clothes or equipment	All that you really need are a good pair of walking shoes and comfortable clothing.
Makes me sore and stiff	Start slowly and gradually increase for no-pain, big-gain payoffs. Include warm-up and cool-down phases; they're essential components of your program.

ARE YOU PHYSICALLY FIT?

Just what does being "fit" mean? Exercise physiologists—the fitness experts—define fitness as the ability of the heart, lungs, and muscles to perform with minimum effort. According to the President's Council on Physical Fitness, fitness means a person can do a day's work with vigor, alertness, and undue fatigue, yet have ample energy left over for leisure time activities and for meeting unforeseen emergencies.

When planning your total fitness program, you should aim for three goals: improved body flexibility, improved muscle strength and endurance, and most important, improved cardiovascular endurance. Improved cardiovascular endurance results from increased oxygen consumption, a by-product of aerobic exercise.

Improving flexibility means you are increasing the body's ability to bend, stretch, and move joints through their full range of motion. Flexibility exercises warm up and stretch muscles and improve their agility. By doing stretching exercises, you can prevent the tightening of muscles and the increasing stiffness that occurs with aging. To decrease the risk of injury, stretching should be done slowly and should not cause pain.

Building muscle strength and endurance increases total body strength, protects joints, aids circulation, and helps to prevent osteoporosis and to maintain good posture. Muscle strength is defined as the greatest force a muscle can produce in one effort, such as a lift or a jump. Muscular endurance refers to the ability to repeat a given movement many times.

You can improve muscle strength and endurance with weight training and calisthenics. When weight training is added to aerobic exercise, the result is improved muscle definition and tone. You can actually reshape your body's dimensions within the limits of your inherited capacity.

Increasing cardiovascular endurance, a vital role of aerobic exercise, improves your body's ability to deliver oxygen to working muscles. Aerobic exercise conditions the heart and lungs, aids circulation, and controls weight. In addition, like others who have made aerobic exercise a part of daily life, you will find emotional and psychological benefits, including a feeling of well-being and increased self-confidence.

HOW TO FILL YOUR EXERCISE PRESCRIPTION

Type: The aerobic workout includes activities such as brisk walking, jogging, aerobic dancing, swimming, rowing, cross-country skiing, and cycling. These keep the large muscles moving continuously and elevate the heart rate into the target zone. Supplement this workout with exercises that enhance flexibility, muscular strength, and endurance as shown on pages 14-15.

Frequency: Regularly scheduled workouts, 3 to 5 sessions a week, are required to achieve and maintain fitness.

Duration: A workout of at least 20 minutes is necessary to obtain cardiovascular conditioning, although exercising 30 minutes or more allows the body to burn a greater percentage of calories from fat stores. Allow a few minutes before the workout for stretching, followed by a warm-up period. At the end of the workout, decrease the intensity to cool down before stretching again.

Intensity: To determine the proper "dose" of exercise, count your heart rate (see below) for 10 seconds and compare it with the target heart rate chart. Your target heart rate, which you want to achieve during exercise, should range between 70 and 85 percent of your maximum heart rate. Adjust the intensity of your workout to stay within these heart rate limits. If you are not reaching your target zone, you may not be exercising vigorously enough. If you are above your target zone, you are working too hard.

TARGET HEART RATE (THR) CHART			
CHECKING YOUR PULSE	Age	Target Heart Rate	
		70%	85%
To check your heart rate, stop your activity and immediately locate a pulse site—either the radial artery on the thumb side of the wrist or the carotid artery on either side of the neck.	20	23	28
	25	23	28
	30	22	27
	35	22	26
Place index and middle fingers over the artery and count the beats for 10 seconds. Check the figures on the chart to see whether you are in your target heart rate zone. To obtain the 1-minute THR in the formula below, multiply the chart values by 6 along with your 10-second heart rate.	40	21	26
	45	20	25
	50	20	24
	55	19	23
	60	19	23
	65	18	22
	70	17	21

MATHEMATICAL FORMULA:
Maximum Heart Rate (MHR) = 220 minus age
MHR x 70% and 85% = Target Heart Rate

A Total Fitness Program

Flexibility, muscular strength and endurance, and cardiovascular (aerobic) endurance are the basic components of a total fitness program. For flexibility, be sure to stretch all major muscle groups before and after exercising, holding each stretch for 30 seconds without bouncing. For strength and endurance, hand-held weights are an option. Try the exercises below for the all-important upper body and abdominal muscles.

Cardiovascular endurance exercises should be done for at least 20 minutes. Intensity and heart-rate are increased by keeping the arms above heart level and varying the movements. If the heart rate rises above the target zone, lower arms below shoulder height. Exercising on a stationary bicycle also has cardiovascular benefits. For variation, listen to music, watch television, or read a book while cycling.

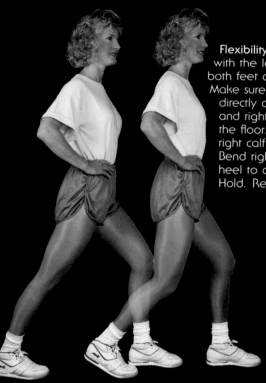

Flexibility—Take a big step with the left foot, keeping both feet directed forward. Make sure left knee is directly above left foot and right heel is flat on the floor. Feel the stretch in right calf muscle. Hold. Bend right knee, allowing heel to come off the floor. Hold. Repeat with other leg.

Flexibility—Place one arm behind your head, grasping that elbow with the opposite hand. Gently press the arm back, feeling a stretch in the tricep, the muscle in back of arm. Repeat with other arm.

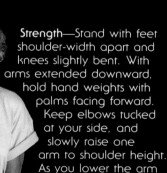

Strength—Stand with feet shoulder-width apart and knees slightly bent. With arms extended downward, hold hand weights with palms facing forward. Keep elbows tucked at your side, and slowly raise one arm to shoulder height. As you lower the arm to starting position, raise other arm. Repeat, alternating arms, 10 to 15 repetitions each.

Strength—Stand with feet shoulder-width apart and knees slight bent. Extend one arm overhead. Bend elbow and slowly lower the weight behind your head. Return to starting position and repeat 10 to 15 times. Repeat with other arm.

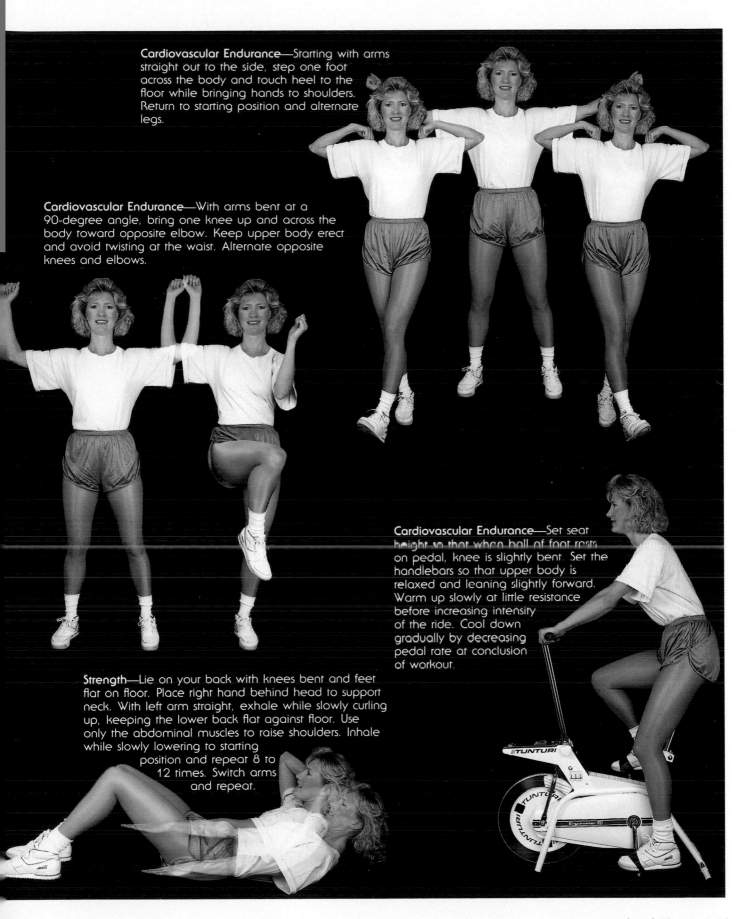

Cardiovascular Endurance—Starting with arms straight out to the side, step one foot across the body and touch heel to the floor while bringing hands to shoulders. Return to starting position and alternate legs.

Cardiovascular Endurance—With arms bent at a 90-degree angle, bring one knee up and across the body toward opposite elbow. Keep upper body erect and avoid twisting at the waist. Alternate opposite knees and elbows.

Cardiovascular Endurance—Set seat height so that when ball of foot rests on pedal, knee is slightly bent. Set the handlebars so that upper body is relaxed and leaning slightly forward. Warm up slowly at little resistance before increasing intensity of the ride. Cool down gradually by decreasing pedal rate at conclusion of workout.

Strength—Lie on your back with knees bent and feet flat on floor. Place right hand behind head to support neck. With left arm straight, exhale while slowly curling up, keeping the lower back flat against floor. Use only the abdominal muscles to raise shoulders. Inhale while slowly lowering to starting position and repeat 8 to 12 times. Switch arms and repeat.

Set Yourself Up for Success

If you want to live healthier as well as longer, look beyond buying a new pair of walking shoes or reading a calorie chart. The key to a healthy lifestyle is behavior. Healthy living means understanding how your behavior affects your daily activities. As you start toward a healthier lifestyle, you may need to modify your daily routine to make time for exercising, eating right, and developing healthy habits that last a lifetime. Also, you may need to redirect your thinking to remove any not-so-healthy habits and at the same time enhance the inner image of your life and its possibilities.

THE ABCs OF BEHAVIOR

Take a look at your actions and behavior. From this, you may learn that a few changes may be beneficial. Gradually reshape your behavior in small, comfortable steps until you achieve the changes you want—changes that fit your lifestyle and that you can live with for the rest of your life.

Sometimes unhealthy behaviors just seem to happen, like when you have overeaten without realizing it. Even so, certain conditions trigger a behavior, and conditions follow that influence whether the behavior will be repeated. Behavioral scientists refer to this chain of events as the ABCs of behavior—**antecedent, behavior,** and **consequences.**

The **antecedents** are the cues, events, feelings, and situations that occur prior to a behavior. Seeing doughnuts in the bakery window may trigger eating, drinking a cup of coffee may be the cue for smoking a cigarette, or viewing a home movie may entice you to make some popcorn. These are the actions or **behavior.** The **consequences** are the feelings and situations following a behavior. When trying to change a behavior such as eating foods high in fat, you may feel guilty and frustrated after you indulge. Recognize these feelings, but do not allow yourself to be discouraged.

A habit is formed when the antecendent, behavior, and consequence are combined like a chain and occur repeatedly. Suppose, for example, that you wake up late and rush to get to work on time. On the way, you buy a fast-food sausage biscuit for breakfast. If this action is repeated often, a habit forms of eating a breakfast high in fat. The short-term consequence is that the day starts with a high-fat meal. The long-term consequence can be elevated blood cholesterol or weight gain.

The key to changing a behavior is finding the place at which you can break the link successfully. To change the antecedent, get up earlier. To change the behavior, prepare Hearty Ham Breakfast Muffins (page 28) the night before, or choose an English muffin at the restaurant. Breaking the chain will adjust the consequence.

SEVEN STEPS IN THE RIGHT DIRECTION

Replace those habits that are deterrents to a healthy lifestyle. But remember that careful planning is needed to attain positive change.

- **Set goals.** Goals provide structure, direction, and a means for measuring your progress. Start by deciding which changes you want to make in your lifestyle, and then set your priorities. Be realistic and select those you believe you can accomplish. Avoid starting with the most difficult one—select an easily achievable goal to keep your motivation high. If your goal is to modify recipes to produce healthier meals, don't try to change them all at once. Instead, select one or two recipes a week. That way, by the year's end you'll have a full set of recipes on which to rely. Breaking down a big task or long-term goal into smaller ones will make the ultimate goal seem more manageable. Learning to set and achieve short-term goals is the key to staying motivated.
- **Keep records.** Before you make a behavioral change, keep a record of how often the behavior occurs and under what circumstances. The record-keeping may be as simple as marking on a calendar the days you exercise or as extensive as a record detailing the time, place, food you ate, and with whom. The more detailed the record, the more information and options you will have.

● **Learn to adapt.** High performers always have alternate plans. They adapt by shifting gears, changing direction, or trying different strategies. If you have lost interest in your walking program, for example, change your exercise to swimming. And on the days you cannot swim, go biking.

● **Plan ahead.** Surveys indicate that exercisers have as much leisure time as non-exercisers; planning makes the difference. Decide where, when, and with whom you plan to achieve your goals. The more specific the plans, the more likely you are to carry them out. Try to anticipate unplanned situations; otherwise, they could keep you from achieving your goals. An example would be having an alternate exercise plan in case inclement weather prevents you from your scheduled session.

● **Think success.** Focus on accomplishments, learn from your lapses, and strive for improvement, not perfection. Frequently remind yourself of your accomplishments. To be successful, avoid vowing to "always" or to "never" do something. If you expect to fail at an exercise program, you probably will.

Instead, expect to succeed. A positive attitude will keep you on the way to a healthier life.

● **Reward yourself.** Reinforce your new behavior by rewarding yourself with something special. Rewards need to be immediate to reinforce the new behavior. Learning to give yourself even the smallest reward encourages you to repeat the healthy behavior. Enjoy a massage or new exercise attire when reaching an exercise goal, but save the larger rewards for major milestones. You are not alone if you have overlooked rewarding yourself—many people frequently see their failures but overlook their successes.

● **Be polite but firm.** Coping with the pressures of well-meaning friends and family can be a major challenge in making lifestyle changes. Refusing a rich dessert can be a challenge when trying to accomplish your goals. So, plan a response for situations that may arise, and stand up for yourself and the goals you hope to achieve. After you refuse politely a few times, most people will learn that pressure tactics will not work on you.

CHANGING TIMES FOR DINING OUT

Eating nutritiously while eating out may initially be a challenge, but you can do it. These pointers will help you reach your goal for healthier eating:

● When in a group, speak up and help select the restaurant; choose one that meets your needs.

● Patronize restaurants that offer salad bars and steamed, baked, or broiled foods.

● Monitor your food intake throughout the day for calories, sodium, fat, and/or sugar according to your health needs.

● Carry low-sodium seasoning blends and packets of low-calorie salad dressing in case these are not available at the restaurant.

● Learn to recognize menu terms that the American Heart Association uses for low-fat food preparation methods: steamed, broiled, roasted, poached, or dry-broiled in lemon juice or wine.

● Learn to recognize menu descriptions that indicate high-calorie

or high-fat food preparation: sautéed, fried, battered, braised, hollandaise, au gratin, escalloped, marinated in oil, basted, prime, and in a cream, butter, or cheese sauce.

● To identify high-sodium foods, watch for these menu terms: pickled, smoked, in cocktail sauce, and in a tomato base.

● To cut down on portion sizes, select appetizers as your main course, order à la carte, or share food with a companion.

● Remember that a restaurant's goal should be to serve you. Do not be intimidated by the menu, atmosphere, or waiter.

● Ask that foods be prepared with less fat and salt and served with salad dressings and sauces on the side. Request substitutions such as a

baked potato instead of french fries or baked chicken instead of fried chicken.

● Enjoy dessert with your friends. Select fresh fruit, fruit ice, sherbet, sorbet, or angel food cake. Also, a cup of espresso or a demitasse coffee with a twist of lemon can provide a polished finish for a gourmet meal.

● Enjoy new fast-food options. Salad bars and low-fat milk are available, and some places offer whole wheat buns and low-calorie dressings. A small hamburger with lettuce, tomato, and onion can be a good selection. But be aware that a double-decker burger, fries, and a milkshake can add more than 1,000 calories, 2,000 milligrams of sodium, and nearly 1/2 cup of fat to your daily diet.

The *Cooking Light* Kitchen

The menu for a Cajun Feast (recipes and complete analysis on page 77) is a perfect example of how preparing foods the *Cooking Light* way allows you to enjoy the foods you like, but still watch the amount of fat, cholesterol, sodium, and calories that you consume. In the traditional catfish recipe, the fish is breaded and deep-fat fried; our version is marinated for extra flavor and cooked in a non-stick skillet with only a small amount of fat. Country Corn Sticks replace Hush Puppies, another commonly deep-fat fried item.

Dirty Rice and Colorful Vegetable Medley help round out the meal by providing attractive, nutritious accompaniments along with Fruity Gelatin Salad. The salad contains no sugar and is sweetened by the fruit. Cranberry-Grape Sorbet finishes off the meal as a contrast to Praline Ice Cream, a dessert abundant in fat, cholesterol, and calories.

This *Cooking Light* menu has only 540 calories per serving. The Spicy Skillet Catfish has less than half the calories of the deep-fried fish because the breading and frying have been eliminated. So sit back and enjoy the meal, knowing what a nutritious feast it will be.

	Cooking Light	Traditional
	Total Calories Per Serving: 540	**Total Calories Per Serving: 1,198**
	PROTEIN 30.2 / FAT 14.9 / CARBOHYDRATES 70.3 / CHOLESTEROL 66 / IRON 4.4 / SODIUM 597 / CALCIUM 157	PROTEIN 28.8 / FAT 75.4 / CARBOHYDRATES 101.2 / CHOLESTEROL 260 / IRON 3.1 / SODIUM 1123 / CALCIUM 240

Cooking Light	Traditional
Spicy Skillet Catfish (3½ ounces)	Deep-Fat Fried Catfish (3½ ounces)
Colorful Vegetable Medley (½ cup)	Tartar Sauce (2 tablespoons)
Dirty Rice (½ cup)	French Fried Potatoes (10 fries)
Country Corn Sticks (1 cornstick)	Hush Puppies (3 hush puppies)
Fruity Gelatin Salad (1 serving)	Creamy Coleslaw (½ cup)
Cranberry-Grape Sorbet (½ cup)	Praline Ice Cream (½ cup)

ALL *COOKING LIGHT* RECIPES TESTED

As a *Cooking Light* cook, you can feel confident as you prepare the recipes in this book. Each has been developed and tested to meet strict standards for sound nutrition, excellent flavor, and visual appeal. Combine the recipes to create your own menus, or follow the suggestions in ''Healthy American Meals'' or the weekly menu plan. Either way, you will have satisfying delights. Featured below are just a few ways to apply *Cooking Light*'s test kitchen techniques to maximize nutrition in your recipes.

PUTTING *COOKING LIGHT* INTO ACTION

Prepare the *Cooking Light* recipes and menus for your family and friends. They'll never guess that the dishes are so healthy. And as you prepare the recipes, be sure to read the food and fitness facts placed throughout the book. Share these with your family and you will encourage even the heartiest eater to be more health-conscious. Look for these facts flagged with the following symbols:

NUTRITION  FITNESS

KEEP IT LIGHT AND KEEP THE FLAVOR

Enhance the flavor of meat, fish, and poultry by placing them in a marinade and refrigerating for several hours. Try this technique in Grilled Lime Chicken (page 159) or Grilled Pompano (page 123) for a flavorful entrée.

Brown meat or sauté foods without fat by spraying a nonstick pan with vegetable cooking spray. Cranberry Pork Chops (page 152) and Artichoke Heart Casserole (page 198) are two of many recipes offering this cooking method.

Reduce the fat content in recipes calling for ground meat such as in Beefy-Tortilla Pie (page 42) or Sloppy Joes (page 55). To do this, thoroughly drain the cooked meat in a strainer or colander, discarding the excess fat.

Fresh herbs can add flavor to almost any recipe. Although a few herbs are seasonal, most can be purchased year round. If it is necessary to use dried herbs, substitute approximately one-third of the fresh amount. Clockwise (from top): parsley, watercress, oregano, thyme, sage, dillweed, basil, oregano, mint. On countertop, rosemary.

Whip evaporated skimmed milk and use in place of fat-laden whipping cream or whipped topping mixes. To prepare, chill a mixing bowl, beaters of an electric mixer, and evaporated skimmed milk in freezer for 30 minutes. Remove and beat milk on high speed until soft peaks form. Use as a topping for Peach-Ginger Crumble (page 234).

Try a flaming dish such as Fresh Peach Flambé (page 220) in which the alcohol burns off, leaving only the flavor, not the calories. Heat the spirit just until warm; remove from heat, and ignite. Do not overheat or the fumes will evaporate and will not ignite. Pour the flaming alcohol over the dessert and serve when the flame dies down.

What's New in the Marketplace?

FITNESS FINESSE

Today's fitness equipment is becoming more sophisticated. Protective eyewear for racquet sports has reached new levels of safety, and exercise shoes are tailored to the biomechanics of every activity from aerobic dancing to walking.

Computerized exercise machines with simulated fitness coaches now offer encouragement and mark your progress along the way. The Liferower® Total Body Conditioner by Life Fitness offers the fitness benefits of a rowing machine as well as the challenge of a video game. Racing your canoe against the machine encourages you to keep up your pace, while the screen displays messages for proper rowing form.

SELECTING SELECT

To ensure selecting a low-fat cut of beef, which grade would you purchase—Prime, Choice, or Good? You are not alone if you answered Prime; the majority of consumers taking part in a national survey gave the same answer. And most felt that Good indicated a meat of poorer quality.

To assist the consumer, the U.S. Department of Agriculture has changed Good to Select, a name perceived to have a more positive connotation. The Department hopes that the new designation will enhance the image of what essentially is leaner beef. Be aware, however, that the grading of meat is voluntary; it is optional for the meat packer to include this designation.

Although the grades serve as a general guide to fat content, continue to look for white specks of fat within the flesh as well as seam fat between the muscles of the meat. Select will have fewer flecks of fat marbling within the muscle, about 32 percent less fat on the average. But when it comes to the amount of protein and vitamins, you will find very little difference in the three grades. If your grocer is not currently carrying Select meat, ask for it by name.

NOUVELLE EATING

In addition to including everyday ingredients in our recipes, *Cooking Light* keeps you up-to-date on the newer, popular foods. Use the following guides for purchasing and preparing these foods.

● **Arugula** is a tender, mustard-flavored green that resembles the leaves of the radish in flavor and appearance. To store, wrap the roots in damp toweling, enclose the bunch in plastic, and refrigerate for no more than a few days. It is an excellent source of calcium, iron, and vitamins A and C.

● **Goat cheese** is a soft, white cheese made from goat's milk. It has a strong, unique flavor that can accent an appetizer or top off a dish.

● **Jicama**, a tuber, is easy to prepare, requiring only the removal of its thin skin. It is available year round. Store unwrapped in the refrigerator; uncut, it keeps 2 to 3 weeks. Once cut, cover tightly and use within a week. Raw or cooked, it can be cut into various shapes and included in recipes ranging from appetizers to desserts. It is a good source of potassium, contains some vitamin C, and has only 25 calories per ½ cup.

● **Starfruit** (carambola) is easy to recognize—the glossy yellow fruit is decorated with five deep ribs that are star-shaped when sliced. It is commonly available during fall and winter. Look for firm fruit, 2 to 5 inches in length. If bought green, allow to ripen until yellow. Select either the sweet variety with thick, fleshy ribs or the tart variety with very narrow ones. Starfruit is a good source of vitamins A and C, potassium, and fiber, and has only 42 calories each.

● **Baby corn** is edible, including the cob. Available either fresh or frozen, it can be added to stir-fried dishes, vegetable combinations, crudités arrangements, or used as a garnish.

● **Tomatillos** are a small, hard, green fruit used mostly in cooked sauces. Remove the papery outer husk before using. This Mexican tomato is available fresh or canned and has only 11 calories per tablespoon.

● **Crimini mushrooms** belong to the large family of mushrooms. Mushrooms are now available fresh, dried, wild, or imported.

● **Chiles** come in many varieties; a few include:
Poblanos are mild to moderately hot. These dark green chiles resemble a small, deflated bell pepper and are good roasted, stuffed, or baked.
Serranos are very hot, and are good seeded, diced, and mixed into guacamole or other sauces. Serranos are a bright, glossy green and are plump but narrow, usually measuring no more than 2 to 2½ inches long. They are one of the smallest and hottest of the chiles.
Jalapeños are hot. To use, remove the seeds and slice into tiny strips for garnishing. Similar in shape to serranos, these are a darker green and somewhat larger, measuring about 3½ inches long and 1½ inches wide at stem end.
Anaheims may be green or red and are often mild. These long, narrow, and slightly twisted peppers are usually light to medium green in color. They are good stuffed or roasted.

● **Jerusalem artichokes** are tannish gold to cream in color, although red or purple varieties may be

1. mango 2. baby corn 3. crimini mushrooms 4. arugula 5. Anaheim 6. poblano 7. serrano 8. jalapeño 9. goat cheese 10. Jerusalem artichoke 11. tomatillos 12. papaya 13. starfruit 14. jicama

seen. The ivory flesh has a crisp texture that makes them a perfect crudité. They add crunch and flavor to salads, vegetables, and meats, whether they are grated, sliced, or chopped, and have only 57 calories in a ½-cup serving. Although available year round, they are at their sweetest from fall through winter. Store wrapped in plastic in the refrigerator.

● **Papayas** are completely yellow when ripe. Select a papaya that yields to the touch. If only partially ripe, leave at room temperature a few days; then store in the refrigerator. A ½-cup serving of papaya supplies the RDA for vitamin C. In addition, it is an excellent source of vitamin A and has only 27 calories.

● **Mangos** are sweet and succulent and are at their peak during the summer months. They range in size from a few ounces to several pounds, are high in vitamins A and C, and have only 54 calories per ½ cup. Allow to ripen at room temperature until soft to the touch.

Healthy American Meals

A nutritionally balanced meal can be elegant entertaining fare as in the "Dinner for the Boss" menu featuring Rack of Lamb Persillade, Herbed Baby Vegetable Sauté, Souffléed Baked Potatoes, and Sparkling Fresh Fruit Cup. A dinner roll and a glass of red wine complete the picture. Edible flower petals add an unusual, gourmet touch to the meal. (Menu begins on page 83.)

Each menu has been carefully developed for your enjoyment, and each meets the *Cooking Light* guidelines for healthy eating. Of the total calories in each menu, more than 50 percent are provided by carbohydrate, about 20 percent are from protein, and less than 30 percent are from fat. This 50-20-30 ratio will allow you to eat healthy, nutritious meals that are balanced and easy to follow.

The four sections of this chapter cover almost every occasion. Whether preparing the simplest of breakfasts, quick and easy lunches, or elegant dinners, you're sure to find the perfect menu for your meal.

Breakfast and Brunch. Whether you are planning a Campfire Brunch, a Hearty Winter Breakfast, Muffins In Minutes, or entertaining for an occasion such as a Wedding Day Brunch, *Cooking Light* can assist. For an island cuisine, try a West Indies Omelet Brunch. Or, if you'd prefer a special Brunch For Two, Eggs and Spinach Goldenrod is the perfect dish.

Quick and Easy. How about a quick Easy Dinner For Two, requiring just a few minutes in preparation time? Or enjoy Crabmeat Imperial at only 153 calories for an After-The-Symphony Supper. Plan a mid-game break of Super Bowl Halftime, or prepare a quick and easy Beefy-Tortilla Pie for Southwestern Fare.

Microwave It Light. Make Family Night Chicken Dinner what it should be—a time for family fun and good food. It features Chicken and Dumplings, a treat the entire family will enjoy. Lunch In A Jiffy is another favorite with all the family, especially the children. For an international flair, Dinner From Down-Under, Island Dinner, and a Mexican Fiesta are sure to provide you with the next-best-thing-to-being-there meal.

That's Entertaining. Whether the menus are for a St. Valentine's Day Dinner For Two, a casual Pizza Party, or a Tapas Party, your friends will be thriled to receive invitations. If you're having a mid-day celebration, Bistro Luncheon will please your palate.

Try Shrimp Mornay Popovers (page 37), Caviar Asparagus (page 38), and Champagne-Peach Melbas for a special-occasion brunch.

Breakfast & Brunch

Wild Pecan Rice Muffins, Blueberry-Poppy Seed Muffins (page 28), Buckwheat-Pear Muffins, Hearty Ham Breakfast Muffins (page 28), and Sesame-Date Muffins (page 28).

Muffins In Minutes

The take-out breakfast has become a major new eating trend. Schedules are busier than ever, yet we're beginning to realize that breakfast really is as important for peak performance as our mothers told us it was. Fast-food chains, delis, supermarkets, and bakeries have all added muffins, croissants, and breakfast sandwiches to their menus. The trouble is that those breakfast choices are generally high in fat, sodium, and calories.

Instead of going out for a breakfast on the run, you can

Buckwheat-Pear Muffins
Wild Pecan Rice Muffins
Blueberry-Poppy Seed Muffins
Sesame-Date Muffins
Hearty Ham Breakfast Muffins
Skim Milk
Coffee

Serves 1
Total calories per serving: 234

have a 2-minute breakfast at home with this wide variety of

scrumptious muffins. With a small investment of time, you can bake two weeks' worth of these high-fiber, low-fat muffins.

Simply store them in zip-top heavy-duty plastic bags in the freezer, and heat muffins in the microwave or toaster oven as needed. With the addition of an 8-ounce glass of skim milk and a cup of coffee, you have a balanced breakfast. And with muffins at 150 calories or less, you're getting much less fat and fewer calories compared with that in giant-sized bakery muffins.

BUCKWHEAT-PEAR MUFFINS

1⅔ cups buckwheat flour
½ cup pan-toasted oats, uncooked
¼ cup firmly packed brown sugar
2 teaspoons baking powder
½ teaspoon ground cinnamon
⅛ teaspoon salt
¼ cup margarine
1 (16-ounce) can unsweetened pears, undrained
½ cup skim milk
1 egg, beaten
Vegetable cooking spray

Combine first 6 ingredients, stirring well. Cut in margarine with a pastry blender until mixture resembles coarse meal. Make a well in center of mixture. Drain pears, reserving juice. Place pears in container of an electric blender or food processor; top with cover, and process until smooth. Combine pureed pears, ½ cup reserved juice, milk, and egg. Add to dry ingredients; stir just until moistened.

Spoon batter into muffin pans that have been coated with cooking spray, filling three-fourths full. Bake at 400° for 20 to 25 minutes or until muffins are lightly browned. Yield: 1 dozen (144 calories each).

PROTEIN 2.6 / FAT 4.9 / CARBOHYDRATE 23.1 / CHOLESTEROL 23 / IRON 0.5 / SODIUM 132 / CALCIUM 57

WILD PECAN RICE MUFFINS

1 cup whole wheat flour
½ cup all-purpose flour
¼ cup shreds of wheat bran cereal
1 teaspoon baking soda
1 teaspoon baking powder
¼ teaspoon salt
1 (8-ounce) carton plain low-fat yogurt
2 tablespoons brown sugar
3 tablespoons vegetable oil
1 egg, beaten
¼ cup skim milk
½ teaspoon vanilla extract
½ cup cooked wild pecan rice (cooked without salt or fat)
¼ cup chopped pecans, toasted
Vegetable cooking spray

Combine first 6 ingredients in a large bowl; make a well in center of mixture. Combine yogurt, sugar, oil, egg, milk, and vanilla; add to dry ingredients, stirring just until moistened. Fold in rice and pecans.

Spoon batter into muffin pans that have been coated with cooking spray, filling two-thirds full. Bake at 400° for 18 to 20 minutes or until lightly browned. Yield: 1 dozen (148 calories each).

PROTEIN 4.2 / FAT 6.4 / CARBOHYDRATE 19.5 / CHOLESTEROL 24 / IRON 1.0 / SODIUM 175 / CALCIUM 83

BLUEBERRY-POPPY SEED MUFFINS

2 cups all-purpose flour
2 tablespoons plus 2 teaspoons sugar
2 teaspoons baking powder
1½ teaspoons poppy seeds
¼ teaspoon salt
1 cup skim milk
¼ cup margarine, melted
1 egg, beaten
1 teaspoon grated lemon rind
¾ cup fresh or frozen blueberries, thawed and drained
Vegetable cooking spray

Combine first 5 ingredients in a large bowl; make a well in center of mixture. Combine milk, margarine, egg, and lemon rind; add to dry ingredients, stirring just until moistened. Fold in blueberries.

Spoon batter into muffin pans that have been coated with cooking spray, filling two-thirds full. Bake at 400° for 20 to 25 minutes or until muffins are golden brown. Yield: 1 dozen (150 calories each).

PROTEIN 3.8 / FAT 4.8 / CARBOHYDRATE 22.7 / CHOLESTEROL 23 / IRON 0.8 / SODIUM 161 / CALCIUM 71

SESAME-DATE MUFFINS

1½ cups whole wheat flour
½ cup wheat germ
¼ cup sesame seeds, toasted
2 teaspoons baking soda
1 cup nonfat buttermilk
1 egg, beaten
3 tablespoons margarine, melted
2 tablespoons molasses
¼ cup chopped dates
Vegetable cooking spray

Combine first 4 ingredients in a large bowl; make a well in center of mixture. Combine buttermilk, egg, margarine, and molasses; add to dry ingredients, stirring just until moistened. Fold in dates.

Spoon batter into muffin pans that have been coated with cooking spray, filling three-fourths full. Bake at 400° for 15 minutes or until lightly browned. Yield: 1 dozen (143 calories each).

PROTEIN 5.4 / FAT 6.1 / CARBOHYDRATE 19.4 / CHOLESTEROL 23 / IRON 1.6 / SODIUM 199 / CALCIUM 79

HEARTY HAM BREAKFAST MUFFINS

1 cup all-purpose flour
½ cup cornmeal
2 teaspoons baking powder
⅛ teaspoon salt
2 ounces chopped lean cooked ham
2 ounces extra-sharp Cheddar cheese, cut into small cubes
1 cup skim milk
½ cup instant grits
3 tablespoons vegetable oil
2 eggs, beaten
Vegetable cooking spray

Combine flour, cornmeal, baking powder, salt, ham, and cheese in a large bowl; make a well in center of mixture. Set aside.

Place milk in a small saucepan; cook over low heat, stirring constantly, until mixture reaches 120° to 130°. Cool to 105° to 115°. Combine milk and grits, stirring well. Combine vegetable oil and eggs in a small bowl. Add grits mixture and egg mixture to dry ingredients, stirring just until moistened.

Spoon batter into muffin pans that have been coated with cooking spray, filling three-fourths full. Bake at 400° for 20 to 25 minutes or until muffins are lightly browned. Yield: 1 dozen (148 calories each).

PROTEIN 5.7 / FAT 6.6 / CARBOHYDRATE 16.1 / CHOLESTEROL 54 / IRON 0.8 / SODIUM 240 / CALCIUM 99

Hearty Winter Breakfast

Grapefruit Half
Cheesy Egg Casserole
Banana Slices
Spiced Black Currant Tea

Serves 6
Total calories per serving: 456

Chilling winds and frosty mornings can make breakfast a comforting meal. Add one-half of a grapefruit and one small sliced banana per person to complete this warming meal.

Cheesy Egg Casserole and Spiced Black Currant Tea will get any chilly winter morning off to a warm beginning.

CHEESY EGG CASSEROLE

4 (1-inch) slices French bread, cubed
Vegetable cooking spray
¾ pound ground lean pork
¼ teaspoon dried whole sage
¼ teaspoon dried whole thyme
⅛ teaspoon dried whole marjoram
⅛ teaspoon freshly ground black pepper
4 eggs, beaten
1½ cups skim milk
¾ cup (3 ounces) shredded 40% less-fat Cheddar cheese
¼ teaspoon dry mustard
⅛ teaspoon ground red pepper
Fresh sage leaves (optional)
Fresh thyme sprigs (optional)

Place bread cubes in a 2-quart baking dish that has been coated with cooking spray, and set aside.

Combine pork, sage, thyme, marjoram, and black pepper in a large nonstick skillet. Cook over medium heat until pork is browned, stirring to crumble. Drain and pat dry with paper towels. Sprinkle meat mixture over bread cubes. Combine eggs and remaining ingredients; stir well. Pour egg mixture over meat mixture. Cover and chill 8 hours.

Bake, uncovered, at 350° for 55 to 60 minutes or until set. If desired, garnish with fresh sage leaves and thyme sprigs. Yield: 6 servings (289 calories per serving).

PROTEIN 23.9 / FAT 13.7 / CARBOHYDRATE 16.0 / CHOLESTEROL 225 / IRON 1.8 / SODIUM 333 / CALCIUM 220

SPICED BLACK CURRANT TEA

6 cups water
1 (3-inch) stick cinnamon
6 whole cloves
5 black currant tea bags
2 tablespoons honey

Combine water, cinnamon, and cloves in a large saucepan; bring to a boil over high heat. Reduce heat and simmer 5 minutes. Remove from heat; discard spices. Add tea bags; cover and let stand 5 minutes. Remove and discard tea bags. Stir in honey. Serve beverage hot. Yield: 6 cups (24 calories per 1-cup serving).

PROTEIN 0.0 / FAT 0.0 / CARBOHYDRATE 6.5 / CHOLESTEROL 0 / IRON 0.1 / SODIUM 7 / CALCIUM 0

To satisfy outdoor appetites, bring along plenty of Maple Apple Rings, Hash Brown Breakfast Pouches, and Creamy Cocoa Mix.

Campfire Brunch

Nothing tastes better than breakfast eaten out-of-doors. On camping trips, the fresh air and beautiful surroundings seem to stimulate the appetite.

But if breakfast has become routine on your trips, try this sunrise special. Everything can be prepared at home, keeping your campside cooking to a

Hash Brown Breakfast Pouches
Maple Apple Rings
Creamy Cocoa Mix

Serves 4
Total calories per serving: 565

minimum. Hash Brown Breakfast Pouches and Maple Apple Rings

are wrapped in individual pouches made from heavy-duty aluminum foil. Store them in the ice chest until it is time to cook them over medium coals of the campfire.

Creamy Cocoa Mix is a convenient dry mix that makes a quick cup of cocoa anytime. Simply add boiling water and stir.

HASH BROWN BREAKFAST POUCHES

2 large baking potatoes (¾ pound)
½ (16-ounce) package 25% less-fat pork sausage
½ cup thinly sliced green onions
½ cup chopped sweet red pepper
½ teaspoon pepper
¼ teaspoon salt
¼ cup grated Parmesan cheese
¼ cup (1 ounce) shredded 40% less-fat Cheddar
  cheese

Cook potatoes in boiling water 30 minutes or until tender; drain. Chill. Peel and coarsely grate potatoes. Set aside.

Combine sausage, onions, and sweet red pepper in a large nonstick skillet. Cook over medium heat until sausage is browned, stirring to crumble meat. Drain and pat dry with paper towels.

Combine potatoes, sausage mixture, pepper, salt, and Parmesan cheese; stir gently. Spoon 1 cup potato mixture onto each of 4 large squares of heavy-duty aluminum foil. Sprinkle 1 tablespoon Cheddar cheese over each serving. Wrap securely, sealing edges well. Store foil-wrapped packets in an ice chest.

To cook, place packets over medium coals for 15 to 20 minutes or until thoroughly heated, turning occasionally. Yield: 4 servings (234 calories per serving).

PROTEIN 14.2 / FAT 10.7 / CARBOHYDRATE 23.3 / CHOLESTEROL 4 /
IRON 2.9 / SODIUM 672 / CALCIUM 169

MAPLE APPLE RINGS

4 medium baking apples, cored and thinly sliced
  into rings
2 tablespoons plus 2 teaspoons reduced-calorie
  maple syrup
2 teaspoons margarine, melted
½ teaspoon ground cinnamon
⅛ teaspoon ground nutmeg
¼ cup sliced natural almonds

Arrange apple rings evenly on 4 large squares of heavy-duty aluminum foil.

Combine syrup, margarine, cinnamon, and nutmeg, stirring well. Spoon 2 teaspoons syrup mixture over each serving of apples. Sprinkle 1 tablespoon almonds over each serving. Wrap securely, sealing edges well. Store foil-wrapped packets in an ice chest.

To cook, place packets over medium coals for 15 minutes or until apples are tender. Yield: 4 servings (183 calories per serving).

PROTEIN 1.6 / FAT 5.8 / CARBOHYDRATE 35.2 / CHOLESTEROL 0 /
IRON 0.7 / SODIUM 26 / CALCIUM 35

CREAMY COCOA MIX

1 cup instant nonfat dry milk powder
2 tablespoons plus 1 teaspoon sugar
2 tablespoons unsweetened cocoa
4 cups boiling water

Combine dry ingredients; stir well. Store in a zip-top plastic bag. To serve, spoon cocoa mix evenly into 4 mugs. Add 1 cup boiling water to each mug; stir well. Yield: 4 cups (149 calories per 1-cup serving).

PROTEIN 11.6 / FAT 0.6 / CARBOHYDRATE 24.2 / CHOLESTEROL 6 /
IRON 0.6 / SODIUM 161 / CALCIUM 381

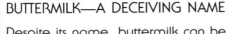

BUTTERMILK—A DECEIVING NAME

Despite its name, buttermilk can be very low in fat. In addition to being made from whole milk, it's available in lower-fat versions made from skim or 1 percent milk. Use it in place of milk in baked goods or breakfast foods such as pancakes or waffles, or drink a glass for an evening snack.

Simple to prepare Glazed Grapefruit and Meringue-Topped Toast start the day off on a sweet note.

Brunch For Two

"Leisurely" and "brunch" can be mutually complementary terms. To keep your weekend brunch as simple as possible, we have put together a Brunch for Two menu that combines make-ahead dishes with others that need a bit of last-minute or joint preparation.

First, chill the ingredients for Faux Pink Champagne, then have your guest gently stir them together while you section the grapefruit, roast the bread, and

Faux Pink Champagne
Glazed Grapefruit
Eggs and Spinach
Goldenrod
Ham Slice
Meringue-Topped Toast

Serves 2
Total calories per serving: 597

slice the ham to ease final preparations. Allow one 3-ounce slice of lean ham per person.

Next, prepare the Eggs and Spinach Goldenrod. Notice that this classic egg and spinach combination has been dressed up and the fat content pared down for a big calorie savings.

Last, prepare a simple glaze for the grapefruit sections using low-sugar orange marmalade. Beat the egg whites, sugar, and vanilla, then slip the Meringue-Topped Toast into the oven until golden brown for an unusual brunch treat.

FAUX PINK CHAMPAGNE

¾ cup sparkling apple cider,
  chilled
¾ cup sparkling cherry-flavored
  mineral water, chilled
½ cup reduced-calorie cranberry
  juice cocktail, chilled

Combine apple cider, mineral water, and cranberry juice cocktail; stir lightly. Pour into 2 champagne glasses. Serve immediately. Yield: 2 cups (55 calories per 1-cup serving).

PROTEIN 0.0 / FAT 0.1 / CARBOHYDRATE 13.8 / CHOLESTEROL 0 / IRON 1.7 / SODIUM 23 / CALCIUM 10

GLAZED GRAPEFRUIT

1 medium-size pink grapefruit
1 tablespoon low-sugar orange marmalade
Fresh mint sprigs (optional)
Grapefruit rind curls (optional)

Peel and section grapefruit, reserving juice. Combine juice and marmalade in a small nonaluminum saucepan; place over medium heat

and cook until marmalade melts.

Place grapefruit sections in 2 dessert dishes. Pour glaze evenly over sections; toss gently. If desired, garnish with fresh mint sprigs and grapefruit rind curls. Yield: 2 servings (84 calories per ½-cup serving).

PROTEIN 1.4 / FAT 0.2 / CARBOHYDRATE 21.0 / CHOLESTEROL 0 / IRON 0.2 / SODIUM 0 / CALCIUM 26

EGGS AND SPINACH GOLDENROD

2 hard-cooked eggs, peeled
1 tablespoon margarine
1 tablespoon all-purpose flour
¾ cup skim milk
¼ teaspoon salt
⅛ teaspoon ground white pepper
¾ pound fresh spinach
⅛ teaspoon ground nutmeg

Cut eggs in half. Remove half of one yolk; chop finely, and set aside. Chop remaining yolk and whites; set aside.

Melt margarine in a small saucepan over low heat; add flour, stirring until smooth. Cook 1 minute, stirring constantly. Gradually add milk; cook over medium-low heat, stirring constantly,

until mixture is thickened and bubbly. Stir in reserved chopped eggs, salt, and pepper. Set aside, and keep warm.

Remove stems from spinach; wash leaves. Place in a large Dutch oven. Cover and cook over medium heat, stirring frequently, until spinach is wilted. Stir in nutmeg.

To serve, spoon spinach evenly onto 2 serving plates. Make a well in center of spinach. Spoon ½ cup reserved egg mixture into each well. Sprinkle reserved chopped yolk evenly over each serving. Serve immediately. Yield: 2 servings (216 calories per serving).

PROTEIN 14.6 / FAT 12.1 / CARBOHYDRATE 14.5 / CHOLESTEROL 276 / IRON 5.8 / SODIUM 611 / CALCIUM 315

MERINGUE-TOPPED TOAST

1 egg white
2 tablespoons sugar
¼ teaspoon vanilla extract
2 slices whole wheat bread, toasted

Beat egg white (at room temperature) at high speed of an electric mixer 1 minute. Gradually add sugar, 1 tablespoon at a time, beating until stiff peaks form and sugar dissolves (2 to 4

minutes). Fold in vanilla.

Cut each piece of toast into 2 triangles. Spread meringue over triangles. Place on an ungreased baking sheet. Bake at 400° for 7 minutes or until meringue is lightly browned. Yield: 2 servings (119 calories per serving).

PROTEIN 4.3 / FAT 0.8 / CARBOHYDRATE 24.8 / CHOLESTEROL 1 / IRON 0.6 / SODIUM 157 / CALCIUM 27

West Indies Omelet Brunch

West Indies Omelet
Garden Medley Tomato
Cups
Lemon-Dill Bread
Orange Juice
Praline Coffee

Serves 4
Total calories per serving: 427

West Indies Omelet, Lemon-Dill Bread, Garden Medley Tomato Cups, and Praline Coffee are a satisfying brunch combination.

This West Indies Omelet Brunch can be prepared leisurely so that the chef may enjoy it as much as the guests. The tangy omelet filling is based upon a Southern favorite, West Indies Salad, and makes a perfect counterpoint to the creamy texture of eggs.

Lemon-Dill Bread may be prepared ahead and frozen or wrapped and stored overnight.

When you come to the kitchen in the morning, toss together the crabmeat mixture for the omelet and the vegetable mixture for the tomato cups. Let these ingredients chill while you sip a 6-ounce serving of freshly squeezed orange juice.

Praline Coffee is the ideal way to end a leisurely meal. Although sweet and rich tasting, it has only 26 calories per serving. It will be as satisfying as the richest dessert, but it won't weigh you down for the rest of the day.

WEST INDIES OMELET

½ pound fresh lump crabmeat, drained and flaked
¼ cup finely chopped celery
¼ cup finely chopped purple onion
2 tablespoons cider vinegar
¼ teaspoon pepper
4 eggs
4 egg whites
¼ cup water
⅛ teaspoon pepper
Vegetable cooking spray
Celery leaves (optional)
Purple onion rings (optional)

Combine first 5 ingredients in a small bowl, and toss gently. Cover and refrigerate at least 2 hours.

Transfer crab mixture to a small nonstick skillet. Cook over low heat until thoroughly heated, stirring occasionally. Drain well, and set aside.

Combine eggs, egg whites, water, and pepper in a medium bowl; beat well with a wire whisk. Coat an 8½-inch nonstick skillet or omelet pan with cooking spray; place over medium heat until hot enough to sizzle a drop of water. Pour in ½ egg mixture. As mixture begins to cook, gently lift edges of omelet with a spatula, and tilt pan to allow uncooked portions to flow underneath. When egg mixture is set, spoon ½ reserved crab mixture over half of omelet; loosen omelet with spatula, and carefully fold in half. Carefully slide omelet onto a warm serving platter. Cut omelet into 2 pieces. Repeat procedure. If desired, garnish omelets with celery leaves and onion rings. Serve immediately. Yield: 4 servings (158 calories per serving).

PROTEIN 20.7 / FAT 6.6 / CARBOHYDRATE 2.6 / CHOLESTEROL 304 / IRON 1.6 / SODIUM 734 / CALCIUM 72

GARDEN MEDLEY TOMATO CUPS

4 medium tomatoes
¾ cup diced zucchini
¾ cup diced yellow squash
¾ cup sliced fresh mushrooms
¾ cup frozen English peas, thawed
2 tablespoons commercial reduced-calorie French dressing
Fresh dillweed sprigs (optional)

Cut off top of each tomato, and scoop out pulp, leaving shells intact (reserve pulp for other uses). Invert tomato shells on paper towels to drain.

Combine zucchini and next 4 ingredients; spoon zucchini mixture evenly into tomato cups Chill thoroughly before serving. Garnish with fresh dillweed sprigs, if desired. Yield: 4 servings (53 calories per serving).

PROTEIN 3.2 / FAT 0.5 / CARBOHYDRATE 10.8 / CHOLESTEROL 0 / IRON 1.3 / SODIUM 121 / CALCIUM 23

LEMON-DILL BREAD

1 package dry yeast
1¼ cups warm water (105° to 115°)
2 tablespoons sugar, divided
2 cups all-purpose flour, divided
1 cup whole wheat flour, divided
2 tablespoons vegetable oil
1 tablespoon plus 1½ teaspoons grated lemon rind
¼ teaspoon salt
¾ teaspoon dried whole dillweed
Vegetable cooking spray

Dissolve yeast and 1 tablespoon sugar in water in a large bowl; stir well. Let stand 5 minutes. Combine yeast mixture, 1 cup all-purpose flour, ½ cup whole wheat flour, oil, lemon rind, salt, and dillweed in a large bowl. Beat at medium speed of an electric mixer 2 minutes, scraping sides of bowl frequently.

Combine remaining 1 cup all-purpose flour, ½ cup whole wheat flour, and 1 tablespoon sugar; add to batter, stirring well. Cover and let rise in a warm place (85°), free from drafts, 40 minutes or until doubled in bulk.

Stir dough down; beat 25 strokes by hand. Spread batter into an 8½- x 4½- x 3-inch loafpan that has been coated with cooking spray. Smooth top with floured hands and pat into loaf shape. Cover and let rise 40 minutes or until doubled in bulk. Bake at 375° for 35 to 45 minutes or until loaf sounds hollow when tapped. Remove from pan, and let cool on a wire rack. Yield: 16 servings (110 calories per ½-inch slice).

PROTEIN 3.0 / FAT 2.1 / CARBOHYDRATE 20.2 / CHOLESTEROL 0 / IRON 0.8 / SODIUM 38 / CALCIUM 8

PRALINE COFFEE

¼ cup ground coffee
2 tablespoons coarsely ground pecans
1 (3-inch) stick cinnamon
3 cups water
1 cup skim milk
1½ teaspoons brown sugar
⅛ teaspoon vanilla, butter, and nut flavoring
4 (3-inch) sticks cinnamon (optional)

Combine first 3 ingredients in basket of a drip coffee maker or electric percolator. Fill pot to the 3-cup mark with water. Prepare coffee according to manufacturer's instructions.

Combine milk and brown sugar in a small saucepan, and heat until sugar dissolves. Stir in flavoring.

Pour ¾ cup coffee into mugs. Pour ¼ cup milk mixture into each mug; stir well. Garnish each serving with a cinnamon stick, if desired. Yield: 4 cups (26 calories per 1-cup serving).

PROTEIN 2.1 / FAT 0.1 / CARBOHYDRATE 4.1 / CHOLESTEROL 1 / IRON 0.1 / SODIUM 32 / CALCIUM 76

Iced Almond Coffee and Chocolate-Almond Crisps make a refreshing, light dessert.

Wedding Day Brunch

A wedding day is an unforgettable experience for those involved. This Wedding Day Brunch menu will be equally memorable from the Champagne Peach Melba to the Chocolate-Almond Crisps. These recipes are a cause for celebration when you know that the calories have been kept to a minimum and flavor and elegance are at a maximum.

What's a wedding without

Champagne-Peach Melba
Shrimp Mornay Popovers
Caviar Asparagus
Chocolate-Almond Crisps
Iced Almond Coffee

Serves 8
Total calories per serving: 458

champagne? Here it is poured over fresh peaches and raspberries for a refreshing appetite teaser. Fresh shrimp are blended into a well-seasoned sauce that is spooned into high-topped Herbed Popovers. To keep things on the elegant side, garnish steamed asparagus with a colorful stripe of caviar.

Relax until the wedding hour arrives with a glass of Iced Almond Coffee and Chocolate-Almond Crisps (4 per person).

CHAMPAGNE-PEACH MELBA

4 fresh peaches, peeled and halved
1 cup fresh raspberries
1 cup champagne, chilled

Place 1 peach half into each of 8 compotes; top each half with 2 tablespoons raspberries and 2 tablespoons champagne. Serve immediately. Yield: 8 servings (48 calories per serving).

PROTEIN 0.5 / FAT 0.1 / CARBOHYDRATE 6.9 / CHOLESTEROL 0 / IRON 0.3 / SODIUM 1 / CALCIUM 6

SHRIMP MORNAY POPOVERS

6 cups water
2 pounds unpeeled medium-size fresh shrimp
1 cup water
1 cup Chablis or other dry white wine
½ cup sliced green onions
¼ cup chopped sweet red pepper
1 tablespoon chicken-flavored bouillon granules
¼ teaspoon ground white pepper
1 cup skim milk, divided
¼ cup cornstarch
½ teaspoon prepared mustard
1 cup (4 ounces) shredded Gouda cheese
3 tablespoons chopped fresh parsley
Herbed Popovers

Bring 6 cups water to a boil; add shrimp, and cook 3 to 5 minutes. Drain well; rinse with cold water. Chill. Peel and devein shrimp. Set aside.

Combine 1 cup water and next 5 ingredients in a large saucepan; bring to a boil. Cover, reduce heat, and simmer 1 minute. Combine ¼ cup skim milk and cornstarch, stirring well. Stir into wine mixture. Add remaining ¾ cup milk and mustard. Cook 2 minutes or until mixture is thickened, stirring constantly. Remove from heat, and stir in shrimp. Stir in cheese and parsley; cook over low heat until cheese melts and mixture is thoroughly heated.

To serve, spoon ¾ cup shrimp mixture over each split popover. Serve immediately. Yield: 8 servings (300 calories per serving).

Herbed Popovers:

1⅓ cups all-purpose flour
1⅓ cups skim milk
¾ teaspoon dried whole chervil
¼ teaspoon salt
3 eggs
Vegetable cooking spray

Combine first 4 ingredients in a medium bowl. Beat at medium speed of an electric mixer just until blended. Add eggs, one at a time, beating just until blended after each addition.

Coat eight (6-ounce) custard cups with cooking spray. Place in a 450° oven for 3 minutes or until a drop of water sizzles when dropped in them. Pour batter into cups, filling half full. Bake at 450° for 15 minutes. Reduce heat to 350° and bake 20 minutes. Yield: 8 popovers.

PROTEIN 26.9 / FAT 8.3 / CARBOHYDRATE 27.7 / CHOLESTEROL 239 / IRON 3.4 / SODIUM 682 / CALCIUM 252

CAVIAR ASPARAGUS

1½ pounds fresh asparagus spears
3 tablespoons plus 1½ teaspoons plain nonfat
  yogurt
2 tablespoons low-fat sour cream
1 teaspoon white wine vinegar
¼ teaspoon garlic powder
¼ teaspoon dry mustard
⅛ teaspoon sugar
1 teaspoon red, black, or golden caviar

Snap off tough ends of asparagus. Remove scales, using a knife or vegetable peeler, if desired. Cook asparagus, covered, in a small amount of boiling water 6 minutes or until crisp-tender. Drain; rinse asparagus with cold water, and drain again. Chill.

Combine yogurt and next 5 ingredients in a small bowl; stir well. Cover and chill thoroughly. Divide asparagus evenly among 8 individual serving plates. Spoon 2 teaspoons yogurt mixture over each serving of asparagus. Top each serving with ⅛ teaspoon of caviar. Yield: 8 servings (25 calories per serving).

PROTEIN 2.5 / FAT 0.7 / CARBOHYDRATE 3.0 / CHOLESTEROL 4 /
IRON 0.5 / SODIUM 23 / CALCIUM 31

CHOCOLATE-ALMOND CRISPS

2 egg whites
¾ cup plus 2 tablespoons sifted powdered sugar
3 tablespoons plus 1½ teaspoons unsweetened
  cocoa
¼ cup semisweet chocolate mini-morsels
¼ cup finely chopped blanched almonds
½ teaspoon almond extract
Vegetable cooking spray

Beat egg whites (at room temperature) at high speed of an electric mixer 1 minute. Combine sugar and cocoa; gradually add sugar mixture to egg whites, 1 tablespoon at a time, beating until stiff peaks form and sugar dissolves (2 to 4 minutes). Fold in mini-morsels, almonds, and almond extract.

Drop by teaspoonfuls, 1 inch apart, onto cookie sheets that have been coated with cooking spray. Bake at 300° for 40 minutes or until set. Cool slightly on cookie sheets; gently remove to wire racks, and cool completely. Store in an airtight container. Yield: 3 dozen (32 calories each).

PROTEIN 0.5 / FAT 0.9 / CARBOHYDRATE 5.8 / CHOLESTEROL 0 /
IRON 0.2 / SODIUM 3 / CALCIUM 4

ICED ALMOND COFFEE

6½ cups freshly brewed strong coffee
¼ cup plus 1 tablespoon superfine sugar
1½ cups skim milk
2 teaspoons almond extract

Combine brewed coffee and sugar; stir until well blended. Let cool. Stir in milk and almond extract. Chill thoroughly. To serve, pour coffee mixture over ice in serving glasses; serve immediately. Yield: 8 cups (53 calories per 1-cup serving).

PROTEIN 1.8 / FAT 0.1 / CARBOHYDRATE 10.8 / CHOLESTEROL 1 /
IRON 0.8 / SODIUM 28 / CALCIUM 60

Ruby-red Burgundy Poached Pears (page 47) are a simple but elegant dessert.

Quick and easy Ham-Broccoli Rollups make an ideal after-work dinner.

Easy Dinner For Two

This menu is devised for days when you just don't have much time or energy to cook. Three simple dishes come together to form a beautiful meal that could compete with one that had taken hours to create.

Prepare the Triple Sec Fruit Salad first. Let the salad chill as long as possible so that the Triple Sec can seep into the fruit for

Ham-Broccoli Rollups
Triple Sec Fruit Salad
Commercial Dinner Rolls
Bavarian Mint Frosty

Serves 2
Total calories per serving: 634

maximum flavor. For the main course, cook broccoli spears, then roll them up in lean ham and

Cheddar cheese slices and bake. Add one commercial dinner roll per person to round out the meal nutritionally.

Dessert couldn't be easier, thanks to the help of an electric blender. Bavarian Mint Frosty is a frosty chocolate concoction reminiscent of a drug-store milk shake with the added flavors of coffee and peppermint.

HAM-BROCCOLI ROLLUPS

1 (8-ounce) package frozen broccoli spears
4 (1-ounce) slices lean cooked ham
2 (1-ounce) slices Swiss cheese
2 tablespoons commercial reduced-calorie creamy
    Italian dressing
Vegetable cooking spray
2 tablespoons (½ ounce) shredded 40% less-fat
    Cheddar cheese

Cook broccoli according to package directions, omitting salt, drain.

Divide ham into 2 portions. Top ham slices with cheese slices. Arrange half of broccoli on each cheese slice; spoon dressing over broccoli. Roll ham and cheese around broccoli; secure with wooden picks.

Place rollups in a 1-quart baking dish that has been coated with cooking spray. Cover and bake at 350° for 15 minutes. Uncover; sprinkle 1 tablespoon shredded cheese over each serving, and bake an additional 2 to 3 minutes or until cheese melts. Remove wooden picks from rollups before serving. Yield: 2 servings (240 calories per serving).

PROTEIN 24.3 / FAT 12.6 / CARBOHYDRATE 9.4 / CHOLESTEROL 61 / IRON 1.3 / SODIUM 1140 / CALCIUM 380

TRIPLE SEC FRUIT SALAD

2 tablespoons process light cream cheese product
¾ teaspoon wheat germ
1 small peach, peeled and sliced
1 small kiwifruit, peeled and sliced
2 large fresh strawberries, sliced
1 tablespoon plus 2 teaspoons Triple Sec or other
    orange-flavored liqueur
Lettuce leaves

Shape cream cheese into 6 balls, using 1 teaspoon cream cheese for each ball; roll in wheat germ. Chill.

Combine peaches, kiwifruit, strawberries, and Triple Sec in a small bowl; toss gently. Cover and chill thoroughly.

To serve, spoon ½ cup fruit mixture onto each of 2 individual lettuce-lined salad plates. Top each serving with 3 cream cheese balls. Yield: 2 servings (120 calories per serving).

PROTEIN 2.8 / FAT 2.9 / CARBOHYDRATE 15.9 / CHOLESTEROL 0 / IRON 0.4 / SODIUM 80 / CALCIUM 37

BAVARIAN MINT FROSTY

2 teaspoons instant coffee granules
1 tablespoon boiling water
1½ cups skim milk
¼ teaspoon peppermint extract
¾ cup chocolate ice milk

Dissolve coffee granules in boiling water; let cool. Combine coffee, milk, and extract in container of an electric blender; top with cover, and process until smooth. Add ice milk, and process until smooth. Serve immediately. Yield: 2 cups (117 calories per 1-cup serving).

PROTEIN 7.2 / FAT 1.2 / CARBOHYDRATE 15.8 / CHOLESTEROL 4 / IRON 0.1 / SODIUM 96 / CALCIUM 228

BLOOD PRESSURE—WHAT'S IT ALL ABOUT?

The first number of your blood pressure reading, the systolic pressure, reflects the heart's squeeze during the pumping of blood. The second number, the diastolic pressure, is the pressure on an artery when the heart is relaxing between beats. Most physicians agree that a blood pressure of 140/80 is borderline high; readings that are consistently above this may require medical attention.

Savour the flavors of the Southwest with Beefy-Tortilla Pie and Southwestern Jicama Salad.

Southwestern Fare

One of those rare evenings when the whole family is at home is not the time to spend hours in the kitchen. We've created a Southwestern menu you can have on the table in an hour—with some time to spare to prop your feet up and catch up with your family.

The Beefy-Tortilla Pie is a lively mixture of ground chuck, onion, green chiles, and cheese baked

Beefy-Tortilla Pie
Southwestern Jicama Salad
Warm Pineapple Sundaes
Commercial Angel Food Cake

Serves 6
Total calories per serving: 619

in a crispy flour tortilla crust. The result is a moist and tasty one-

dish meal. While the pie is baking, prepare the Southwestern Jicama Salad. Next, make the pineapple sauce for Warm Pineapple Sundaes. If necessary, reheat the sauce while the table is being cleared. Serve the warm sauce over a scoop of ice milk and a 2-ounce slice of commercial angel food cake to end the meal on a sweetly balanced note.

BEEFY-TORTILLA PIE

Vegetable cooking spray
5 (6-inch) flour tortillas
½ pound ground chuck
1 (4-ounce) can chopped green chiles, drained
1 small onion, chopped
½ cup (2 ounces) shredded 40% less-fat Cheddar
  cheese
3 eggs, beaten
½ cup skim milk
3 tablespoons all-purpose flour
½ teaspoon baking powder
½ teaspoon chili powder
Jalapeño pepper flowers (optional)
Fresh cilantro sprigs (optional)

Coat bottom and sides of a 9-inch pieplate with cooking spray and line with tortillas. Set aside.

Cook ground chuck in a large nonstick skillet over medium heat until browned, stirring to crumble. Drain and pat dry with paper towels. Combine meat, chiles, onion, and cheese; stir well. Spoon mixture into prepared dish.

Combine eggs and remaining ingredients in a large bowl; beat with a wire whisk until well blended. Pour egg mixture over beef mixture. Bake at 350° for 45 minutes or until set. If desired, garnish with jalapeño pepper flowers and fresh cilantro sprigs. Yield: 6 servings (268 calories per serving).

PROTEIN 15.8 / FAT 11.8 / CARBOHYDRATE 25.3 / CHOLESTEROL 160 /
IRON 2.0 / SODIUM 170 / CALCIUM 160

SOUTHWESTERN JICAMA SALAD

½ cup vinegar
1 tablespoon plus 2 teaspoons sugar
1 tablespoon minced fresh cilantro
⅛ teaspoon salt
⅛ teaspoon pepper
Dash of hot sauce
2 cups shredded jicama
4 small tomatoes, sliced
2 fresh tomatillos, husked and sliced

Combine first 6 ingredients in a medium bowl; stir with a wire whisk until well blended. Add jicama, and toss gently.

Arrange tomato slices and tomatillo slices on individual salad plates, and top with ⅓ cup jicama mixture. Yield: 6 servings (57 calories per serving).

PROTEIN 1.7 / FAT 0.3 / CARBOHYDRATE 13.7 / CHOLESTEROL 0 /
IRON 0.9 / SODIUM 62 / CALCIUM 16

WARM PINEAPPLE SUNDAES

1 (8-ounce) can unsweetened pineapple tidbits,
  undrained
2 tablespoons brown sugar
1 tablespoon water
2 teaspoons cornstarch
3 tablespoons raisins
1½ teaspoons margarine
¼ teaspoon ground cinnamon
⅛ teaspoon ground nutmeg
½ teaspoon vanilla extract
3 cups vanilla ice milk
1 tablespoon flaked coconut, toasted

Drain pineapple, reserving juice. Set pineapple aside.

Combine reserved juice, sugar, water, and cornstarch in a small nonaluminum saucepan; stir well. Cook over medium heat until thickened, stirring constantly. Stir in pineapple, raisins, margarine, cinnamon, and nutmeg. Cook over low heat, stirring frequently, until thoroughly heated. Stir in vanilla.

To serve, place ½ cup ice milk in individual dessert dishes. Spoon 3 tablespoons warm pineapple mixture over each serving of ice milk. Sprinkle 1 teaspoon coconut over each serving. Serve immediately. Yield: 6 servings (147 calories per serving).

PROTEIN 2.9 / FAT 4.3 / CARBOHYDRATE 25.6 / CHOLESTEROL 9 /
IRON 0.4 / SODIUM 68 / CALCIUM 96

Christmas Night Supper

No matter how much we eat during the holiday season, we always seem to want "a little something" for supper in the evenings. This simple supper fills the bill and has the additional bonus of using many ingredients that may be left over from holiday dinners.

Start with a steamy bowl of Fresh Mushroom Soup. It's a simple mix of beef-flavored bouillon granules, shallots, and fresh

Fresh Mushroom Soup
Festive Turkey Salad with
Cranberry-French Dressing
Commercial Hard Rolls
Gingerbread Spritz Cookies
Steamy Grape Tea

Serves 4
Total calories per serving: 619

mushrooms. Make a tasty Festive Turkey Salad from leftover turkey

and cranberry sauce. Add one commercial hard roll per person to balance the menu.

For dessert, try a cup of flavorful Steamy Grape Tea along with spicy Gingerbread Spritz Cookies (2 per person). To make the tea, mix brewed tea with red grape juice, a little brown sugar, and orange and lemon flavorings. Thoroughly heat the tea, then sit back with an aromatic cupful and remember a special day.

FRESH MUSHROOM SOUP

Vegetable cooking spray
½ pound fresh mushrooms, sliced
1 shallot, chopped
4 cups water
1 tablespoon beef-flavored bouillon granules
⅛ teaspoon garlic powder
⅛ teaspoon pepper

Coat a large nonstick skillet with cooking spray; place over medium-high heat until hot.

Add mushrooms and shallot, and sauté until tender. Set aside.

Combine water, beef bouillon, garlic powder, and pepper in a large saucepan; bring to a boil. Add mushroom mixture, reduce heat, and simmer 5 minutes or until thoroughly heated. Yield: 4 cups (25 calories per 1-cup serving).

PROTEIN 1.2 / FAT 1.2 / CARBOHYDRATE 3.0 / CHOLESTEROL 0 / IRON 0.7 / SODIUM 711 / CALCIUM 4

FESTIVE TURKEY SALAD

3 cups coarsely chopped cooked turkey breast
   (skinned before cooking and cooked without salt)
¼ cup chopped celery
1 cup chopped Red Delicious apple
¼ cup coarsely chopped pecans
3 tablespoons reduced-calorie mayonnaise
Red leaf lettuce leaves
Cranberry-French Dressing
Fresh celery leaves (optional)

Combine first 5 ingredients in a large bowl; stir well. Cover and chill thoroughly. To serve, place 1 cup turkey mixture onto each of 4 lettuce-lined salad plates. Top each serving with 2 tablespoons Cranberry-French Dressing. Garnish with fresh celery leaves, if desired. Yield: 4 servings (271 calories per serving).

Cranberry-French Dressing:

¼ cup jellied cranberry sauce
⅛ teaspoon salt
⅛ teaspoon paprika
⅛ teaspoon dry mustard
⅛ teaspoon pepper
2 tablespoons vinegar
1 tablespoon vegetable oil

Combine first 5 ingredients in a small bowl, stirring with a wire whisk until smooth. Gradually add vinegar to cranberry mixture alternately with oil, beginning and ending with vinegar; stir well after each addition. Yield: ½ cup.

PROTEIN 26.0 / FAT 14.3 / CARBOHYDRATE 9.0 / CHOLESTEROL 62 / IRON 1.4 / SODIUM 226 / CALCIUM 26

Restore your energy with Festive Turkey Salad, Gingerbread Spritz Cookies, and Steamy Grape Tea.

GINGERBREAD SPRITZ COOKIES

¼ cup margarine
2 tablespoons brown sugar
⅓ cup molasses
½ teaspoon vanilla extract
1½ cups all-purpose flour
½ teaspoon salt
¼ teaspoon baking soda
¼ teaspoon baking powder
¼ teaspoon ground cinnamon
¼ teaspoon ground ginger
¼ teaspoon ground cloves

Cream margarine; add sugar, beating at medium speed of an electric mixer until light and fluffy. Add molasses and vanilla; mix well.

Combine flour and remaining ingredients; stir well. Add to creamed mixture, ¼ cup at a time, mixing to form a stiff dough. Chill at least 2 hours. Using a cookie press, press dough into desired shapes onto ungreased cookie sheets. Bake at 375° for 6 to 8 minutes or until lightly browned. Cool on wire racks. Yield: 2½ dozen (50 calories each).

PROTEIN 0.7 / FAT 1.6 / CARBOHYDRATE 8.1 / CHOLESTEROL 0 / IRON 0.4 / SODIUM 68 /

STEAMY GRAPE TEA

3 cups water
3 regular-size tea bags
1 cup unsweetened red grape juice
1 tablespoon brown sugar
¾ teaspoon orange extract
¾ teaspoon lemon extract
Orange rind curls (optional)

Bring water to a boil in a large saucepan; add tea bags. Remove from heat; cover and let stand 5 minutes. Remove and discard tea bags. Add juice and next 3 ingredients; cook over medium heat until sugar dissolves and mixture is thoroughly heated. Garnish with orange rind curls, if desired. Serve hot. Yield: 4 cups (67 calories per 1-cup serving).

PROTEIN 0.0 / FAT 0.0 / CARBOHYDRATE 14.6 / CHOLESTEROL 0 / IRON 0.3 / SODIUM 9 / CALCIUM 11

After an evening at the symphony, try Crabmeat Imperial and Green Salad with Herb Vinaigrette.

After-The-Symphony Supper

Late-night dining can be an elegant change of pace. The secret to this type of entertaining is to serve guests with the least amount of last-minute preparation possible, as in this After-The-Symphony Supper.

The heady flavor of the Herb Vinaigrette salad dressing intensifies as it stands, so prepare it several hours in advance. Have the greens washed and torn so they

Crabmeat Imperial
Green Salad with Herb Vinaigrette
Commercial Hard Rolls
Burgundy Poached Pears

Serves 8
Total calories per serving: 389

only need to be tossed with the dressing just before serving. Bur-

gundy Poached Pears make an elegant dessert. The rich flavor and color of red wine penetrates the pears during poaching and chilling. Add one commercial hard roll per person to the meal for balance.

Prepare the entrée last by making the simple crabmeat mixture and spooning it into attractive serving shells to bake while guests are assembling.

CRABMEAT IMPERIAL

Vegetable cooking spray
½ cup chopped celery
½ cup chopped green pepper
½ cup chopped sweet red pepper
2 tablespoons chopped fresh parsley
1 teaspoon prepared mustard
⅛ teaspoon ground white pepper
⅛ teaspoon ground red pepper
⅛ teaspoon hot sauce
2 eggs, beaten
⅓ cup reduced-calorie mayonnaise
2 pounds fresh lump crabmeat, drained and flaked

Coat a large nonstick skillet with cooking

spray; place over medium-high heat until hot. Add celery, green pepper, and sweet red pepper, and sauté until tender. Remove from heat, and stir in parsley, mustard, white pepper, red pepper, and hot sauce. Set aside.

Combine eggs and mayonnaise in a small bowl; stir with a wire whisk until smooth. Add vegetable mixture; stir well. Add crabmeat, stirring gently. Spoon crabmeat mixture evenly into 8 baking shells. Arrange shells on a baking sheet. Bake at 375° for 20 to 25 minutes. Yield: 8 servings (153 calories per serving).

PROTEIN 21.4 / FAT 6.0 / CARBOHYDRATE 2.2 / CHOLESTEROL 125 / IRON 1.4 / SODIUM 1190 / CALCIUM 73

GREEN SALAD WITH HERB VINAIGRETTE

2 tablespoons white wine vinegar
¼ teaspoon dried whole thyme
¼ teaspoon dried whole oregano
⅛ teaspoon ground red pepper
⅛ teaspoon hot sauce
⅓ cup canned no-salt-added chicken broth, undiluted
2 tablespoons water
1 tablespoon vegetable oil
1 clove garlic, sliced
3 cups torn Boston lettuce
3 cups torn romaine lettuce
2 cups chopped watercress
1 small sweet red pepper, seeded and cut into rings

Combine white wine vinegar, thyme, oregano, ground red pepper, hot sauce, chicken broth, water, vegetable oil, and garlic in a jar. Cover tightly, and shake vigorously. Chill dressing several hours.

Combine Boston lettuce, romaine lettuce, chopped watercress, and sweet red pepper rings in a large bowl. Remove and discard garlic slices from vinaigrette. Shake vinaigrette vigorously, and pour over lettuce mixture; toss well. Serve immediately. Yield: 8 servings (27 calories per serving).

PROTEIN 0.9 / FAT 1.9 / CARBOHYDRATE 1.9 / CHOLESTEROL 0 / IRON 0.6 / SODIUM 13 / CALCIUM 21

BURGUNDY POACHED PEARS

8 medium pears
¼ cup unsweetened orange juice
2 cups Burgundy or other dry red wine
1 cup reduced-calorie cranberry juice cocktail
4 orange slices
1 (3-inch) stick cinnamon
Orange rind curls (optional)
Fresh mint sprigs (optional)

Peel pears and core just from the bottom, cutting to but not through the stem end. Brush pears with orange juice to prevent browning.

Combine wine, cranberry juice cocktail,

orange slices, and cinnamon stick in a Dutch oven; bring to a boil. Place pears in Dutch oven in an upright position; spoon wine mixture over pears. Cover; reduce heat, and simmer 15 to 20 minutes or until tender. Transfer pears and liquid to a large bowl; cover and chill.

Discard cinnamon sticks and orange slices. Place pears in individual dessert dishes; spoon wine mixture evenly over pears. If desired, garnish with orange rind curls and fresh mint sprigs. Yield: 8 servings (53 calories per serving).

PROTEIN 0.3 / FAT 0.2 / CARBOHYDRATE 13.3 / CHOLESTEROL 0 / IRON 1.1 / SODIUM 4 / CALCIUM 14

Super Bowl Halftime

Artichoke Dip
Spicy Marinated Green
Beans
Chunky Chicken-Potato
Soup
Apple-Pecan Brownies

Serves 8
Total calories per serving: 502

What is more fun than having friends over to watch the biggest game of the football season? Since this is also traditionally four quarters of snacking and eating, make sure to offer your guests more nutritious food than chips and dip.

Set out Artichoke Dip and Spicy Marinated Green Beans for munching during the game. During halftime, bring out steaming bowls of hearty Chunky Chicken-Potato Soup garnished with reduced-calorie sour cream, low-fat Cheddar cheese, and chives. Serve rich Apple-Pecan Brownies (one per person) to satisfy any sweet tooth as your guests settle down for the second half.

Chunky Chicken-Potato Soup is a winning halftime idea.

ARTICHOKE DIP

1 cup low-fat cottage cheese
2 tablespoons reduced-calorie mayonnaise
2 tablespoons plain nonfat yogurt
¼ cup grated Parmesan cheese
1 (14-ounce) can artichoke hearts, drained and finely chopped
⅛ teaspoon paprika
1 (5¼-ounce) box whole grain melba rounds

Combine first 4 ingredients in container of an electric blender or food processor; top with cover, and process until smooth. Stir in chopped artichoke hearts. Cover and chill thoroughly. Sprinkle with paprika just before serving. Serve with melba toast rounds. Yield: 8 appetizer servings (136 calories per ¼ cup plus 1 tablespoon dip and 5 melba toast rounds).

PROTEIN 8.4 / FAT 3.3 / CARBOHYDRATE 18.6 / CHOLESTEROL 6 / IRON 1.0 / SODIUM 247 / CALCIUM 87

SPICY MARINATED GREEN BEANS

2 (10-ounce) packages frozen Italian-cut green
  beans
2 cups cherry tomatoes, halved
1 teaspoon dillseeds
½ teaspoon salt
½ teaspoon sugar
½ teaspoon ground red pepper
2 cloves garlic, sliced
½ cup water
½ cup cider vinegar

Cook green beans according to package directions, omitting salt. Drain; rinse beans with cold water, and drain again. Combine beans and tomatoes in a 12- x 8- x 2-inch baking dish. Set aside.

Combine dillseeds, salt, sugar, and pepper; sprinkle over reserved bean mixture. Stir in garlic slices. Combine water and vinegar in a small saucepan; bring mixture to a boil. Pour vinegar mixture over bean mixture; stir well. Cover and chill thoroughly, stirring occasionally. Yield: 8 appetizer servings (38 calories per ¾-cup serving).

PROTEIN 2.1 / FAT 0.2 / CARBOHYDRATE 9.2 / CHOLESTEROL 0 /
IRON 0.4 / SODIUM 151 / CALCIUM 11

CHUNKY CHICKEN-POTATO SOUP

3 medium baking potatoes, peeled and cubed
2 cups chopped onion
4 cups water
1 tablespoon chicken-flavored bouillon granules
¼ teaspoon salt
¼ teaspoon ground red pepper
⅛ teaspoon pepper
2 cups chopped cooked chicken breast (skinned
  before cooking and cooked without salt)
¼ cup skim milk
2 tablespoons plus 2 teaspoons chopped pimiento
⅓ cup low-fat sour cream
⅓ cup (1⅓ ounces) shredded 40% less-fat Cheddar
  cheese
2 tablespoons plus 2 teaspoons chopped fresh chives

Combine first 7 ingredients in a large Dutch oven; bring to a boil. Cover; reduce heat, and simmer 30 minutes or until potatoes are tender.

Place half of potato mixture in container of an electric blender or food processor; top with cover, and process until smooth. Add pureed mixture, chicken, and milk to Dutch oven; cook over medium heat until thoroughly heated. Stir in pimiento.

Ladle soup into serving bowls. Top each serving with 2 teaspoons sour cream, 2 teaspoons cheese, and 1 teaspoon chives. Yield: 8 cups (175 calories per 1-cup serving).

PROTEIN 17.2 / FAT 4.2 / CARBOHYDRATE 17.0 / CHOLESTEROL 40 /
IRON 1.2 / SODIUM 457 / CALCIUM 81

APPLE-PECAN BROWNIES

1¼ cups all-purpose flour
½ cup sugar
¼ cup unsweetened cocoa
1½ teaspoons baking powder
½ teaspoon ground cinnamon
¼ teaspoon salt
½ cup margarine, melted
2 eggs, beaten
2 teaspoons vanilla extract
1 cup peeled, grated apple
¼ cup chopped pecans
Vegetable cooking spray

Combine first 6 ingredients in a large bowl. Add margarine, eggs, and vanilla; beat at medium speed of an electric mixer until well blended. Stir in apple and pecans.

Spoon batter into a 9-inch square baking pan that has been coated with cooking spray. Bake at 325° for 25 to 30 minutes or until a wooden pick inserted in center comes out clean. Cool on a wire rack. Cut into 2-inch squares. Yield: 16 brownies (153 calories each).

PROTEIN 2.5 / FAT 8.0 / CARBOHYDRATE 18.0 / CHOLESTEROL 34 /
IRON 0.8 / SODIUM 141 / CALCIUM 30

Colorful Antipasto Cups add fun and flair to dining outdoors.

Dining Alfresco

Dining outdoors is decidedly one of the greatest pleasures of warm summer weather. Long evenings and gentle breezes make outdoor meals a natural. This Dining Alfresco menu is as satisfying and carefree as a summer evening.

Antipasto Cups start the meal in a spectacular fashion with an arrangement of fresh vegetables, Italian peppers, and part-skim mozzarella cheese cubes in an assortment of colorful sweet pepper cups. Try to choose sweet peppers that stand upright and are approximately the same size and shape.

Veal chops are a fresh new idea for the grill. The simple

Antipasto Cups
Grilled Veal Chops with
Jicama Salsa
Creamy Potatoes and Peas
Tossed Green Salad
Commercial Hard Rolls
Strawberries with
Honey-Almond Sauce
White Wine

Serves 6
Total calories per serving: 774

basting sauce of lemon juice and crushed garlic gives off an enticing aroma while the veal chops are grilling. Jicama Salsa, flavored with minced fresh cilantro, is a

crunchy and colorful accompaniment. Make the salsa early in the day so that the flavors have a chance to blend.

Creamy Potatoes and Peas is a simple make-ahead side dish that is trouble free at serving time. To complete this festive alfresco meal, add one commercial hard roll, a tossed green salad topped with 1 tablespoon commercial oil-free Italian dressing, and a 6-ounce serving of white wine per person.

Fresh strawberries are the ultimate summertime dessert, especially when they are topped with a silky honey-almond-flavored custard sauce as in Strawberries with Honey-Almond Sauce.

ANTIPASTO CUPS

2 medium-size sweet red peppers
2 medium-size sweet yellow peppers
2 medium-size green peppers
2 medium carrots, quartered and cut into 3-inch strips
12 radish roses
12 green onion fans
6 pepperocini peppers
2 ounces part-skim mozzarella cheese, cubed
6 commercial breadsticks

Cut a thin slice from the top of each pepper, reserving tops for other uses; remove seeds. Cut a thin slice from the bottom of each pepper, if necessary, to help pepper stand upright.

Arrange equal amounts of carrots and remaining ingredients except breadsticks in each pepper cup. Chill thoroughly. Serve each pepper cup with 1 breadstick. Yield: 6 servings (89 calories per serving).

PROTEIN 4.3 / FAT 2.8 / CARBOHYDRATE 13.3 / CHOLESTEROL 5 / IRON 2.4 / SODIUM 290 / CALCIUM 92

 LOW-IMPACT EXERCISE

Fitness experts contend that high-impact exercises are detrimental to the body. Repetitive high-impact activities can place strain on joints, causing stress injuries such as sprains and fractures.

The fitness-minded and experts alike agree that low-impact aerobics such as walking, swimming, rowing, and bicycling are all effective exercise choices that allow you to reach healthy fitness levels. However, activities such as walking may require that you exercise longer before you achieve health benefits. Extending the activity without increasing intensity helps to reduce the risk of injury.

Choosing only low-impact exercises may not be the best strategy, however. Studies show that weight-bearing activities may be necessary to increase bone density. Such findings suggest that the best all-around program may be to cross-train. Varying the exercise routine by alternating high- and low-impact activities avoids stressing any one muscle or joint while getting total body results. This sensible approach may be the most productive for fitness goals while also providing the variety to keep the fitness-minded enthusiastic.

GRILLED VEAL CHOPS WITH JICAMA SALSA

¼ cup finely chopped jicama
¼ cup finely chopped tomato
¼ cup finely chopped cucumber
1 tablespoon minced fresh cilantro
1 tablespoon white wine vinegar
½ teaspoon vegetable oil
¼ teaspoon sugar
⅛ teaspoon celery salt
⅛ teaspoon dry mustard
6 (6-ounce) lean loin veal chops (1-inch thick)
½ cup lemon juice
2 cloves garlic, crushed
Vegetable cooking spray

Combine jicama, tomato, cucumber, and cilantro in a small bowl; set aside. Combine vinegar and next 4 ingredients; stir well. Pour over vegetables, stirring well. Cover and chill 2 hours.

Trim fat from chops. Place chops in a large shallow dish. Combine lemon juice and garlic; stir well. Pour over chops; let stand 10 minutes at room temperature.

Remove chops from marinade, reserving marinade. Coat grill rack with cooking spray; place on grill over medium-hot coals. Grill chops on rack, and cook 10 to 15 minutes or to desired degree of doneness, turning and basting frequently with reserved marinade. To serve, spoon 2 tablespoons salsa mixture over each veal chop. Yield: 6 servings (199 calories per serving).

PROTEIN 20.8 / FAT 10.9 / CARBOHYDRATE 3.2 / CHOLESTEROL 79 / IRON 2.6 / SODIUM 108 / CALCIUM 15

CREAMY POTATOES AND PEAS

3 small baking potatoes (1 pound)
¾ cup frozen English peas, thawed
¼ cup commercial reduced-calorie ranch-style
  dressing
1 tablespoon skim milk
¼ teaspoon pepper

Combine potatoes and water to cover in a large saucepan; bring to a boil. Cover, reduce heat, and simmer 20 minutes or until tender. Drain, and let cool. Peel and cube potatoes.

Combine potato cubes and peas in a medium bowl. Set aside. Combine dressing, milk, and pepper; stir well. Pour over potato mixture; toss gently. Cover and chill thoroughly. Yield: 6 servings (98 calories per ½-cup serving).

PROTEIN 2.2 / FAT 3.1 / CARBOHYDRATE 18.7 / CHOLESTEROL 0 / IRON 0.6 / SODIUM 108 / CALCIUM 14

STRAWBERRIES WITH HONEY-ALMOND SAUCE

1 egg
1 tablespoon honey
1 tablespoon sugar
¾ cup skim milk
½ teaspoon almond extract
6 cups fresh strawberries, hulled

Beat egg in a small bowl at medium speed of an electric mixer until foamy. Add honey and sugar; beat until thickened. Stir in milk. Transfer mixture to a medium saucepan. Cook over low heat, stirring constantly, about 15 minutes or until mixture thickens and coats a metal spoon. Remove from heat; stir in almond extract. Cover and chill thoroughly.

To serve, place strawberries in individual dessert dishes. Spoon 2 tablespoons sauce over each serving. Yield: 6 servings (88 calories per serving).

PROTEIN 3.0 / FAT 1.5 / CARBOHYDRATE 17.0 / CHOLESTEROL 46 / IRON 0.8 / SODIUM 29 / CALCIUM 63

A taste of Tex-Mex with Zucchini-Beef Burritos, Mexican Rice, and Cherry Tomato Salad (menu begins on page 65).

Herbed Corn on the Cob is cooked in its husk in the microwave.

Lunch In A Jiffy

Busy lifestyles often leave little time to prepare a healthy, nutritious lunch. But that's no reason to skip meals or eat high-fat, high-calorie meals on the run. Instead, use the microwave oven to cook a wholesome lunch in record time.

Quick and easy Sloppy Joes feature ground chuck cooked with chunks of onion and celery in a lightly sweetened tomato sauce, then spooned over toasted English muffin halves. From start to finish, this dish takes

Sloppy Joes
Herbed Corn on the Cob
Tossed Green Salad
Easy Strawberry Sundaes
Iced Tea

Serves 6
Total calories per serving: 540

about 15 minutes to prepare.

Herbed Corn on the Cob is a tasty meal accompaniment. The corn is cooked in its husk on paper towels to ease preparation

and clean-up. Dried salad herbs are mixed with margarine and spread over the hot corn for extra flavor appeal. Add iced tea and a tossed green salad with 1 tablespoon commercial oil-free Italian dressing per person.

Dessert is a simple matter, too. Easy Strawberry Sundaes require just 3 minutes of cooking time to melt low-sugar strawberry spread mixed with orange juice for a quick sauce. Simply spoon the sauce over scoops of ice milk and banana slices.

SLOPPY JOES

1 pound ground chuck
½ cup chopped onion
¼ cup chopped celery
2 cloves garlic, minced
1 (8-ounce) can no-salt-added tomato sauce
1 (6-ounce) can no-salt-added tomato paste
1 tablespoon vinegar
2 teaspoons sugar
½ teaspoon dry mustard
½ teaspoon salt
3 English muffins, split and toasted

Combine ground chuck, onion, celery, and garlic in a 2½-quart baking dish. Cover and microwave at HIGH for 5½ to 6½ minutes or until meat is no longer pink, stirring every 2 minutes. Drain and pat dry with paper towels. Wipe pan drippings from dish with a paper towel.

Return meat to baking dish; stir in tomato sauce and next 5 ingredients. Cover and microwave at HIGH for 3 to 4 minutes or until thoroughly heated, stirring once. To serve, place ½ cup meat mixture over each English muffin half. Yield: 6 servings (277 calories per serving).

PROTEIN 19.3 / FAT 10.0 / CARBOHYDRATE 28.6 / CHOLESTEROL 46 / IRON 3.0 / SODIUM 416 / CALCIUM 75

HERBED CORN ON THE COB

6 ears fresh corn
2 tablespoons margarine, softened
1 teaspoon dried salad herbs

Pull back husks from corn, leaving husks attached at base of cob; remove silks. Rinse corn and pat dry. Pull husks up over corn. Rinse corn in husks; do not drain. Arrange corn on paper towels in microwave oven. Cover with wax paper. Microwave at HIGH for 16 to 18 minutes, rearranging after 8 minutes. Let stand 5 minutes; remove husks.

Combine margarine and salad herbs; spread 1 teaspoon margarine mixture over each ear of corn. Yield: 6 servings (100 calories per serving).

PROTEIN 2.0 / FAT 4.6 / CARBOHYDRATE 15.3 / CHOLESTEROL 0 / IRON 0.6 / SODIUM 55 / CALCIUM 10

EASY STRAWBERRY SUNDAES

½ cup plus 2 tablespoons low-sugar strawberry
  spread
2 tablespoons unsweetened orange juice
3 cups vanilla ice milk
2 medium bananas, sliced

Combine strawberry spread and orange juice in a 2-cup glass measure; cover with wax paper. Microwave at MEDIUM (50% power) for 2 to 3 minutes or until mixture is thoroughly heated, stirring once.

Scoop ½ cup ice milk into 6 dessert dishes; top evenly with banana slices. Spoon 2 tablespoons warm strawberry mixture over each serving. Serve immediately. Yield: 6 servings (151 calories per serving).

PROTEIN 3.0 / FAT 3.0 / CARBOHYDRATE 29.3 / CHOLESTEROL 9 / IRON 0.2 / SODIUM 53 / CALCIUM 91

MICROWAVING IT LIGHT

Microwaving is ideal for *Cooking Light* cooks. When cooking foods such as vegetables, microwave cooking retains the crisp texture, color, and flavor better than conventional cooking methods do. In addition, more of the nutrients, especially water-soluble vitamins, are retained. All this adds up to quick food preparation for dishes full of flavor and good nutrition.

Family Night Chicken Dinner

Chicken and Dumplings
Two-Squash Toss
Pineapple Salad with
Poppy Seed Dressing
Lemon Pudding Cakes
Skim Milk

Serves 6
Total calories per serving: 584

Chicken and Dumplings sports chunks of savory chicken nestled among carrots, potatoes, onion, and celery for a satisfying home-style entrée. For added interest, cut thyme-flavored dumplings into fanciful shapes and place on casserole. Serve each person an 8-ounce glass of skim milk to round out this family-style meal.

For a quick dessert from the microwave, try individual Lemon Pudding Cakes.

CHICKEN AND DUMPLINGS

1 cup thinly sliced carrots
1 cup peeled, cubed red potato
½ cup chopped onion
½ cup sliced celery
1 cup canned no-salt-added chicken broth, undiluted
¼ teaspoon salt
3 (6-ounce) skinned chicken breast halves
1 tablespoon all-purpose flour
½ cup water
1 cup all-purpose flour
2 teaspoons dried parsley flakes
1 teaspoon baking powder
½ teaspoon dried whole thyme
¼ teaspoon salt
2 tablespoons shortening
⅓ cup plus 1 tablespoon nonfat buttermilk

Combine first 6 ingredients in a 12- x 8- x 2-inch baking dish. Place chicken over vegetable mixture with thickest portions towards outside of dish. Cover with wax paper and microwave at HIGH for 12 minutes or until chicken is tender, rotating dish a half-turn after every 4 minutes. Remove chicken; bone and chop. Set aside.

Cover vegetable mixture with wax paper and microwave at HIGH for 3 minutes. Combine 1 tablespoon flour and water, stirring well. Stir flour mixture into vegetable mixture. Cover and microwave for 4 minutes, stirring once. Stir in reserved chicken.

Combine 1 cup flour, parsley, baking powder, thyme, and ¼ teaspoon salt. Cut in shortening with a pastry blender until mixture resembles coarse meal. Add buttermilk to dry ingredients, stirring with a fork just until moistened. Roll dough to ¼-inch thickness; cut into twelve 1½-inch rounds. Place flat side down over chicken mixture. Cover with wax paper; microwave at HIGH for 4 minutes, rotating dish a half-turn after 2 minutes. Let stand, covered, 5 minutes. Yield: 6 servings (241 calories per serving).

PROTEIN 20.2 / FAT 5.1 / CARBOHYDRATE 27.2 / CHOLESTEROL 39 / IRON 1.8 / SODIUM 345 / CALCIUM 60

TWO-SQUASH TOSS

3 small yellow squash, cut into ½-inch slices
2 medium zucchini, cut into ½-inch slices
1 (2-ounce) jar sliced pimiento, drained
½ teaspoon dried Italian seasoning
¼ teaspoon salt
¼ teaspoon garlic powder
3 tablespoons water
2 teaspoons margarine

Combine yellow squash, zucchini, pimiento, Italian seasoning, salt, and garlic powder in a 2½-quart casserole. Add water and dot with margarine. Cover with heavy-duty plastic wrap and vent; microwave at HIGH for 8 to 10 minutes or until vegetables are tender, stirring at 3 minute intervals. Let stand, covered, 2 minutes. Yield: 6 servings (30 calories per ½-cup serving).

PROTEIN 1.2 / FAT 1.5 / CARBOHYDRATE 3.9 / CHOLESTEROL 0 / IRON 0.6 / SODIUM 117 / CALCIUM 21

PINEAPPLE SALAD WITH POPPY SEED DRESSING

Curly leaf lettuce leaves
1 medium-size fresh pineapple
2 medium kiwifruit, peeled
Poppy Seed Dressing

Place lettuce leaves on a serving platter; set aside.

Peel and trim eyes from pineapple, removing core. Cut pineapple into 6 slices. Arrange over lettuce leaves. Cut kiwifruit into 6 slices; arrange over pineapple slices. Pour 2 tablespoons Poppy Seed Dressing over each serving. Yield: 6 servings (111 calories per serving).

Poppy Seed Dressing:

¾ cup unsweetened orange juice
2 teaspoons cornstarch
1 tablespoon honey
1½ teaspoons poppy seeds
¼ teaspoon grated orange rind

Combine orange juice and cornstarch in a 2-cup glass measure, stirring well. Microwave at HIGH for 2½ minutes or until thickened, stirring once. Add honey, poppy seeds, and orange rind; stir well. Cover and chill. Yield: ¾ cup.

PROTEIN 1.4 / FAT 1.1 / CARBOHYDRATE 26.2 / CHOLESTEROL 0 / IRON 0.8 / SODIUM 4 / CALCIUM 34

LEMON PUDDING CAKES

¼ cup plus 2 tablespoons sugar
⅓ cup all-purpose flour
¼ teaspoon salt
2 eggs, separated
¾ cup skim milk
2 tablespoons lemon juice
1 tablespoon grated lemon rind
Vegetable cooking spray
Fresh blueberries (optional)
Lemon slices (optional)
Fresh mint sprigs (optional)

Combine first 3 ingredients in a medium bowl; set aside.

Beat egg yolks at high speed of an electric mixer until thick and lemon colored; add milk and lemon juice, beating well. Add mixture to dry ingredients; beat well. Beat egg whites (at room temperature) at high speed of an electric mixer until soft peaks form. Gently fold egg whites and lemon rind into milk mixture.

Pour batter evenly into 6 (6-ounce) custard cups that have been coated with cooking spray. Place 3 custard cups in microwave oven. Microwave, uncovered, at MEDIUM HIGH (70% power) for 2 to 2½ minutes, rotating a half-turn after 1 minute. Let stand 2 minutes. Repeat procedure with remaining custard cups. If desired, garnish with blueberries, lemon slices, and fresh mint sprigs. Serve warm. Yield: 6 servings (116 calories per serving).

PROTEIN 3.9 / FAT 2.2 / CARBOHYDRATE 20.5 / CHOLESTEROL 92 / IRON 0.6 / SODIUM 137 / CALCIUM 51

Southern Supper

The microwave oven is perfect for cooking fish without adding unnecessary fat and calories. What's more, this fast method of cooking maintains the delicate flavor and moist texture of fish.

Southern Pecan Catfish boasts a light topping of corn flake crumbs and chopped pecans. The mild flavor of farm-raised catfish comes through without deep-fat frying in the traditional Southern manner.

Southern Pecan Catfish
Garden Corn and Okra
Candied Sweet Potatoes
Peaches 'n' Cream

Serves 4
Total calories per serving: 598

When gardens and orchards are brimming with nature's bounty, Southern produce is never better. Fresh corn, okra, green peppers, and tomatoes bring color and just-picked flavor to the meal when you serve Garden Corn and Okra. The classic combination of sweet potatoes and brown sugar in Candied Sweet Potatoes is sure to please everyone.

And you'll reap the benefits of the Southern peach harvest for dessert. Peaches 'n' Cream lets you enjoy the natural sweetness of fresh peaches without overwhelming amounts of sugar.

SOUTHERN PECAN CATFISH

½ cup corn flake crumbs
¼ teaspoon salt
⅛ teaspoon paprika
⅛ teaspoon pepper
2 tablespoons finely chopped pecans
4 (4-ounce) farm-raised catfish fillets
2 egg whites, beaten
1 tablespoon margarine
Lemon twists (optional)
Fresh parsley sprigs (optional)

Combine crumbs, salt, paprika, pepper, and pecans; stir well.

Rinse fillets with cold water; pat dry. Dip in egg white; dredge in crumb mixture.

Arrange fillets in an 11- x 7- x 2-inch baking dish with thickest portions to the outside of dish.

Place margarine in a 1-cup glass measure. Microwave at HIGH for 35 seconds or until melted; drizzle over fish. Cover with wax paper; microwave at HIGH for 4 to 6 minutes or until fish flakes easily when tested with a fork. Rearrange after 3 minutes. Let stand 1 minute. If desired, garnish with lemon twists and parsley sprigs. Yield: 4 servings (246 calories per serving).

PROTEIN 23.7 / FAT 10.2 / CARBOHYDRATE 14.1 / CHOLESTEROL 66 / IRON 2.2 / SODIUM 409 / CALCIUM 55

GARDEN CORN AND OKRA

¾ cup fresh corn
¾ cup sliced fresh okra
⅓ cup chopped green pepper
1 small onion, chopped
1 tablespoon water
1 teaspoon margarine
1 teaspoon sugar
½ teaspoon salt
⅛ teaspoon pepper
1 medium tomato, chopped
⅛ teaspoon hot sauce

Combine corn, okra, green pepper, onion, water, margarine, sugar, salt, and pepper in a 1-quart baking dish, tossing well. Cover with wax paper and microwave at HIGH for 8 to 10 minutes, stirring at 3 minute intervals. Add chopped tomato and hot sauce. Cover and microwave at HIGH for 1½ to 2 minutes or until mixture is thoroughly heated. Yield: 4 servings (65 calories per ½-cup serving).

PROTEIN 2.1 / FAT 1.5 / CARBOHYDRATE 12.5 / CHOLESTEROL 0 / IRON 0.8 / SODIUM 315 / CALCIUM 30

A Southern supper from the microwave: Southern Pecan Catfish, Garden Corn and Okra, Candied Sweet Potatoes, and Peaches 'n' Cream.

CANDIED SWEET POTATOES

2 large sweet potatoes (1¾ pounds)
3 tablespoons brown sugar
1 tablespoon margarine
1 tablespoon unsweetened
   orange juice

Wash sweet potatoes and pat dry; prick each sweet potato several times with a fork. Arrange sweet potatoes 1 inch apart on a layer of paper towels in microwave oven. Microwave, uncovered, at HIGH for 8 to 10 minutes or until sweet potatoes are tender, turning and rearranging potatoes after 4 minutes. Let potatoes stand 5 minutes.

Peel sweet potatoes and cut into ½-inch slices. Combine brown sugar and margarine in a 2-quart casserole. Microwave, uncovered, at HIGH for 1 to 1½ minutes or until sugar and margarine melt, stirring after 1 minute. Stir in orange juice. Add sweet potato slices, and toss gently. Cover with wax paper and microwave at HIGH for 1 to 2 minutes or until potatoes are thoroughly heated. Toss gently before serving. Serve immediately. Yield: 4 servings (158 calories per serving).

PROTEIN 1.7 / FAT 3.2 / CARBOHYDRATE 31.3 / CHOLESTEROL 0 / IRON 0.8 / SODIUM 49 / CALCIUM 29

PEACHES 'N' CREAM

1 cup vanilla ice milk, softened
½ teaspoon ground cinnamon
1 tablespoon plus 1½ teaspoons brown sugar
1 tablespoon plus 1½ teaspoons cornstarch
½ teaspoon ground cinnamon
¼ teaspoon ground ginger
1 tablespoon lemon juice
½ teaspoon almond extract
3 cups peeled, sliced peaches
Vegetable cooking spray
Fresh mint sprigs (optional)

Combine ice milk and ½ teaspoon cinnamon, stirring well. Cover and freeze until firm.

Combine sugar and next 5 ingredients in a large bowl. Add peaches and toss gently. Spoon into an 8-inch square baking dish that has been coated with cooking spray. Cover with wax paper and microwave at HIGH for 6 to 8 minutes or until peaches are tender, giving dish a half-turn after 4 minutes. Let stand 2 minutes. Spoon ½ cup peach mixture into individual dessert dishes. Top each serving with ¼ cup ice milk. Garnish with fresh mint sprigs, if desired. Yield: 4 servings (129 calories per serving).

PROTEIN 2.2 / FAT 1.7 / CARBOHYDRATE 28.2 / CHOLESTEROL 5 / IRON 0.5 / SODIUM 27 / CALCIUM 61

Island Dinner

This Island Dinner menu is reminiscent of food served on the sandy beaches of one of the Caribbean Islands.

Start with a refreshing Starfruit Sipper—a white wine cooler made with sodium-free seltzer water, fresh strawberries, and crystallized ginger. Coat the rims of tall glasses with sugar for an eye-catching presentation. Garnish each serving with a colorful slice of carambola or starfruit, as it is more commonly known.

Chicken Teriyaki
Sweet Pepper Salad
Coconut Custard
Starfruit Sippers

Serves 4
Total calories per serving: 703

Prepare the simple Sweet Pepper Salad using sweet red and green pepper strips, and let it chill thoroughly for maximum flavor. Continue with an easy-to-prepare microwave version of

Chicken Teriyaki. Chicken breast halves are marinated in a flavorful mixture of white wine, low-sodium soy sauce, pineapple juice, and honey. Add crunchy water chestnuts and serve the chicken on a bed of fluffy rice.

For a light but satisfying dessert, enjoy Coconut Custard—a fluffy coconut meringue sitting on top of a luscious pineapple custard. The dessert cooks in less than 10 minutes in the microwave.

CHICKEN TERIYAKI

⅓ cup Chablis or other dry white wine
¼ cup low-sodium soy sauce
3 tablespoons unsweetened pineapple juice
2 tablespoons honey
4 (4-ounce) skinned, boned chicken breast halves
1 (8-ounce) can sliced water chestnuts, drained
1 tablespoon water
2½ teaspoons cornstarch
2 cups hot cooked long-grain rice (cooked without salt or fat)

Combine wine, soy sauce, pineapple juice, and honey; stir well. Set aside.

Trim fat from chicken. Rinse with cold, running water and pat dry. Place chicken in an 11- x 7- x 2-inch baking dish with thickest portions toward outside of dish. Pour wine mixture over chicken. Cover and marinate in refrigerator 2 hours, turning occasionally.

Top chicken with water chestnuts. Cover with wax paper and microwave at HIGH for 8 to 10 minutes or until chicken is tender, rearranging after 5 minutes.

Remove chicken from marinade, reserving marinade. Set chicken aside, and keep warm.

Combine water and cornstarch in a glass measure, stirring well. Gradually stir in reserved marinade. Microwave at HIGH for 3 to 4 minutes or

until thickened. Arrange chicken over hot cooked rice. Spoon sauce evenly over chicken. Yield: 4 servings (355 calories per serving).

PROTEIN 30.1 / FAT 1.6 / CARBOHYDRATE 52.4 / CHOLESTEROL 66 / IRON 2.6 / SODIUM 681 / CALCIUM 33

SWEET PEPPER SALAD

2 medium-size green peppers, cut into julienne strips
1 medium-size sweet red pepper, cut into julienne strips
¼ cup thinly sliced green onions
2 tablespoons red wine vinegar
1 tablespoon olive oil
1 tablespoon water
1 small clove garlic, minced
1 teaspoon sugar
½ teaspoon dried Italian seasoning
⅛ teaspoon salt

Combine pepper strips in a large bowl; set aside. Combine green onions and remaining ingredients in a 1-cup glass measure; stir well. Microwave, uncovered, at HIGH for 1½ to 2½ minutes or until mixture boils. Pour over pepper strips. Cover and chill thoroughly. Yield: 4 servings (56 calories per ½-cup serving).

PROTEIN 0.8 / FAT 3.7 / CARBOHYDRATE 5.5 / CHOLESTEROL 0 / IRON 1.2 / SODIUM 76 / CALCIUM 15

Tropical Starfruit Sippers (page 62) are garnished with slices of starfruit.

COCONUT CUSTARD

1 cup skim milk
2 tablespoons sugar
2 tablespoons cornstarch
1 tablespoon margarine
2 eggs, separated
1 cup unsweetened pineapple juice
1 tablespoon lime juice
¼ teaspoon rum extract
2 tablespoons powdered sugar
½ teaspoon coconut extract
2 tablespoons plus 2 teaspoons unsweetened grated coconut, toasted

Combine milk, sugar, cornstarch, and margarine in a 1-quart glass measure. Microwave, uncovered, at HIGH for 2 to 3 minutes or until mixture begins to boil, stirring once. Combine egg yolks and pineapple juice in a medium bowl; beat well with a wire whisk. Gradually stir about one-fourth of hot milk mixture into egg mixture; add to remaining milk mixture, stirring constantly. Microwave, uncovered, at HIGH for 3 to 5 minutes or until thickened, stirring after every minute. Remove from oven; stir in lime juice and rum extract.

Spoon mixture evenly into four 6-ounce custard cups. Beat egg whites (at room temperature) at high speed of an electric mixer 1 minute. Gradually add sugar, 1 tablespoon at a time, beating until stiff peaks form and sugar dissolves (2 to 4 minutes). Gently fold in coconut extract. Spread meringue mixture evenly over custard. Microwave, uncovered, at HIGH for 1 to 1½ minutes or until meringue is set. Sprinkle 2 teaspoons coconut over each serving. Serve immediately. Yield: 4 servings (200 calories per serving).

PROTEIN 5.6 / FAT 8.0 / CARBOHYDRATE 26.5 / CHOLESTEROL 138 / IRON 0.8 / SODIUM 102 / CALCIUM 102

STARFRUIT SIPPERS

2 tablespoons sugar
2 tablespoons water
1 tablespoon chopped crystallized ginger
2 medium starfruit (6½ ounces), sliced and seeded
1 cup sliced fresh strawberries
Sugar
2 cups Chablis or other dry white wine, chilled
¾ cup sodium-free seltzer water, chilled
Starfruit slices (optional)

Combine 2 tablespoons sugar, water, and ginger in a 1-cup glass measure. Microwave, uncovered, at HIGH for 2 to 3 minutes or until mixture forms a light syrup, stirring after every minute. Cool slightly. Place starfruit, strawberries, and sugar mixture in container of an electric blender; top with cover, and process until smooth. Cover and chill thoroughly.

To serve, lightly moisten the rims of four 10-ounce glasses. Place sugar in a saucer; spin rim of each glass in sugar. Combine fruit mixture and wine, stirring well. Pour evenly into glasses. Add 3 tablespoons seltzer water to each glass; stir gently. Garnish with starfruit slices, if desired. Serve immediately. Yield: 4 servings (93 calories per 1-cup serving).

PROTEIN 0.6 / FAT 0.3 / CARBOHYDRATE 23.2 / CHOLESTEROL 0 / IRON 1.5 / SODIUM 19 / CALCIUM 28

EXERCISE AS PREVENTIVE MEDICINE

Several studies now suggest that exercise may reduce the risk of developing cancer. A study of nearly 17,000 Harvard alumni found that the cancer mortality rate was significantly lower in people who burned more than 2,000 calories per week during aerobic exercise than in those who burned less than 500 calories per week.

The reasons are not clear, but the benefits of exercise, such as reducing obesity and increasing components of the immune system, may play a role. Also, exercisers tend to have other healthy habits as well, including a diet lower in fat and not smoking.

Typical Australian fare: Rosemary Grilled Lamb Chops, Minted Peas and Carrots, and Tropical Trifle (page 64).

Dinner From Down-Under

Come to the vast land down-under and sample the bounty of fresh foods native to Australia for a dinner that would please the whole outback.

To begin your culinary journey to the country where there are more sheep than men, try Rosemary Grilled Lamb Chops marinated in a mixture of wine, garlic, and rosemary, then cooked in the microwave oven and finished on the grill. Team

Rosemary Grilled Lamb Chops
Minted Peas and Carrots
Baked Potato
Tropical Trifle
Hot Tea

Serves 6
Total calories per serving: 698

the lamb chops with Minted Peas and Carrots and one baked

potato per person.

Tropical Trifle, a colorful layered dessert, begins with a variety of fresh fruit commonly enjoyed in Australia—pineapples, kiwifruit, strawberries, and mangos. Top the fresh fruit mixture with pieces of commercial angel food cake, then pour the rich custard sauce over the cake and garnish with slices of starfruit. Serve hot tea with dessert in typical Australian fashion.

ROSEMARY GRILLED LAMB CHOPS

½ cup Chablis or other dry white wine
2 tablespoons lemon juice
1 tablespoon vegetable oil
4 cloves garlic, minced
2 teaspoons dried whole rosemary
⅛ teaspoon salt
¼ teaspoon pepper
6 (6-ounce) lamb loin chops (1-inch thick)
Vegetable cooking spray

Combine first 7 ingredients in an 11- x 7- x 2-inch baking dish, stirring well.

Trim fat from chops; place chops in baking dish. Cover and marinate in refrigerator at least 8 hours, turning chops occasionally.

Arrange chops with thickest portion towards outside of dish. Cover with wax paper and microwave at MEDIUM (50% power) for 8 minutes, turning chops over and rearranging after 4 minutes. Drain chops, reserving marinade.

Coat grill rack with cooking spray; place on grill over medium-hot coals. Place chops on rack, and cook 14 minutes or to desired degree of doneness, turning and basting frequently with reserved marinade. Serve immediately. Yield: 6 servings (264 calories per serving).

PROTEIN 33.9 / FAT 12.4 / CARBOHYDRATE 2.2 / CHOLESTEROL 119 / IRON 3.1 / SODIUM 178 / CALCIUM 32

MINTED PEAS AND CARROTS

¼ cup thinly sliced green onions
1 (16-ounce) package frozen green peas and carrots
3 tablespoons water
¼ cup chopped fresh mint leaves
⅛ teaspoon salt
⅛ teaspoon pepper
Fresh mint sprigs (optional)

Place first 3 ingredients in a 1-quart casserole. Cover with heavy-duty plastic wrap; microwave at HIGH for 5 to 8 minutes or until tender, stirring after 3 minutes. Stir in remaining ingredients. Garnish with mint sprigs, if desired. Yield: 6 servings (53 calories per ½-cup serving).

PROTEIN 3.3 / FAT 0.3 / CARBOHYDRATE 9.8 / CHOLESTEROL 0 / IRON 1.2 / SODIUM 125 / CALCIUM 25

TROPICAL TRIFLE

¼ cup sugar
¼ teaspoon salt
3 tablespoons cornstarch
1¾ cups plus 2 tablespoons skim milk
1 egg yolk
2 tablespoons cream sherry
1 (8-ounce) can unsweetened pineapple chunks, drained
1 kiwifruit, peeled and sliced
½ cup fresh strawberries, sliced
1 medium mango, peeled, seeded, and cubed
4 (1-ounce) slices angel food cake, cut into ½-inch cubes
1 starfruit, sliced and seeded
Strawberry fan (optional)
Fresh mint sprigs (optional)

Combine sugar, salt, and cornstarch in a 1½-quart casserole. Gradually add milk, stirring with a wire whisk. Microwave, uncovered, at MEDIUM HIGH (70% power) for 5 to 6 minutes or until thickened, stirring every 2 minutes.

Combine egg yolk and sherry, beating with a wire whisk. Gradually stir about one-fourth of hot mixture into egg mixture; add to remaining hot mixture, stirring constantly. Microwave, uncovered, at MEDIUM HIGH for 1 minute. Cover with plastic wrap, gently pressing directly on pudding. Chill until thickened.

Combine pineapple, kiwifruit, strawberries, and mango. Line bottom of a 2-quart glass bowl with half of fruit. Cover fruit with angel food cake. Spread half of chilled pudding over cake. Spoon remaining half of fruit over pudding. Cover with remaining pudding. Top with starfruit. Chill thoroughly. If desired, garnish with strawberry fan and fresh mint sprigs. Yield: 6 servings (197 calories per serving).

PROTEIN 4.7 / FAT 1.4 / CARBOHYDRATE 42.7 / CHOLESTEROL 47 / IRON 0.5 / SODIUM 168 / CALCIUM 131

Mexican Fiesta

Zucchini-Beef Burritos
Mexican Rice
Cherry Tomato Salad
Rum-Pineapple Boat
Light Beer

Serves 6
Total calories per serving: 683

This Mexican Fiesta fare is high in complex carbohydrates yet low in fat. Spicy Zucchini-Beef Burritos begin with flank steak marinated in commercial oil-free Italian dressing, then cooked quickly. Next it is rolled up in a tortilla along with zucchini, green onions, and cherry tomatoes, then topped with two cheeses. Include a 12-ounce serving of light beer per person.

Rum-Pineapple Boat is an easy but impressive way to serve fruit for dessert.

ZUCCHINI-BEEF BURRITOS

¾ pound lean flank steak
½ cup commercial oil-free Italian dressing
1 clove garlic, minced
6 (8-inch) flour tortillas
1 cup shredded zucchini
½ cup chopped green onions
6 cherry tomatoes, quartered
Vegetable cooking spray
1 (8-ounce) can no-salt-added tomato sauce
½ teaspoon chili powder
¼ teaspoon garlic powder
⅛ teaspoon onion powder
¼ cup (1 ounce) finely shredded Monterey Jack cheese with jalapeño peppers
¼ cup (1 ounce) finely shredded 40% less-fat Cheddar cheese

Partially freeze steak; trim fat from steak. Slice steak diagonally across grain into thin strips. Cut each strip in half lengthwise. Arrange in a 2½-quart shallow casserole. Combine dressing and garlic; pour over beef. Cover and marinate in refrigerator at least 2 hours.

Cover casserole with wax paper. Microwave at MEDIUM HIGH (70% power) for 5 minutes; stir. Cover and microwave at MEDIUM HIGH an additional 7 minutes or to desired degree of doneness, stirring after 3 minutes. Let stand, covered, 5 minutes. Drain and discard marinade.

Place tortillas between paper towels and microwave at HIGH for 40 seconds to 1 minute or until softened. Distribute beef, zucchini, green onions, and tomato evenly down center of each tortilla. Roll up and place seam side up in a 13- x 9- x 2-inch baking dish that has been coated with cooking spray.

Combine tomato sauce, chili powder, garlic powder, and onion powder; stir well. Pour over burritos. Cover with wax paper. Microwave at MEDIUM HIGH for 2 to 3 minutes or until thoroughly heated. Uncover; sprinkle with cheeses. Microwave, uncovered, at HIGH 1 to 2 minutes or until cheese melts. Serve immediately. Yield: 6 servings (313 calories per serving).

PROTEIN 17.8 / FAT 12.1 / CARBOHYDRATE 35.9 / CHOLESTEROL 34 / IRON 2.5 / SODIUM 197 / CALCIUM 122

MEXICAN RICE

1⅔ cups water
½ teaspoon dry mustard
½ teaspoon beef-flavored bouillon granules
1½ cups uncooked instant rice
¼ cup chopped green pepper
1 (4-ounce) can chopped green chiles, undrained

Combine water, dry mustard, and bouillon granules in a 2-quart casserole. Stir in rice and chopped green pepper. Cover with heavy-duty plastic wrap, and microwave at HIGH for 8 to 10 minutes or until liquid is absorbed. Let stand 3 minutes. Stir in chopped green chiles. Fluff with a fork before serving. Yield: 6 servings (97 calories per ½-cup serving).

PROTEIN 2.0 / FAT 0.2 / CARBOHYDRATE 21.1 / CHOLESTEROL 0 / IRON 0.9 / SODIUM 79 / CALCIUM 3

CHERRY TOMATO SALAD

⅓ pound cherry tomatoes, quartered
¼ pound yellow plum tomatoes, quartered
1 small purple onion, thinly sliced and halved
¼ cup plus 2 tablespoons commercial
  reduced-calorie ranch-style dressing
½ small avocado, peeled, pitted, and diced

Arrange tomatoes and onion on a large serving platter. Drizzle dressing down center of salad. Top with diced avocado. Yield: 6 servings (76 calories per serving).

PROTEIN 1.0 / FAT 6.2 / CARBOHYDRATE 9.6 / CHOLESTEROL 0 / IRON 0.5 / SODIUM 130 / CALCIUM 13

RUM-PINEAPPLE BOAT

1 tablespoon unsweetened grated coconut
1 large fresh pineapple
3 tablespoons dark rum
2 tablespoons brown sugar

Place coconut in a custard cup; microwave at HIGH for 3 to 4 minutes or until toasted, stirring after every minute. Set aside.

Cut a slice from side of pineapple, leaving top intact to form a boat. Scoop out pulp, leaving ¼- to ½-inch-thick shell; set aside. Discard slice.

Cut pineapple pulp into bite-size pieces, discarding core. Combine pulp, rum, and sugar in a medium bowl; stir well. Cover with heavy-duty plastic wrap and microwave at HIGH for 4 to 5 minutes or until thoroughly heated. Spoon pineapple mixture into reserved shell. Sprinkle with toasted coconut. Serve warm. Yield: 6 servings (98 calories per ½-cup serving).

PROTEIN 0.5 / FAT 1.0 / CARBOHYDRATE 19.3 / CHOLESTEROL 0 / IRON 0.6 / SODIUM 3 / CALCIUM 12

Wild Mushroom Pizzas (page 75) topped with goat cheese and Warm Green-and-Red Salad (page 76) with pine nuts take pizza and salad out of the ordinary.

Bistro Luncheon

The word "bistro" means different things to different people, but in terms of the type of food that is served in a bistro, one common definition emerges—dishes that are light, simple, and unpretentious. The first bistros in Europe were simple neighborhood cafés or taverns that served inexpensive, quickly prepared foods. Today our American bistros are in the forefront of creative cookery techniques and trends, but they still adhere to a light approach to food preparation.

Our bistro-inspired luncheon is

Tuna Salad Niçoise
Raisin Bread Pudding
Commercial French Bread
Rolls
Champagne Kir

Serves 6
Total calories per serving: 615

quickly prepared, yet festive and pretty. Champagne Kir sets the mood with a colorful mixture of black currant syrup and champagne. Tuna Salad Niçoise, a contemporary adaptation of a European bistro classic, is light

and lively in its presentation and easily assembled just before serving. The individually served Raisin Bread Pudding is made with a rich-tasting custard base laced with the flavor of fresh raspberries. The puddings can be assembled in advance and baked while guests are enjoying their salad.

Round out the meal with one crusty commercial French bread roll per person. Then relax and enjoy, along with the guests, the ambience created by this special bistro luncheon.

TUNA SALAD NIÇOISE

1 (12½-ounce) can water-packed Albacore tuna, drained
2 tablespoons lemon juice
1 tablespoon capers
¼ teaspoon salt
¼ teaspoon pepper
¾ pound fresh baby green beans
1 pound small red potatoes, unpeeled
¾ pound cherry tomatoes, halved
1 medium-size sweet yellow pepper, seeded and cut into julienne strips
½ medium-size purple onion, thinly sliced
Vinaigrette (recipe follows)
1 large head curly leaf lettuce, torn
¼ cup Niçoise olives
2 tablespoons chopped fresh parsley

Combine tuna, lemon juice, capers, salt, and pepper; toss gently and set aside.

Wash beans; trim ends, and remove strings. Cook beans in a small amount of boiling water 5 minutes or until crisp-tender. Drain. Plunge beans into ice water to cool; drain again and set aside.

Cook potatoes in boiling water 15 minutes or until tender. Drain; plunge potatoes into ice water to cool. Drain again and let cool. Cut potatoes into quarters.

Place beans, potatoes, tomatoes, yellow pepper strips, and onion in separate bowls. Add 2 tablespoons Vinaigrette to each bowl; toss gently. Cover and chill thoroughly.

Arrange lettuce leaves on a large serving platter. Mound tuna mixture in center of platter. Arrange chilled vegetables around tuna. Drizzle remaining 2 tablespoons Vinaigrette over salad. Sprinkle with olives and parsley. Yield: 6 servings (216 calories per serving).

Vinaigrette:

½ teaspoon chicken-flavored bouillon granules
½ cup boiling water
2 tablespoons red wine vinegar
1 tablespoon lemon juice
2 cloves garlic, minced
1 tablespoon vegetable oil
¼ teaspoon dried whole oregano

Dissolve bouillon granules in boiling water; set aside and let cool. Combine bouillon and remaining ingredients, stirring with a wire whisk until blended. Yield: ¾ cup.

PROTEIN 16.0 / FAT 5.6 / CARBOHYDRATE 28.3 / CHOLESTEROL 17 / IRON 2.5 / SODIUM 474 / CALCIUM 52

A richly flavored custard laced with raspberries makes Raisin Bread Pudding a flavorful dessert.

RAISIN BREAD PUDDING

12 (½-inch) slices raisin bread
Vegetable cooking spray
½ cup fresh raspberries
2 cups skim milk
1 egg
2 egg yolks
¼ cup sugar
¼ teaspoon vanilla extract
Fresh mint sprigs (optional)

Trim crust from bread; cut bread into 12 rounds using a 2½-inch biscuit cutter. Place 1 round into each of six (6-ounce) custard cups that have been coated with cooking spray.

Press raspberries through a fine sieve to yield ¼ cup juice; discard seeds. Spoon 2 teaspoons juice onto each bread round in custard cups. Top with remaining bread rounds; set aside.

Place milk in top of a double boiler; bring water to a boil. Cook until milk is thoroughly heated. Set aside.

Combine egg, yolks, sugar, and vanilla in a medium bowl, stirring well. Gradually add milk, stirring constantly with a wire whisk until well blended. Pour milk mixture evenly into prepared custard cups.

Place custard cups in a 13- x 9- x 2-inch baking dish; pour hot water into baking dish to a depth of 1 inch. Bake at 350° for 40 to 45 minutes or until set. Remove cups from water. Serve warm or chilled. Garnish with fresh mint sprigs, if desired. Yield: 6 servings (140 calories per serving).

PROTEIN 5.7 / FAT 3.6 / CARBOHYDRATE 21.2 / CHOLESTEROL 139 / IRON 0.7 / SODIUM 109 / CALCIUM 126

CHAMPAGNE KIR

1 (25.4-ounce) bottle champagne, chilled
1 tablespoon black currant syrup
Lemon rind curls (optional)

Pour champagne evenly into 6 champagne glasses. Add ½ teaspoon syrup to each glass; stir gently. Garnish with lemon rind curls, if desired. Yield: 3 cups (104 calories per ½-cup serving).

PROTEIN 0.4 / FAT 0.0 / CARBOHYDRATE 3.6 / CHOLESTEROL 0 / IRON 0.7 / SODIUM 5 / CALCIUM 7

(Clockwise from top): Cauliflower Medley, Spicy Garlic Shrimp, Potato Omelet, Marinated Squid Salad, Black-and-White Bean Salad, Spanish Vegetable Ragout, and Fresh Mushroom Salad.

Tapas Party

Tapas, those delicious little dishes of Spain, are a centuries-old social institution in Spain. Consumed with zeal in bars and taverns before lunch and again before dinner, they are an integral part of the Spanish life-style. Tapas, besides being a social phenomenon in Spain, are also a way to satisfy appetites between meals in a country where lunch is rarely eaten before 2 or 3 p.m. and dinner is around 10 p.m. Tapas are not necessarily a particular kind of food, but rather a casual style of eating.

However, tapas bars and parties are quickly proliferating in the United States as many people are discovering the benefits of eating in the tapas style and spirit. Viewed as a new way of entertaining, tapas bridge the gap between the not-so-filling cocktail party and a full-course, sit-down dinner party. Tapas have most certainly found a comfortable niche in the United States as a way to entertain that is readily

Spicy Garlic Shrimp
Marinated Squid Salad
Black-and-White Bean Salad
Cauliflower Medley
Fresh Mushroom Salad
Potato Omelet
Spanish Vegetable Ragout

Serves 16
Total calories per serving: 302

adaptable to our fast-paced American lifestyle.

Tapas take appetizers into a whole new world. These fun, interesting "little bites" range from the simple to the sophisticated; there are as many varieties of tapas as the imagination can create. A tapas menu is generally served in small portions and contains a variety of colors, tastes, and textures that are complementary to one another.

Traditionally, tapas contain a large amount of oil. To lighten this menu without sacrificing

flavor, we have used marinade mixtures containing dry sherry, wine, red wine vinegar, chicken broth, olive oil, or lemon juice with liberal amounts of seasonings such as garlic, cumin, and crushed red pepper.

This Tapas Party menu may be considered an appetizer menu, but the dishes are quite substantial and will certainly satisfy the appetites of the heartiest of eaters. Most of the dishes can be prepared in advance with only the Spicy Garlic Shrimp and Potato Omelet being cooked right before serving.

Serve all the tapas dishes on large, colorful platters with small individual plates and forks on the side. For those guests who are less calorie conscious, be sure to include some very dry fino sherry to lend an authentic Spanish touch to the party.

As a unique Spanish cuisine, tapas should be served in a setting of friendship, spontaneity, and good times.

SPICY GARLIC SHRIMP

2 pounds unpeeled large fresh shrimp
½ cup dry sherry
¼ cup freshly squeezed lemon juice
1 tablespoon olive oil
1½ cloves garlic, minced
2 teaspoons paprika
1 teaspoon crushed red pepper
Lemon wedges (optional)

Devein shrimp by cutting down the back through the shell with a small pair of scissors, leaving shell, legs, and tail intact. Place in a

large shallow baking dish.

Combine sherry and next 5 ingredients; pour over shrimp. Cover and marinate in refrigerator 8 hours.

Place shrimp and marinade in broiler pan. Broil 6 inches from heat 3 to 4 minutes on each side or until shrimp are done, basting with marinade. Transfer shrimp to a serving platter; serve with lemon wedges, if desired. Yield: 16 servings (36 calories per serving).

PROTEIN 5.8 / FAT 0.9 / CARBOHYDRATE 0.9 / CHOLESTEROL 43 / IRON 0.7 / SODIUM 42 / CALCIUM 16

MARINATED SQUID SALAD

½ pound cleaned, skinned calamari (squid)
1½ cups diagonally sliced celery
1 small sweet red pepper, seeded and
  cut into julienne strips
½ small purple onion, sliced
¼ cup red wine vinegar
2 tablespoons Chablis or other dry
  white wine
1 tablespoon olive oil
3 cloves garlic, minced
¼ teaspoon freshly ground pepper
¼ teaspoon crushed red pepper

Slice calamari into ½-inch rings. Drop into boiling water for 15 to 20 seconds or until calamari begins to curl around edges. Drain; rinse with cold water. Drain again.

Combine calamari, celery, red pepper, and onion in a large bowl. Combine vinegar and remaining ingredients; pour over calamari mixture, tossing well. Cover and marinate in refrigerator 8 hours. Yield: 16 servings (26 calories per ¼-cup serving).

PROTEIN 2.4 / FAT 1.1 / CARBOHYDRATE 1.4 / CHOLESTEROL 33 /
IRON 0.2 / SODIUM 15 / CALCIUM 10

BLACK-AND-WHITE BEAN SALAD

7 ounces dried black beans
7 ounces dried Great Northern beans
1 cup sliced green onions
1 cup diced sweet red pepper
1 cup diced green pepper
1¾ cups peeled, seeded, and chopped tomato
3 tablespoons red wine vinegar
2 tablespoons canned no-salt-added chicken broth,
  undiluted
1 tablespoon olive oil
1 teaspoon salt
1 clove garlic, minced
½ teaspoon freshly ground pepper

Sort and wash beans; place in separate large Dutch ovens. Cover with water 3 inches above

beans. Bring to a boil; boil 5 minutes. Remove from heat. Cover and let stand 1 hour. Drain; return beans to Dutch ovens. Cover with water 3 inches above beans. Bring to a boil. Reduce heat, and simmer 1 hour or until beans are tender. Drain; rinse with cold water. Drain again.

Combine beans, onions, red pepper, green pepper, and tomato in a serving bowl. Combine vinegar and remaining ingredients, stirring with a wire whisk until well blended. Pour over bean mixture; toss gently. Cover and marinate in refrigerator at least 4 hours. Yield: 16 servings (102 calories per ½-cup serving).

PROTEIN 5.8 / FAT 1.3 / CARBOHYDRATE 17.9 / CHOLESTEROL 0 /
IRON 2.1 / SODIUM 152 / CALCIUM 45

CAULIFLOWER MEDLEY

1 large cauliflower (3 pounds)
2 tablespoons lemon juice
½ cup commercial reduced-calorie Italian dressing
2 tablespoons capers
¼ teaspoon cracked pepper
2 tablespoons sliced ripe olives
1 (4-ounce) jar sliced pimiento, drained

Wash cauliflower, and break into small flowerets. Arrange cauliflower in a steaming basket. Plunge into boiling water to which

lemon juice has been added. Blanch for 4 minutes or until crisp-tender. Drain and transfer to a large bowl of ice water to cool. Drain well, and pat dry.

Combine dressing and remaining ingredients in a large bowl; stir well. Add cauliflower, and toss gently. Cover and marinate in refrigerator at least 2 hours. Yield: 16 servings (20 calories per ½-cup serving).

PROTEIN 1.2 / FAT 0.2 / CARBOHYDRATE 4.1 / CHOLESTEROL 0 /
IRON 0.4 / SODIUM 87 / CALCIUM 19

FRESH MUSHROOM SALAD

¼ cup canned no-salt-added chicken broth, undiluted
2 tablespoons minced fresh parsley
3 tablespoons lemon juice
1 teaspoon olive oil
1 teaspoon salt
1 clove garlic, minced
½ teaspoon ground cumin
¼ teaspoon freshly ground pepper
1½ pounds fresh mushrooms, quartered
Fresh basil sprigs (optional)

Combine first 8 ingredients in a large bowl. Add mushrooms; toss gently. Cover; marinate in refrigerator 2 hours, tossing occasionally. Garnish with basil sprigs, if desired. Yield: 16 servings (15 calories per ¼-cup serving).

PROTEIN 1.0 / FAT 0.5 / CARBOHYDRATE 2.4 / CHOLESTEROL 0 / IRON 0.6 / SODIUM 151 / CALCIUM 5

POTATO OMELET

2 pounds red potatoes, peeled
1 cup sliced green onions
6 eggs, beaten
½ teaspoon salt
¼ teaspoon freshly ground pepper
¼ teaspoon hot sauce
Vegetable cooking spray
Green onion fans (optional)

Cook potatoes in boiling water to cover 15 minutes or until tender. Drain; chill thoroughly.

Combine green onions, eggs, salt, pepper, and hot sauce in a large bowl. Thinly slice potatoes, and add to egg mixture.

Coat a 10-inch nonstick skillet with cooking spray. Place over medium heat until hot. Spoon potato mixture into skillet. Cook 20 minutes or until outer edge is set. Broil 6 inches from heat 5 minutes or until set and golden brown. Remove from oven; let rest 10 minutes.

To serve, invert omelet onto serving platter. Cut into 1-inch squares. Garnish with green onion fans, if desired. Serve warm or cold. Yield: 16 servings (74 calories per serving).

PROTEIN 3.7 / FAT 2.2 / CARBOHYDRATE 9.9 / CHOLESTEROL 103 / IRON 1.2 / SODIUM 104 / CALCIUM 24

SPANISH VEGETABLE RAGOUT

2 medium-size sweet red peppers
2 medium-size green peppers
Vegetable cooking spray
2 medium onions, cut into ½-inch slices
¼ cup water
2 medium zucchini, sliced
5 large cloves garlic, minced
1 (28-ounce) can whole tomatoes, undrained
⅛ teaspoon ground saffron
⅛ teaspoon freshly ground pepper
2 tablespoons chopped fresh parsley

Wash and dry peppers; place on an ungreased baking sheet. Broil 3 to 4 inches from heat until blistered on all sides, turning often with tongs. Immediately place peppers in a plastic bag; seal and let stand 10 minutes to loosen skins.

Peel peppers; remove core and seeds. Slice peppers into ½-inch strips. Set aside.

Coat a large Dutch oven with cooking spray. Place over medium-high heat until hot. Add onion slices and water, and cook 7 minutes or until water is evaporated. Add pepper strips, zucchini, and remaining ingredients; bring to a boil. Uncover, reduce heat, and simmer 20 minutes. Serve immediately. Yield: 16 servings (29 calories per ½-cup serving).

PROTEIN 1.3 / FAT 0.3 / CARBOHYDRATE 6.0 / CHOLESTEROL 0 / IRON 0.8 / SODIUM 83 / CALCIUM 27

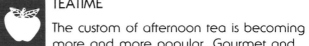 TEATIME

The custom of afternoon tea is becoming more and more popular. Gourmet and specialty stores are displaying endless varieties, and hotels and restaurants are adding specialty teas to their menus. Interestingly, all of the 3,000 varieties of tea come from the same plant, the tea plant. The differences in color, flavor, and aroma of teas depend on where the tea plant is grown. Black tea is oxidized, or fermented, which causes the leaves to darken and contributes to a dark, hearty brew. Oolong tea is semi-fermented, imparting a tender brown color and a light brew. Green teas make a very light cup of tea because the leaves require no oxidation. Teabags may contain 20 to 30 varieties of tea leaves blended to match American tastes.

Crisp Hazelnut Meringues and creamy Cappuccino make a satisfying ending to a meal.

Pizza Party

Remember those teenage pizza parties? Well, we've grown up and so have our tastes in pizzas. Here's a Pizza Party menu to suit our more sophisticated adult palates. Serve these exotic Wild Mushroom Pizzas, and let the good times roll.

First, toss together a Warm Green-and-Red Salad. Use raddi-chio and escarole enlivened with a splash of balsamic vinegar and

Wild Mushroom Pizzas
Warm Green-and-Red Salad
Hazelnut Meringues
Cappuccino

Serves 6
Total calories per serving: 702

topped with toasted pine nuts. Next, bake the individual Wild

Mushroom Pizzas using a mixture of fresh and dried wild and domestic mushrooms on a whole wheat crust.

For dessert, what could be better than blender-made Cappuccino accompanied by crunchy Hazelnut Meringues laced with Frangelico. You won't miss too much of the fun, because most of the preparation can be done in advance of the party.

WILD MUSHROOM PIZZAS

½ ounce dried porcini mushrooms
8 ounces fresh crimini mushrooms, sliced
8 ounces fresh mushrooms, sliced
½ cup part-skim ricotta cheese
4 ounces crumbled goat cheese
1 tablespoon water
½ cup chopped purple onion
½ teaspoon dried whole thyme
½ teaspoon dried whole basil
½ teaspoon dried whole oregano
⅛ teaspoon salt
⅛ teaspoon freshly ground
   pepper
2 tablespoons Chablis or other
   dry white wine
¾ cup tomato puree
1 large clove garlic, minced
Whole Wheat Pizza Crust
6 large fresh basil leaves, cut into
   julienne strips
Fresh oregano sprigs (optional)
Fresh thyme sprigs (optional)

Pour boiling water over dried porcini mushrooms to cover; let stand 20 minutes. Drain and coarsely chop.

Combine mushrooms, and set aside.

Combine ricotta and goat cheese in a small bowl; stir well. Set aside.

Place a large nonstick skillet over medium-high heat until hot. Add water and chopped purple onion, and cook 1 minute. Add reserved mushrooms, thyme, basil, oregano, salt, and ⅛ teaspoon freshly ground pepper, and cook 8 to 10 minutes or until mushrooms are lightly browned. Add wine, and remove from heat. Set mixture aside.

Combine tomato puree and minced garlic, stirring well. Spread tomato mixture evenly over pizza crusts, leaving a ½-inch border around edges. Spread reserved mushroom mixture evenly over pizzas. Top each pizza with 2 tablespoons plus 2 teaspoons reserved cheese mixture. Sprinkle fresh basil strips evenly over top.

Bake at 500° for 10 minutes or until crusts are lightly browned. If desired, garnish with fresh oregano and thyme sprigs. Serve immediately. Yield: 6 servings (393 calories per serving).

Whole Wheat Pizza Crust:

1 package dry yeast
1 cup warm water (105° to 115°), divided
1 tablespoon honey
2 cups plus 2 tablespoons all-purpose flour, divided
½ cup whole wheat flour
½ cup cornmeal
1 teaspoon salt
Vegetable cooking spray
1 teaspoon all-purpose flour

Dissolve yeast in ¼ cup warm water in a large mixing bowl; let stand 5 minutes.

Combine remaining ¾ cup warm water and honey; add to yeast mixture, stirring gently.

Gradually stir 2 cups all-purpose flour, ½ cup whole wheat flour, cornmeal, and salt into the yeast mixture to form a soft dough. Remove dough to a lightly floured surface. Knead 2 minutes or until dough is soft and elastic, kneading in remaining 2 tablespoons all-purpose flour. Place dough in a bowl that has been coated with cooking spray, turning to grease top. Sprinkle 1 teaspoon flour over dough; cover and let rise in a warm place (85°), free from drafts, 30 minutes.

Punch dough down, and divide into 6 equal portions. Form into small balls. Cover with a towel, and let rest 5 minutes.

Roll each ball into a 7-inch circle, and place on baking sheets that have been coated with cooking spray. Yield: 6 (7-inch) pizza crusts.

PROTEIN 15.2 / FAT 7.1 / CARBOHYDRATE 67.5 / CHOLESTEROL 23 / IRON 4.2 / SODIUM 805 / CALCIUM 183

A HEALTHY WAIST

Excess fat, especially around the waist area, is known to be bad for health. People with "spare tires" around their mid-section are more prone to high blood pressure, elevated blood sugars, heart disease, and strokes than those having excess fat elsewhere in the body. Many researchers believe that fat stored around the waist increases triglycerides and may raise blood sugar levels.

If your waist is too large, consider losing weight with exercise. Exercise burns fat, and when aerobic exercise is combined with prudent eating, weight loss and a trimmer waistline result.

WARM GREEN-AND-RED SALAD

3 tablespoons balsamic vinegar
½ teaspoon sugar
½ teaspoon salt
1 tablespoon olive oil
¼ cup canned no-salt-added chicken broth, undiluted
3 cups torn raddichio
3 cups torn escarole
¼ teaspoon freshly ground pepper
2 tablespoons pine nuts, toasted

Combine first 5 ingredients in a large skillet, and bring to a boil. Add torn raddichio and escarole, tossing gently for 15 seconds or until slightly wilted. Remove greens to a serving bowl; sprinkle with freshly ground pepper, and toss gently. Sprinkle with toasted pine nuts; serve immediately. Yield: 6 servings (60 calories per 1-cup serving).

PROTEIN 2.2 / FAT 4.9 / CARBOHYDRATE 3.7 / CHOLESTEROL 0 / IRON 1.3 / SODIUM 214 / CALCIUM 46

HAZELNUT MERINGUES

¼ cup plus 2 tablespoons hazelnuts, divided
3 egg whites
¼ teaspoon cream of tartar
⅛ teaspoon salt
½ cup superfine sugar
1½ cups chocolate ice milk
2 tablespoons Frangelico or other hazelnut-flavored liqueur
Fresh mint sprigs (optional)

Toast hazelnuts at 400° for 6 minutes. Rub briskly with a towel to remove skins. Chop hazelnuts, and set aside.

Line a large baking sheet with parchment paper; draw six 3½-inch circles on paper.

Beat egg whites (at room temperature), cream of tartar, and salt in a large bowl at high speed of an electric mixer 1 minute. Gradually add sugar, 1 tablespoon at a time, beating until stiff peaks form and sugar dissolves (2 to 4 min-

utes). Gently fold in ¼ cup reserved chopped hazelnuts.

Spoon meringue into a decorating bag fitted with a No. 6 round tip. Pipe meringue evenly in circles on paper. Working quickly, smooth meringue circles, using the back of a spoon. Form a well in center of each meringue by pushing excess meringue up to the edges. Bake at 225° for 2 hours. Turn oven off, and cool meringues in oven for 1 hour. Store in zip-top plastic bags.

To serve, place meringues on a serving platter. Top each meringue with ¼ cup scoop of ice milk. Pour 1 teaspoon liqueur over each serving. Sprinkle 1 teaspoon reserved chopped hazelnuts over each serving. Garnish with fresh mint sprigs, if desired. Serve immediately. Yield: 6 servings (192 calories per serving).

PROTEIN 4.4 / FAT 8.1 / CARBOHYDRATE 26.1 / CHOLESTEROL 5 / IRON 0.4 / SODIUM 109 / CALCIUM 66

CAPPUCCINO

1½ cups skim milk
2 egg whites
1 tablespoon sugar
4½ cups freshly brewed hot coffee
2 tablespoons shaved semisweet chocolate
6 (3-inch) sticks cinnamon

Place milk in a small saucepan; place over low heat, stirring constantly, until mixture reaches 120° to 130°. Remove from heat.

Place egg whites in container of an electric

blender; top with cover, and process at high speed 10 seconds or until frothy. Slowly add hot milk and sugar, blending at high speed 30 seconds.

Pour ¾ cup hot coffee into 6 mugs. Pour milk mixture evenly into coffee. Top each serving with 1 teaspoon chocolate, and add 1 cinnamon stick. Yield: 6 servings (57 calories per 1-cup serving).

PROTEIN 3.5 / FAT 1.4 / CARBOHYDRATE 8.2 / CHOLESTEROL 1 / IRON 1.0 / SODIUM 52 / CALCIUM 86

The flavors of cranberries, grapes, and champagne blend in a delicious fashion in Cranberry-Grape Sorbet.

Cajun Feast

In Cajun cookery, you'll find a greater variety of peppers than in any other ethnic cuisine. Along with onions, garlic, celery, and a number of robust herbs, creative blends of hot and mild peppers give Cajun dishes their unique, fiery flavor.

Spicy Skillet Catfish and Dirty Rice highlight this menu and include ground red, white, and black peppers. Add a Colorful Vegetable Medley featuring

Spicy Skillet Catfish
Colorful Vegetable Medley
Fruity Gelatin Salad
Dirty Rice
Country Corn Sticks
Cranberry-Grape Sorbet

Serves 6
Total calories per serving: 540

zucchini, sweet red and green peppers, okra, and green onions,

all native Louisiana produce. A half hour prior to dinnertime, bake Country Corn Sticks, a tasty meal accompaniment.

Prepare Fruity Gelatin Salad and Cranberry-Grape Sorbet several hours in advance, allowing plenty of time for the gelatin to set and the sorbet to freeze. The sorbet, a light combination of cran-grape juice cocktail and champagne, will cool and refresh the palate.

SPICY SKILLET CATFISH

6 farm-raised catfish fillets
¼ cup lemon juice
1 teaspoon hot sauce
1 tablespoon paprika
1 teaspoon onion powder
1 teaspoon garlic powder
½ teaspoon ground white pepper
½ teaspoon ground red pepper
½ teaspoon dried whole oregano
¼ teaspoon dried whole thyme
¼ teaspoon dry mustard
1 tablespoon plus 1½ teaspoons
  skim milk
2 tablespoons margarine
Lemon twists (optional)
Fresh oregano sprigs (optional)
Fresh thyme sprigs (optional)

Rinse fillets with cold, running water, and pat dry. Place in a shallow dish. Combine lemon juice and hot sauce. Pour over fillets. Cover and marinate in refrigerator at least 30 minutes.

Combine paprika and next 7 ingredients, stirring well. Remove fillets from marinade mixture; discard marinade. Brush fillets with skim milk. Dredge in seasoning mixture.

Preheat a nonstick electric skillet to 400°. Add margarine and heat until margarine melts. Cook fillets, uncovered, 3 minutes on each side or until browned and fish flakes easily when tested with a fork. If desired, garnish with lemon twists, and fresh oregano and thyme sprigs. Yield: 6 servings (178 calories per serving).

PROTEIN 21.2 / FAT 8.9 / CARBOHYDRATE 2.7 / CHOLESTEROL 66 / IRON 1.6 / SODIUM 125 / CALCIUM 60

COLORFUL VEGETABLE MEDLEY

Vegetable cooking spray
2 teaspoons vegetable oil
4 green onions, cut into 1-inch pieces
1½ cups sliced fresh okra
1 medium carrot, scraped and cut into julienne strips
1 medium zucchini, cut into julienne strips
1 small sweet red pepper, seeded and cut into
  julienne strips
¾ teaspoon dried whole basil
¼ teaspoon dried whole thyme
¼ teaspoon salt
¼ teaspoon hot sauce

Coat a large nonstick skillet with vegetable cooking spray. Add vegetable oil to skillet, and place over medium-high heat until hot. Add green onion pieces, sliced okra, carrot, zucchini, and sweet red pepper strips to skillet. Stir in basil, thyme, salt, and hot sauce, and sauté 8 to 10 minutes or until vegetables are crisp-tender. Remove skillet from heat. Serve vegetable mixture immediately. Yield: 6 servings (38 calories per ½-cup serving).

PROTEIN 1.1 / FAT 1.7 / CARBOHYDRATE 5.3 / CHOLESTEROL 0 / IRON 0.8 / SODIUM 107 / CALCIUM 34

FRUITY GELATIN SALAD

2 envelopes unflavored gelatin
2 cups unsweetened orange juice
1 (15¼-ounce) can unsweetened crushed
  pineapple, undrained
2 cups sliced fresh strawberries
1 medium banana, sliced
Vegetable cooking spray
Lettuce leaves (optional)

Sprinkle gelatin over orange juice in a nonaluminum saucepan; let stand 1 minute. Cook over low heat; stir until gelatin dissolves.

Drain pineapple, reserving ⅓ cup juice; stir juice into orange juice mixture. Chill until the consistency of unbeaten egg white.

Add pineapple, strawberries, and banana to gelatin mixture; stir gently. Spoon mixture into a 10- x 6- x 2-inch baking dish that has been coated with cooking spray. Cover and chill until firm. Cut into squares and place each serving on a lettuce-lined salad plate, if desired. Yield: 6 servings (112 calories per serving).

PROTEIN 3.4 / FAT 0.7 / CARBOHYDRATE 25.1 / CHOLESTEROL 0 / IRON 0.6 / SODIUM 5 / CALCIUM 22

DIRTY RICE

½ teaspoon salt
½ teaspoon paprika
¼ teaspoon ground red pepper
¼ teaspoon freshly ground black pepper
¼ teaspoon dry mustard
¼ teaspoon dried whole basil
¼ teaspoon dried whole thyme
1 tablespoon margarine
½ cup chopped onion
½ cup chopped celery
½ cup chopped green pepper
1 clove garlic, minced
⅔ cup uncooked long-grain rice
1⅓ cups water

Combine first 7 ingredients in a small bowl; stir well. Set aside.

Melt margarine in a large saucepan. Add onion, celery, green pepper, and garlic, and sauté until vegetables are crisp-tender. Stir in rice, and sauté until lightly browned. Stir in reserved seasoning mixture and water; bring to a boil. Cover, reduce heat, and simmer 20 minutes or until liquid is absorbed. Yield: 6 servings (104 calories per ½-cup serving).

PROTEIN 1.8 / FAT 2.2 / CARBOHYDRATE 19.0 / CHOLESTEROL 0 / IRON 1.0 / SODIUM 228 / CALCIUM 19

COUNTRY CORN STICKS

¼ cup plus 2 tablespoons cornmeal
2 tablespoons all-purpose flour
1 teaspoon sugar
¼ teaspoon baking powder
¼ teaspoon baking soda
⅛ teaspoon salt
½ cup nonfat buttermilk
1 egg white
2 teaspoons vegetable oil
Vegetable cooking spray

Combine cornmeal, flour, sugar, baking powder, soda, and salt in a medium bowl. Combine buttermilk, egg white, and oil; gradually add to dry ingredients, stirring just until moistened.

Place a cast-iron corn stick pan coated with cooking spray in a 425° oven for 3 minutes or until hot. Remove pan from oven; spoon batter into pan, filling two-thirds full. Bake at 425° for 14 to 16 minutes or until lightly browned. Remove from pan, and serve warm. Yield: ½ dozen (67 calories each)

PROTEIN 2.3 / FAT 1.9 / CARBOHYDRATE 9.9 / CHOLESTEROL 0 / IRON 0.3 / SODIUM 126 / CALCIUM 17

 THESE SHOES ARE MADE FOR WALKING

Shoes designed for walking have become as popular as the sport itself. Base your selection on overall comfort, and make sure they have these features:
*A roomy "toe-box" that allows the foot to spread out and prevents pain and blisters.
*A midsole that absorbs shock while propelling you to take the next step.
*A firm heel and an arch support to guide the foot through its roll forward.
*Thick, cushioned soles to provide protection from the shock of impact.
Remember, you will walk more miles in shoes that provide cushioning and, most of all, comfort.

CRANBERRY-GRAPE SORBET

2½ cups cran-grape juice cocktail
½ cup champagne
1 egg white
1 tablespoon sugar

Pour cran-grape juice cocktail into 2 freezer trays; freeze until almost firm. Spoon mixture into a large mixing bowl, and beat at high speed of an electric mixer until slushy. Gently stir in champagne.

Beat egg white (at room temperature) at high speed of an electric mixer 1 minute. Add sugar, beating until soft peaks form. Carefully fold beaten egg white into juice mixture; pour into freezer can of a hand-turned or electric freezer. Freeze according to manufacturer's instructions. Scoop sorbet into individual dessert bowls, and serve immediately. Yield: 6 cups (41 calories per ½-cup serving).

PROTEIN 0.4 / FAT 0.1 / CARBOHYDRATE 8.3 / CHOLESTEROL 0 / IRON 0.1 / SODIUM 6 / CALCIUM 5

Beautifully arranged Lobster Nouvelle makes a special entrée for a special someone.

St. Valentine's Day Dinner For Two

A very special person deserves a very special dinner like this St. Valentine's Day Dinner for Two menu. Not only is the meal special in flavor and elegant in appearance, but it is also balanced nutritionally.

Elegant, special-occasion dinners needn't be loaded with calorie- and fat-laden butter and cream sauces. Lobster and caviar, long associated with food indulgence, are usually prepared with heavy, rich sauces. In this menu, we have lightened our lobster sauce by using vegetables as a thickener and a low-fat cottage cheese for richness. Each serving of Lobster Nouvelle is accompanied by a fan of notched snow

New Potatoes with Sour Cream and Caviar
Lobster Nouvelle
Heavenly Heart Meringues
Blush Wine

Serves 2
Total calories per serving: 710

pea pods and garnished with fresh basil for an impressive visual display.

For the appetizer, begin with small new potatoes that are cooked and cut into wedges, then topped with low-fat sour cream and a colorful sprinkling of red, black, or golden caviar— a delicious but light combination.

Nestle the potato wedges on a bed of rock salt to serve. Accompany the meal with a 6-ounce serving of delicately tinted blush wine per person.

For dessert we suggest serving romantic, heart-shaped Heavenly Heart Meringues. Easily prepared in advance, these delicate chocolate-flavored meringue shells can be filled at the last moment with fresh peaches, blueberries, and strawberry slices. Be sure to store empty meringue shells in zip-top plastic bags in order to preserve their crispness.

Set the table with lace and flowers, light the candles, and put on beautiful music for a special evening meal for two.

NEW POTATOES WITH SOUR CREAM AND CAVIAR

4 small new potatoes (⅓ pound)
Rock salt
2 teaspoons low-fat sour cream
1 teaspoon red, black, or golden caviar

Place potatoes in a medium saucepan; cover with water, and bring to a boil. Cover, reduce heat, and cook 15 to 20 minutes or until tender. Drain and cool.

Cut each potato into 4 wedges, cutting to but not through base of potato. Spread wedges slightly apart. Fill 2 small serving plates with rock salt. Arrange potatoes on top of salt. Top each potato with ½ teaspoon sour cream and ¼ teaspoon caviar. Yield: 2 servings (68 calories per serving).

PROTEIN 2.7 / FAT 1.1 / CARBOHYDRATE 12.1 / CHOLESTEROL 13 / IRON 1.3 / SODIUM 69 / CALCIUM 22

NO PAIN, BIG GAIN

The theory of "no-pain, no-gain" exercise has been revised. Muscle pain while exercising is called overload training and is the result of working at high intensity. The pain felt during a burst of hard exercise is due in part to the swelling of a contracted muscle. This swelling and pressure reduces the blood flow to the muscle and prevents the individual muscle fibers from receiving sufficient oxygen. This is what many athletes call "the burn." When exercise is stopped, blood circulation returns to normal and the pain is relieved. For most exercisers, overload training and "feeling the burn" can lead to injury and should not be practiced.

Exercising in your target heart rate zone should not be painful. If pain does occur, stop and rest the stressed muscles. Pain is the body's warning signal that something is not right. Working through pain is not necessary for fitness and may lead to burnout or injuries to the muscles.

LOBSTER NOUVELLE

1 stalk celery, cut into 2-inch pieces
1 medium carrot, scraped and cut into 2-inch pieces
½ medium onion, quartered
2 bay leaves
2 fresh parsley sprigs
1 fresh thyme sprig or 1 teaspoon dried whole thyme
¼ teaspoon black peppercorns
2 quarts water
2 cups Chablis or other dry white wine
2 (¾-pound) live lobsters
6 ounces snow pea pods
1 tablespoon margarine
½ cup diced carrot
½ cup diced celery
½ cup diced onion
2 tablespoons tomato paste
½ cup low-fat cottage cheese
1 cup hot cooked fettuccine (cooked without salt or fat)
¼ cup seeded and chopped tomato
2 fresh basil leaves, cut into julienne strips
Fresh basil sprigs (optional)

Combine first 9 ingredients in a large stockpot; bring to a boil. Plunge lobsters, head first, into boiling liquid. Return to a boil; cover and simmer 10 minutes. Remove lobster from liquid; cool. Strain liquid, reserving 2 cups; place in a medium saucepan, and reduce by half.

Place lobster on its back. Cut lobster in half lengthwise. Remove the stomach (located just back of the head) and the intestinal vein (runs from the stomach to the tip of the tail). Remove tail meat from lobster in one piece. Cut into diagonal slices. Gently crack claws, and remove meat in one piece. Set lobster meat aside.

Trim ends from snow peas. Arrange snow peas in a vegetable steamer over boiling water. Cover and steam 1 minute or until crisp-tender.

Melt margarine in a medium saucepan over low heat. Add diced carrot, celery, and onion, and sauté 5 to 10 minutes or until tender. Add reserved reduced liquid and tomato paste, stirring with a wire whisk until well blended. Simmer, uncovered, 5 minutes. Set aside.

Place cottage cheese in container of an electric blender or food processor; top with cover, and process until smooth. Add vegetable mixture, and process until smooth. Transfer mixture to a skillet. Add lobster meat, and cook over low heat until thoroughly heated. Remove from heat. Remove lobster from sauce. Spoon ¼ cup sauce onto each serving plate. Stir hot cooked fettuccine into remaining sauce; divide evenly among serving plates. Top evenly with lobster meat. Arrange half of snow peas on each serving plate. Top each serving with chopped tomato and fresh basil strips. Garnish with fresh basil sprigs, if desired. Yield: 2 servings (407 calories per serving).

PROTEIN 30.0 / FAT 9.3 / CARBOHYDRATE 51.3 / CHOLESTEROL 76 / IRON 4.7 / SODIUM 366 / CALCIUM 149

HEAVENLY HEART MERINGUES

2 egg whites
¼ teaspoon cream of tartar
¼ cup superfine sugar
1 teaspoon unsweetened cocoa
½ teaspoon vanilla extract
½ cup chopped fresh peaches
¼ cup fresh blueberries
3 large fresh strawberries, sliced

Line a large baking sheet with parchment paper; draw two 5-inch hearts 3 inches apart.

Beat egg whites (at room temperature) and cream of tartar at high speed of an electric mixer 1 minute. Combine sugar and cocoa. Gradually add sugar mixture, 1 tablespoon at a time, beating until stiff peaks form and sugar dissolves (2 to 4 minutes). Fold in vanilla.

Spoon meringue into a decorating bag fitted with a No. 4 star tip. Pipe a small amount evenly inside heart shapes; smooth meringue, using the back of a spoon. Pipe around edge of heart shapes; repeat piping around outer edge, forming a 1-inch heart border.

Bake at 225° for 2 hours. Turn oven off; cool in oven 1 hour. Carefully peel off paper, and store meringues in zip-top plastic bags.

Combine peaches, blueberries, and strawberries; toss gently. Place meringue hearts on individual dessert plates. Spoon fruit mixture evenly into meringues. Serve immediately. Yield: 2 servings (157 calories per serving).

PROTEIN 4.2 / FAT 0.3 / CARBOHYDRATE 35.3 / CHOLESTEROL 0 / IRON 0.3 / SODIUM 77 / CALCIUM 11

Sweet Red Pepper Soup is garnished with an edible flower for a gourmet touch.

Dinner For The Boss

Pull out all the stops—this is a special menu designed to impress your most sophisticated guest but not overwhelm.

The first course, a beautiful, intensely colored Sweet Red Pepper Soup, can be prepared the day before the dinner party. Garnish the soup with an edible flower for a gourmet touch.

Have your butcher bone the rack of lamb, but save the bones to create an almost instant lamb sauce that can be prepared the morning of the dinner.

**Sweet Red Pepper Soup
Rack of Lamb Persillade
Herbed Baby Vegetable
Sauté
Souffléed Baked Potatoes
Commercial Dinner Rolls
Sparkling Fresh Fruit Cup
Red Wine**

Serves 8
Total calories per serving: 679

The Herbed Baby Vegetable Sauté is simple but elegant with its use of baby eggplant and zucchini. If these trendy vegetables are not available in your area, try substituting eggplant strips and zucchini slices.

Souffléed Baked Potatoes complete the elegant picture, along with one commercial dinner roll and a 6-ounce glass of red wine per person.

On the morning of the dinner party choose the freshest fruit available for a Sparkling Fresh Fruit Cup—a light ending to a rich-tasting dinner.

SWEET RED PEPPER SOUP

3½ cups chopped onion
2 teaspoons olive oil
9 large sweet red peppers (4½ pounds), seeded and chopped
3 (10½-ounce) cans no-salt-added chicken broth, undiluted
1 tablespoon sherry wine vinegar
¼ teaspoon salt
¼ teaspoon pepper
Fresh chives (optional)
Edible flowers (optional)

Sauté onion in olive oil in a large Dutch oven 5 minutes or until tender. Add sweet red pepper and broth; bring to a boil. Cover, reduce heat, and simmer 15 minutes. Remove from heat.

Transfer pepper mixture in batches to container of an electric blender or food processor; top with cover, and process until smooth. Return pureed mixture to Dutch oven. Add vinegar, salt, and pepper. Cook over medium-low heat until thoroughly heated.

Serve soup in individual soup bowls. If desired, garnish with fresh chives and edible flowers. Yield: 8 cups (84 calories per 1-cup serving).

PROTEIN 2.3 / FAT 2.0 / CARBOHYDRATE 14.2 / CHOLESTEROL 0 / IRON 2.4 / SODIUM 93 / CALCIUM 25

CHILDREN HAVE SPECIAL NEEDS

Although medical research continues to emphasize that most people should follow a prudent diet, one age group should be excluded—children under 2 years of age. The Nutrition Committee of the American Academy of Pediatrics reports that while most of us need to reduce fat intake to less than 30 percent of our daily calories, 40 percent is a safer limit for those under 2 years of age.

Research shows that severe growth problems in children may be the result of an overly strict diet. Children need dietary fats to metabolize fat-soluble vitamins and to promote proper development. In addition, severely limiting children's dietary cholesterol could deprive them of the cholesterol needed to form body cells, especially those of the nervous system. Thus, while the rest of the family is enjoying a low-fat meal, do not restrict the fat intake of children under 2 years of age.

RACK OF LAMB PERSILLADE

2 (3½-pound) racks of lamb (16 chops)
½ cup soft breadcrumbs
½ teaspoon minced garlic
1 tablespoon chopped fresh parsley
½ teaspoon dried whole rosemary
2 teaspoons olive oil
Vegetable cooking spray
Red Wine Sauce

Remove chine bones from lamb; reserve for wine sauce. Trim fat from racks, leaving only small eye of rib. Strip rib tips of all meat and fat. Reserve meat for sauce; discard fat.

Combine breadcrumbs and next 4 ingredients; stir well. Pat mixture over meat portion of racks. Place lamb in a shallow roasting pan that has been coated with cooking spray. Insert meat thermometer, making sure it does not touch bone. Bake at 450° for 20 minutes or until thermometer registers 160° (medium). Remove from oven and let stand for 5 minutes before slicing. Place chops on a serving plate; spoon 1 tablespoon Red Wine Sauce over each chop. Yield: 8 servings (195 calories per serving).

Red Wine Sauce:

Reserved bones and meat from racks of lamb
1 carrot, scraped and chopped
1 stalk celery, chopped
⅓ cup chopped onion
1 cup Burgundy or other dry red wine
4 cups canned no-salt-added chicken broth, undiluted
1 teaspoon dried whole rosemary
⅛ teaspoon salt
⅛ teaspoon freshly ground pepper

Place bones and meat, carrot, celery, and onion in a shallow roasting pan. Bake at 450° for 35 to 40 minutes or until browned, turning once. Drain; pat dry with paper towels. Transfer to a heavy saucepan. Add wine; cook, uncovered, over medium heat 15 minutes or until liquid evaporates. Add broth and rosemary; cook until mixture is reduced by half. Strain; discard bones, meat, and vegetables. Add salt and pepper to sauce; stir well. Yield: 1 cup.

PROTEIN 20.0 / FAT 9.9 / CARBOHYDRATE 4.5 / CHOLESTEROL 67 / IRON 2.0 / SODIUM 202 / CALCIUM 26

HERBED BABY VEGETABLE SAUTÉ

Vegetable cooking spray
1½ teaspoons olive oil
2 cloves garlic, crushed
½ teaspoon dried whole thyme
½ teaspoon dried whole rosemary,
  crushed
⅛ teaspoon salt
⅔ pound baby eggplant, halved
⅔ pound baby zucchini, halved
2 teaspoons chopped fresh parsley

Coat a large nonstick skillet with cooking spray; add oil and place over medium-high heat until hot. Add garlic, thyme, rosemary, and salt, and sauté 1 minute. Add remaining ingredients, and sauté 5 minutes or until crisp-tender, stirring occasionally. Yield: 8 servings (22 calories per serving).

PROTEIN 0.8 / FAT 1.0 / CARBOHYDRATE 3.2 / CHOLESTEROL 0 /
IRON 0.5 / SODIUM 39 / CALCIUM 20

SOUFFLÉED BAKED POTATOES

4 small baking potatoes (1¼ pounds)
¼ cup skim milk
2 tablespoons low-fat sour cream
2 tablespoons chopped fresh chives
¼ teaspoon salt
¼ teaspoon pepper
2 egg whites
⅓ cup (1⅓ ounces) finely shredded 40% less-fat
  Cheddar cheese
⅛ teaspoon paprika

Wash potatoes; bake at 400° for 1 hour or until tender. Allow potatoes to cool completely. Cut in half lengthwise; carefully scoop out pulp, leaving ⅛-inch-thick shells. Combine potato pulp, milk, sour cream, chives, salt, and pepper in a bowl; mash with a potato masher until smooth. Set aside.

Beat egg whites (at room temperature) at high speed of an electric mixer until stiff peaks form; fold into potato mixture. Spoon potato mixture into shells; place on an ungreased bak-

ing sheet. Sprinkle 1 tablespoon cheese over each serving. Sprinkle paprika evenly over each serving. Bake at 375° for 15 minutes or until thoroughly heated. Yield: 8 servings (78 calories per serving).

PROTEIN 4.1 / FAT 1.4 / CARBOHYDRATE 12.6 / CHOLESTEROL 2 /
IRON 0.9 / SODIUM 128 / CALCIUM 62

DON'T PASS UP POTATOES

If you think of potatoes as a "fattening" food, read further. Nutritionists report that potatoes are a filling, nutrient-dense food. A 5-ounce potato has only 150 calories, considerably less than a 5-ounce serving of prime rib, which has more than 550 calories. Potatoes are rich in potassium and vitamin C and supply other minerals as well. In addition, potatoes provide complex carbohydrates, a nutrient that should be the base of every meal. Eat the skin and get the added bonus of a healthy dose of fiber. Adding a serving of potatoes will allow you to reduce the portion of meat you eat—and you won't go hungry. Try Souffléed Baked Potatoes for a nutritious base for your next meal.

SPARKLING FRESH FRUIT CUP

4 medium-size fresh pears, cored and diced
2 tablespoons lemon juice
2 cups halved fresh strawberries
¾ pound fresh plums, pitted and thinly sliced
2 cups peeled, diced fresh peaches
2 cups sparkling apple cider, chilled
Fresh mint sprigs (optional)

Place diced pears in a large bowl, and sprinkle with lemon juice; toss gently. Add strawberries, plums, and peaches; toss gently to combine.

To serve, place 1 cup fruit mixture in individual dessert cups. Pour ¼ cup sparkling apple cider over each serving. Garnish with fresh mint sprigs, if desired. Serve immediately. Yield: 8 servings (133 calories per serving).

PROTEIN 1.2 / FAT 0.8 / CARBOHYDRATE 33.3 / CHOLESTEROL 0 /
IRON 0.7 / SODIUM 2 / CALCIUM 23

Light Recipes

Healthy American meals revolve around attractive, good-for-you foods such as (clockwise from left): Refreshing Fruit Spritzer (page 97), Mexican Bean Salad (page 172), Chocolate-Chocolate Chip Ice Milk (page 221), Bourbon-Walnut Brownies (page 241), Peppery Pasta Salad (page 174), Maple-Spice Chiffon Cake (page 232), Hearty Hero Sandwiches (page 185), and Fresh Rhubarb Pie (page 236).

With a little planning, you can turn healthy recipes into nutritionally balanced meals whose taste and appearance say "delicious." Planning healthy meals begins with recipes that include nutrient-dense foods. This does not mean, however, that you'll have to spend more time or money to purchase or prepare food.

Many nutritious recipes are as close as your own recipe file. A quick assessment of the ones you use most often is a good way to begin cooking the light way. Check to see which recipes already are low in saturated fat and cholesterol or are high in complex carbohydrate and fiber. You may discover that many of your recipes can be made healthier by modifying certain ingredients or by changing cooking methods as described in the *Cooking Light* Kitchen.

However, it takes more than a healthy recipe to make a balanced meal. The nutrient analysis that follows each recipe will help you create nutritionally sound meals.

Win hearts by the presentation and taste of the meals. Appearances do count, especially when introducing new and different foods to family and friends. Follow our garnishing suggestions to make even the simplest of dishes look special. If the recipe calls for a food that may be new to you, look in the Marketplace for tips on buying and preparing the newer items.

Light Recipes contains a variety of recipes. From entrées of beef, pork, fish, poultry, and meatless main dishes to accompaniments of pastas, grains, salads, fruits, and vegetables, your family is sure to enjoy the variety that *Cooking Light* offers. And there is no better way to top off a meal than by including a *Cooking Light* dessert. Whether the dessert is baked fruit, cookies, a cheesecake, or a luscious tart, no one could guess that each has less than 200 calories per serving. Enjoy!

Serve Baked Brie with Strawberries and Kiwifruit (page 94) with gingersnaps to get any meal off to a spectacular start.

Appetizers & Beverages

TANGY MARINATED BRUSSELS SPROUTS

1 pound small fresh brussels sprouts
¼ cup red wine vinegar
3 tablespoons water
2 tablespoons grated Parmesan
  cheese
1 tablespoon lemon juice
1 tablespoon olive oil
1 clove garlic, crushed
⅛ teaspoon hot sauce
1 teaspoon sesame seeds, toasted

Wash brussels sprouts thoroughly, and remove discolored leaves. Cut off stem ends, and slash bottom of each sprout with a shallow X. Place brussels sprouts in a vegetable steamer over boiling water. Cover and steam 6 to 8 minutes or until crisp-tender. Drain; place brussels sprouts in a bowl and set aside.

Combine vinegar and remaining ingredients except toasted sesame seeds in container of an electric blender; top with cover, and process until smooth. Pour vinegar mixture over reserved brussels sprouts; toss gently to coat. Sprinkle toasted sesame seeds over brussels sprouts mixture. Cover and marinate in refrigerator 8 hours. Drain well before serving. Yield: 36 appetizers (9 calories each).

PROTEIN 0.5 / FAT 0.5 / CARBOHYDRATE 0.7 / CHOLESTEROL 0 /
IRON 0.1 / SODIUM 8 / CALCIUM 10

CAVIAR POTATOES

5 small new potatoes (½ pound)
¼ cup plus 2 teaspoons low-fat sour cream
2 tablespoons plus 1 teaspoon red, black,
  or golden caviar

Place potatoes in a vegetable steamer over boiling water. Cover and steam 20 minutes or until tender; drain. Chill.

Slice potatoes crosswise into ¼-inch slices. Place potato slices on a serving platter. Top each slice with ½ teaspoon sour cream and ¼ teaspoon caviar. Yield: 28 appetizers (14 calories each).

PROTEIN 0.7 / FAT 0.5 / CARBOHYDRATE 1.5 / CHOLESTEROL 6 /
IRON 0.3 / SODIUM 33 / CALCIUM 8

CRAB CANAPÉS

1 (18-inch) French bread baguette
1 pound fresh lump crabmeat, drained and flaked
1 cup finely chopped celery
⅓ cup soft breadcrumbs
⅛ teaspoon dry mustard
¼ cup reduced-calorie mayonnaise
¼ cup plain nonfat yogurt
1 tablespoon chopped pimiento
1 teaspoon lemon juice
¾ teaspoon Worcestershire sauce

Cut bread into ¼-inch slices. Set aside.
Combine crabmeat and remaining ingredients; stir well. Spoon 2 teaspoons crab mixture onto each bread slice. Yield: 6 dozen appetizers (16 calories each).

PROTEIN 1.3 / FAT 0.4 / CARBOHYDRATE 1.7 / CHOLESTEROL 6 /
IRON 0.1 / SODIUM 37 / CALCIUM 6

 RICE CAKES—A POPULAR TREAT

Sales of rice cakes have increased more than 2,000 percent during the 1980s. Perfect for snacks, rice cakes are nutritionally fat-free and most are sodium-free as well. Pair them with low-fat cheeses or spreads for a healthy snack.

GARDEN CHEESE BALL

1 cup shredded carrot
½ cup shredded zucchini
½ cup shredded yellow squash
1 (8-ounce) package Neufchâtel cheese, softened
1 cup (4 ounces) shredded 40% less-fat Cheddar
  cheese
1 tablespoon grated onion
1 clove garlic, minced
⅓ cup nut-like cereal nuggets
1 tablespoon chopped fresh parsley

Press shredded carrot, zucchini, and yellow squash between paper towels to remove excess moisture.

Combine cheeses, grated onion, and garlic in a large bowl; stir well. Stir in shredded vegetables. Cover and chill at least 2 hours.

Shape chilled cheese mixture into a ball. Combine cereal nuggets and parsley, stirring well. Coat cheese ball with cereal mixture. Wrap in wax paper, and chill thoroughly. Serve with unsalted crackers. Yield: 3 cups (23 calories per tablespoon).

PROTEIN 1.0 / FAT 1.5 / CARBOHYDRATE 1.6 / CHOLESTEROL 4 / IRON 0.1 / SODIUM 25 / CALCIUM 21

BLUE CHEESE MOLD

1½ teaspoons unflavored gelatin
¼ cup cold water
½ cup plain nonfat yogurt
½ cup crumbled blue cheese
¼ cup reduced-calorie mayonnaise
Vegetable cooking spray

Soften gelatin in cold water in a small saucepan; let stand 1 minute. Cook over low heat, stirring constantly, until gelatin dissolves. Stir in yogurt. Chill until consistency of unbeaten egg white (about 10 minutes).

Combine cheese and mayonnaise in a small bowl; beat at medium speed of an electric mixer until creamy. Fold cheese mixture into gelatin mixture. Spoon into a 1-cup mold that has been coated with cooking spray. Cover and chill until set. Unmold onto a serving plate. Serve with fresh fruit. Yield: 1 cup (28 calories per tablespoon).

PROTEIN 1.4 / FAT 2.1 / CARBOHYDRATE 0.9 / CHOLESTEROL 4 / IRON 0.0 / SODIUM 83 / CALCIUM 33

CHEESE-STUFFED JALAPEÑO PEPPERS

15 fresh jalapeño peppers (½ pound)
3 tablespoons process light cream cheese product
2 tablespoons unsweetened crushed pineapple, drained
1 tablespoon minced sweet red pepper
2 teaspoons minced fresh cilantro

Slice peppers lengthwise and remove seeds. Place peppers in a saucepan; add water to cover. Bring to a boil; cook 2 to 3 minutes or until crisp-tender. Drain and let cool.

Combine cheese and remaining ingredients in a small bowl, stirring until smooth. Chill thoroughly. Stuff peppers with 1 teaspoon cream cheese mixture. Cover and chill thoroughly. Yield: 30 appetizers (6 calories each).

PROTEIN 0.3 / FAT 0.3 / CARBOHYDRATE 0.8 / CHOLESTEROL 0 / IRON 0.1 / SODIUM 8 / CALCIUM 3

GARLIC SPREAD

1 (8-ounce) package Neufchâtel cheese, softened
2 tablespoons grated Parmesan cheese
3 tablespoons chopped fresh chives
2 cloves garlic, minced

Combine all ingredients in a small bowl, stirring until well blended. Cover and chill thoroughly. Serve spread with unsalted crackers or fresh raw vegetables. Yield: 1 cup (40 calories per tablespoon).

PROTEIN 1.7 / FAT 3.5 / CARBOHYDRATE 0.6 / CHOLESTEROL 11 / IRON 0.1 / SODIUM 68 / CALCIUM 20

QUICK SALMON SPREAD

1 (15½-ounce) can red salmon, drained
¼ cup thinly sliced celery
¼ cup chopped onion
2 tablespoons reduced-calorie mayonnaise
1 tablespoon reduced-calorie chili sauce
1 teaspoon lemon juice
½ teaspoon dried whole dillweed
¼ teaspoon paprika
⅛ teaspoon Worcestershire sauce

Combine all ingredients in container of an electric blender or food processor; top with cover, and process until smooth. Transfer salmon mixture to a small bowl. Cover and chill thoroughly. Serve spread with unsalted rye crackers or melba rounds. Yield: 2 cups (23 calories per tablespoon).

PROTEIN 2.2 / FAT 1.4 / CARBOHYDRATE 0.3 / CHOLESTEROL 4 / IRON 0.1 / SODIUM 14 / CALCIUM 15

Simply tie the ends of fresh corn husks, and you have unique serving containers for Fresh Corn Relish Dip.

FRESH CORN RELISH DIP

1 cup fresh corn
3 ounces Neufchâtel cheese, softened
2 tablespoons low-fat sour cream
1 tablespoon reduced-calorie mayonnaise
1 tablespoon lime juice
2 tablespoons finely chopped sweet red pepper
2 tablespoons finely chopped green onions
1 tablespoon minced fresh cilantro
1 teaspoon chopped jalapeño pepper
Fresh corn husks (optional)
Sweet red pepper ring (optional)
Fresh parsley sprigs (optional)

Cook corn in a small amount of water until tender. Drain. Mash gently with a fork; set aside.

Combine Neufchâtel cheese, sour cream, mayonnaise, and lime juice in a small bowl. Beat at medium speed of an electric mixer until smooth. Stir in red pepper, onions, cilantro, jalapeño pepper, and reserved corn. Chill.

Serve dip in corn husks, if desired, with raw vegetables or unsalted tortilla chips. If desired, garnish with pepper ring and parsley sprigs. Yield: 1½ cups (19 calories per tablespoon).

PROTEIN 0.6 / FAT 1.2 / CARBOHYDRATE 1.6 / CHOLESTEROL 3 / IRON 0.1 / SODIUM 20 / CALCIUM 5

CREAMY ORANGE DIP

1 (8-ounce) package Neufchâtel cheese, softened
2 tablespoons powdered sugar
2 tablespoons plain nonfat yogurt
2 tablespoons unsweetened orange juice
1 tablespoon plus 1 teaspoon grated orange rind

Combine all ingredients in a small bowl; stir until smooth. Cover and chill thoroughly. Serve with fresh fruit or unsalted crackers. Yield: 1⅓ cups (28 calories per tablespoon).

PROTEIN 1.0 / FAT 2.2 / CARBOHYDRATE 1.2 / CHOLESTEROL 7 / IRON 0.0 / SODIUM 39 / CALCIUM 10

CHUNKY PEANUT BUTTER DIP

2 (6-ounce) cartons orange low-fat yogurt
¾ cup no-sugar-added chunky peanut butter
1 tablespoon unsweetened orange juice

Combine all ingredients in a small bowl; stir well. Cover and chill thoroughly. Serve with fresh fruit. Yield: 2 cups (46 calories per tablespoon).

PROTEIN 2.1 / FAT 3.2 / CARBOHYDRATE 3.0 / CHOLESTEROL 0 / IRON 0.1 / SODIUM 7 / CALCIUM 17

PICADILLO DIP

½ pound ground chuck
½ cup chopped green pepper
2 medium tomatoes, peeled, seeded, and chopped
¼ cup raisins
¼ teaspoon onion salt
¼ teaspoon pepper
⅛ teaspoon dried whole oregano
⅓ cup water
¼ cup no-salt-added tomato sauce
3 tablespoons no-salt-added tomato paste

Cook ground chuck in a large nonstick skillet over medium heat until browned, stirring to crumble. Drain and pat dry with paper towels. Wipe pan drippings from skillet with a paper towel. Return meat to skillet; add chopped green pepper and remaining ingredients. Simmer, uncovered, for 30 minutes over low heat,

stirring occasionally. Transfer mixture to a chafing dish; serve with unsalted tortilla chips. Yield: 2½ cups (17 calories per tablespoon).

PROTEIN 1.3 / FAT 0.7 / CARBOHYDRATE 1.4 / CHOLESTEROL 3 / IRON 0.2 / SODIUM 16 / CALCIUM 2

INCREASING ATHLETIC PERFORMANCE

A study of Swedish cyclists showed that a 10-minute massage before a workout increased their performance by 11 percent. This may be partially due to increased blood circulation, which helps prevent lactic acid buildup, the main cause of muscle soreness. The massage may also promote the feeling of well-being, a psychological boost that helps relax the muscles. So, if the occasion should arise, enjoy the benefits of a sports massage.

HOT SPINACH DIP LOAF

1 (1-pound) round loaf sourdough bread
1 (10-ounce) package frozen chopped spinach, thawed
1 (8-ounce) package Neufchâtel cheese, softened
1 (8-ounce) carton plain nonfat yogurt
1¼ cups (5 ounces) shredded 40% less-fat Cheddar cheese
½ cup low-fat sour cream
1 (1-ounce) package no-oil Italian dressing mix
1 (2-ounce) jar sliced pimiento, drained

Cut off top one-fourth of loaf; set aside. Hollow out center of loaf, and cut bread into 1-inch cubes. Place bread cubes on an ungreased baking sheet. Bake at 350° for 15 minutes or until golden brown. Set aside.

Drain spinach; press between paper towels to remove excess moisture. Combine spinach and remaining ingredients in a large bowl; stir well. Spoon mixture into bread cavity. Cover with top of loaf. Wrap loaf in heavy-duty aluminum foil, and place on an ungreased baking sheet. Bake at 325° for 1½ hours or until thoroughly heated. Unwrap and serve with bread cubes. Yield: 3 cups dip plus 4 dozen bread cubes (36 calories per tablespoon of dip and 1 bread cube).

PROTEIN 1.7 / FAT 1.9 / CARBOHYDRATE 3.5 / CHOLESTEROL 5 / IRON 0.2 / SODIUM 38 / CALCIUM 42

TEQUILA DIP WITH JICAMA CHIPS

¾ cup plus 1 tablespoon low-fat sour cream
¾ cup plain nonfat yogurt
2 tablespoons tequila
1 tablespoon chili powder
½ teaspoon grated lime rind
¼ teaspoon hot sauce
1 (2-pound) jicama, peeled and cut into ¼-inch
    slices

Combine first 6 ingredients; stir well. Cover and chill. Cut jicama into rounds, using a 2-inch cookie cutter. Serve with tequila dip. Yield: 1¾ cups dip plus 4 dozen jicama chips (24 calories per tablespoon dip and 2 jicama chips).

PROTEIN 0.8 / FAT 0.9 / CARBOHYDRATE 2.6 / CHOLESTEROL 3 /
IRON 0.2 / SODIUM 12 / CALCIUM 23

NACHO CRACKERS

36 garlic-flavored melba rounds
¾ cup (3 ounces) shredded Monterey Jack cheese
    with jalapeño peppers
1½ teaspoons chili powder

Arrange melba rounds on an ungreased baking sheet. Top each with 1 teaspoon cheese. Sprinkle with chili powder. Broil 4 inches from heat for 30 seconds or until cheese melts. Serve hot. Yield: 36 appetizers (21 calories each).

PROTEIN 1.0 / FAT 1.0 / CARBOHYDRATE 2.0 / CHOLESTEROL 2 /
IRON 0.1 / SODIUM 40 / CALCIUM 18

SWEET CHEESE BUNDLES

2 (12- x 18½-inch) sheets commercial frozen phyllo
    pastry, thawed
Vegetable cooking spray
4½ ounces Neufchâtel cheese, softened
2 tablespoons gingersnap crumbs
1 tablespoon brown sugar
1 tablespoon low-sugar strawberry spread
2 tablespoons finely chopped pecans, toasted

Spray one sheet of phyllo lightly with cooking spray. Top with second sheet and spray lightly. Cut in half lengthwise; place one half on top of the other, forming four layers. Cut into twelve 2½-inch circles, using a cookie cutter; gently press into ungreased miniature muffin pans.

Combine cheese and next 3 ingredients; stir well. Spoon 1 tablespoon cheese mixture into each cup. Sprinkle evenly with pecans. Bake at 400° for 6 to 8 minutes or until lightly browned. Yield: 12 appetizers (60 calories each).

PROTEIN 1.5 / FAT 4.3 / CARBOHYDRATE 4.5 / CHOLESTEROL 9 /
IRON 0.2 / SODIUM 45 / CALCIUM 12

BAKED BRIE WITH STRAWBERRIES AND KIWIFRUIT

1 (8-ounce) round Brie cheese
1 cup sliced fresh strawberries
1 kiwifruit, peeled and sliced
Fresh mint sprigs (optional)

Place Brie on an ovenproof serving platter. Arrange fruit over top. Bake at 350° for 10 minutes or until cheese is bubbly. Serve immediately with gingersnaps. Garnish with fresh mint sprigs, if desired. Yield: 16 appetizer servings (53 calories per serving).

PROTEIN 3.1 / FAT 4.0 / CARBOHYDRATE 1.3 / CHOLESTEROL 14 /
IRON 0.1 / SODIUM 89 / CALCIUM 29

MUSHROOM-GOAT CHEESE TART

Vegetable cooking spray
1 cup thinly sliced fresh mushrooms
3 tablespoons finely chopped onion
½ teaspoon finely chopped fresh rosemary
4 ounces goat cheese, softened
1 (12-ounce) carton low-fat cottage cheese
2 eggs

Coat a large nonstick skillet with cooking spray; place over medium-high heat until hot. Add mushrooms and onion, and sauté until tender. Stir in rosemary; set aside.

Combine goat cheese and remaining ingredients in container of an electric blender or food processor; top with cover, and process until smooth. Pour into a 9-inch pieplate that has been coated with cooking spray. Spoon reserved mushroom mixture evenly over cheese mixture.

Bake at 325° for 40 minutes or until set. Cool 10 minutes; cut into 8 wedges and serve immediately. Yield: 8 appetizers (100 calories each).

PROTEIN 9.6 / FAT 5.4 / CARBOHYDRATE 3.0 / CHOLESTEROL 85 /
IRON 0.5 / SODIUM 349 / CALCIUM 107

WARM PEACH FONDUE

2 cups peeled, sliced fresh peaches
2 tablespoons sugar
1 tablespoons cornstarch
¼ cup unsweetened orange juice
¼ cup water
2 tablespoons peach schnapps
½ (8-ounce) package Neufchâtel cheese, softened

Place sliced peaches in a medium saucepan. Mash until smooth. Combine sugar and cornstarch; sprinkle over peaches. Stir in orange juice, water, and schnapps. Cook over medium heat, stirring constantly, until mixture is thickened and bubbly. Add cheese, stirring until cheese melts. Transfer mixture to a fondue pot. Serve with fresh fruit. Yield: 2¾ cups (14 calories per tablespoon).

PROTEIN 0.3 / FAT 0.6 / CARBOHYDRATE 1.9 / CHOLESTEROL 2 / IRON 0.0 / SODIUM 10 / CALCIUM 3

COLORFUL BROCCOLI QUICHE BITES

Vegetable cooking spray
1 teaspoon olive oil
¾ cup finely chopped fresh broccoli
¼ cup finely chopped sweet red pepper
1 clove garlic, minced
4 eggs, separated
½ cup (2 ounces) finely shredded Swiss cheese
3 tablespoons grated Parmesan cheese
½ teaspoon dried whole basil
⅛ teaspoon ground red pepper
Vegetable cooking spray

Coat a large nonstick skillet with cooking spray; add olive oil, and place over medium-high heat until hot. Add broccoli, chopped sweet red pepper, and garlic, and sauté until crisp-tender. Set aside.
Combine egg yolks, cheeses, basil, and red pepper in a large bowl; stir well. Beat egg whites (at room temperature) in a large bowl until stiff but not dry; gently fold into egg yolk mixture. Gently fold in reserved broccoli mixture.
Spoon batter into miniature muffin pans that have been coated with cooking spray, allowing 1 tablespoon batter per cup. Bake at 425° for 10 minutes or until set. Cool in pans 1 minute. Remove from pans, and serve immediately. Yield: 1½ dozen appetizers (39 calories each).

PROTEIN 2.7 / FAT 2.8 / CARBOHYDRATE 0.6 / CHOLESTEROL 64 / IRON 0.3 / SODIUM 40 / CALCIUM 51

CARIBBEAN MEATBALLS WITH TROPICAL SAUCE

½ (16-ounce) package frozen raw ground turkey, thawed
1 cup soft, whole wheat breadcrumbs
2 tablespoons minced green pepper
2 tablespoons finely chopped macadamia nuts
1 egg, beaten
1 teaspoon minced fresh cilantro
⅛ teaspoon salt
Vegetable cooking spray
Tropical Sauce

Combine turkey and next 6 ingredients, stirring well. Shape mixture into 24 (1-inch) meatballs. Arrange on rack of a roasting pan that has been coated with cooking spray. Bake at 400° for 12 minutes or until meatballs are browned. To serve, combine meatballs and Tropical Sauce in a chafing dish. Yield: 24 appetizers (40 calories per meatball and 1 tablespoon sauce).

Tropical Sauce:

1 medium mango, peeled, seeded, and coarsely chopped
1 tablespoon cornstarch
1 tablespoon brown sugar
½ cup water
2 tablespoons lime juice
2 tablespoons teriyaki sauce
1 teaspoon grated fresh gingerroot
¼ teaspoon grated lime rind

Place mango in container of an electric blender or food processor; top with cover, and process until smooth. Combine cornstarch and brown sugar in a small saucepan. Add pureed mango, water, and remaining ingredients. Cook over medium-low heat, stirring constantly, until thickened. Yield: 1½ cups.

PROTEIN 2.8 / FAT 1.3 / CARBOHYDRATE 4.4 / CHOLESTEROL 17 / IRON 0.3 / SODIUM 89 / CALCIUM 8

(Left to right): Sparkling Cassis Cider, Bellini Freeze (page 98), Piña Colada, Blushing Bull, Mint Tea Julep (page 98).

CARROT DELIGHT

1 pound carrots, scraped and sliced
1½ cups water
1½ cups unsweetened pineapple juice
1½ cups unsweetened orange juice
2 tablespoons honey
½ cup water

Combine carrots and 1½ cups water in a saucepan; bring to a boil. Cover; reduce heat, and simmer 25 to 30 minutes or until carrots are very tender. Place carrots and cooking liquid in container of an electric blender or food processor; top with cover, and process until smooth. Add juices and honey; process until smooth. Place carrot mixture in a pitcher; stir in ½ cup water. Chill thoroughly. Yield: 6 cups (110 calories per 1-cup serving).

PROTEIN 1.2 / FAT 0.2 / CARBOHYDRATE 27.1 / CHOLESTEROL 0 / IRON 0.6 / SODIUM 22 / CALCIUM 33

BLUSHING BULLS

1½ teaspoons beef-flavored bouillon granules
½ cup boiling water
3½ cups no-salt-added tomato juice
1 tablespoon lemon juice
1 tablespoon low-sodium Worcestershire sauce
2 teaspoons lime juice
¼ teaspoon hot sauce
⅛ teaspoon pepper
Lime slices (optional)

Dissolve bouillon granules in ½ cup boiling water; allow to cool. Combine tomato juice, lemon juice, Worcestershire sauce, lime juice, hot sauce, and pepper, stirring well. Chill thoroughly. Serve over ice. Garnish each serving with a lime slice, if desired. Yield: 4 cups (51 calories per 1-cup serving).

PROTEIN 2.2 / FAT 0.4 / CARBOHYDRATE 12.0 / CHOLESTEROL 0 / IRON 0.0 / SODIUM 394 / CALCIUM 1

REFRESHING FRUIT SPRITZER

1 cup boiling water
6 orange herb tea bags
1 (6-ounce) can frozen lemonade concentrate, thawed and undiluted
2 cups apricot nectar
4 cups lime-flavored sparkling mineral water, chilled
Lemon slices (optional)

Pour boiling water over tea bags; cover and steep 5 minutes. Discard tea bags. Stir in lemonade concentrate and nectar. Chill thoroughly. Stir in mineral water just before serving. Serve over ice. Garnish with lemon slices, if desired. Yield: 8 cups (74 calories per 1-cup serving).

PROTEIN 0.3 / FAT 0.1 / CARBOHYDRATE 19.0 / CHOLESTEROL 0 / IRON 0.4 / SODIUM 28 / CALCIUM 6

STRAWBERRY-MELON COOLER

2 cups fresh strawberries, washed and hulled
2 cups diced cantaloupe
2 tablespoons honey
2 teaspoons vanilla extract
1 cup club soda

Combine first 4 ingredients in container of an electric blender; top with cover, and process until smooth. Stir in club soda. Serve over ice. Yield: 4 cups (90 calories per 1-cup serving).

PROTEIN 1.2 / FAT 0.4 / CARBOHYDRATE 21.4 / CHOLESTEROL 0 / IRON 0.4 / SODIUM 20 / CALCIUM 22

BROWN COW SHAKE

1 cup skim milk
½ cup unsweetened orange juice
8 dried, pitted prunes
1 teaspoon vanilla extract
8 ice cubes

Combine first 4 ingredients in container of an electric blender; top with cover, and process until smooth. Gradually add ice cubes, processing until smooth. Serve immediately. Yield: 3 cups (100 calories per 1-cup serving).

PROTEIN 3.4 / FAT 0.6 / CARBOHYDRATE 20.4 / CHOLESTEROL 2 / IRON 0.4 / SODIUM 52 / CALCIUM 112

PIÑA COLADAS

1 (8-ounce) can unsweetened pineapple chunks, undrained
1 large banana, sliced
15 ice cubes
1 (12-ounce) can evaporated skimmed milk
½ cup pineapple-orange banana juice
½ teaspoon rum extract
½ teaspoon coconut extract

Combine all ingredients in container of an electric blender; top with cover, and process until smooth. Yield: 6 cups (99 calories per 1-cup serving).

PROTEIN 4.8 / FAT 0.3 / CARBOHYDRATE 19.8 / CHOLESTEROL 2 / IRON 0.4 / SODIUM 66 / CALCIUM 172

SOFT DRINK ALTERNATIVES

Over the past several years, consumption of soft drinks has jumped by 126 percent. Unfortunately, except for calories and fluid, soft drinks provide no nutritional value.

When compared with other beverages, soft drinks fall short. A 4-ounce portion of orange juice provides the Recommended Dietary Allowance (RDA) for vitamin C, as well as some beta carotene.

Still thirsty? Skim milk should not be overlooked. Pour some in the blender with ice and add a banana for a low-calorie milkshake that adds vitamins A and D as well as calcium and potassium.

SPARKLING CASSIS CIDER

1 (25.4-ounce) bottle sparkling cider, chilled
½ cup lemon-flavored mineral water, chilled
¼ cup crème de cassis
2 tablespoons lemon juice
Lemon twists (optional)

Combine first 4 ingredients in a large pitcher; stir gently. Pour into glasses and garnish with lemon twists, if desired. Serve immediately. Yield: 4 cups (111 calories per 1-cup serving).

PROTEIN 0.1 / FAT 0.2 / CARBOHYDRATE 23.7 / CHOLESTEROL 0 / IRON 0.7 / SODIUM 13 / CALCIUM 15

BELLINI FREEZE

1 (10-ounce) package frozen sliced peaches
1 cup unsweetened orange juice
1 cup champagne, chilled
½ cup club soda, chilled
Fresh peach slices (optional)

Let peaches stand at room temperature 10 minutes to thaw slightly. Combine peaches and orange juice in container of an electric blender; top with cover, and process until smooth. Pour into a large pitcher. Slowly pour in champagne and club soda; stir gently. Serve immediately. Garnish with fresh peach slices, if desired. Yield: 4 cups (104 calories per 1-cup serving).

PROTEIN 1.0 / FAT 0.2 / CARBOHYDRATE 15.2 / CHOLESTEROL 0 / IRON 0.4 / SODIUM 10 / CALCIUM 12

MINT TEA JULEPS

3½ cups water
½ cup bourbon
1 tablespoon sugar
8 mint herb tea bags
Fresh mint sprigs (optional)

Combine water, bourbon, and sugar in a large saucepan; bring mixture to a boil. Pour mixture over tea bags; cover and steep 5 minutes. Remove and discard tea bags. Chill thoroughly. Serve over crushed ice. Garnish with fresh mint sprigs, if desired. Yield: 4 cups (12 calories per 1-cup serving).

PROTEIN 0.0 / FAT 0.0 / CARBOHYDRATE 3.1 / CHOLESTEROL 0 / IRON 0.0 / SODIUM 0 / CALCIUM 0

CHOCOLATE-PRALINE COFFEE

4 cups strong, hot coffee
2 tablespoons chocolate-flavored syrup
¼ cup praline-flavored liqueur

Combine coffee and syrup in a medium saucepan. Cook over medium heat, stirring constantly, until thoroughly heated (do not boil). Stir in liqueur. Serve immediately. Yield: 4 cups (78 calories per 1-cup serving).

PROTEIN 0.5 / FAT 0.2 / CARBOHYDRATE 10.8 / CHOLESTEROL 0 / IRON 1.1 / SODIUM 11 / CALCIUM 6

FROSTED COFFEE

1 cup chocolate-swirl ice milk
4 cups strong hot coffee

Place ¼ cup ice milk in 4 mugs. Add 1 cup coffee to each mug. Serve immediately. Yield: 4 cups (60 calories per 1-cup serving).

PROTEIN 1.25 / FAT 1.0 / CARBOHYDRATE 12 / CHOLESTEROL 6.75 / IRON 1.0 / SODIUM 37 / CALCIUM 5

HOT SPICED TEA

2 cups boiling water
4 mint herb tea bags
1 cup water
2 (1-inch) sticks cinnamon
2 tablespoons sugar
¾ cup unsweetened orange juice
¼ cup unsweetened pineapple juice

Pour boiling water over tea bags; cover and steep 5 minutes. Remove and discard tea bags. Set aside.

Combine water, cinnamon sticks, and sugar in a saucepan; bring to a boil. Reduce heat and simmer 10 minutes. Remove and discard cinnamon sticks. Cool.

Combine tea, sugar mixture, and juices; stir well. Reheat to serve hot, or chill thoroughly and serve over ice. Yield: 4 cups (54 calories per 1-cup serving).

PROTEIN 0.4 / FAT 0.0 / CARBOHYDRATE 13.4 / CHOLESTEROL 0 / IRON 0.1 / SODIUM 1 / CALCIUM 7

A spectacular selection of hearty, homemade breads that taste as good as they look! Clockwise from top left: Glazed Orange-Rum Buns (page 104), Poppy Seed-Onion Twists (page 107), Blueberry English Muffins (page 104), Cheddar Cheese Crescent Rolls (page 106), and Cracked Wheat-Zucchini Bread (page 102).

Breads, Grains & Pastas

Ladder loaf-style Fig Coffee Cake is generously filled with rich-tasting figs.

FIG COFFEE CAKE

3 cups chopped dried figs
¼ cup Marsala wine
2 tablespoons honey
1 teaspoon grated lemon rind
3¾ cups all-purpose flour, divided
1 package dry yeast
⅓ cup sugar
½ teaspoon salt
½ cup water
½ cup skim milk
¼ cup unsalted margarine
1 egg
Vegetable cooking spray

Position knife blade in food processor bowl; add first 4 ingredients. Top with cover, and process until smooth; set aside.

Combine 2 cups flour and yeast in a large mixing bowl; stir well. Set aside.

Combine sugar, salt, water, milk, and margarine in a small saucepan; cook over medium heat until very warm (120° to 130°). Add milk mixture to reserved flour mixture; beat at low speed of an electric mixer until well blended. Add egg; beat an additional 3 minutes at medium speed. Gradually stir in enough remaining flour to make a soft dough.

Turn dough out onto a lightly floured surface, and knead until dough is smooth and elastic (about 8 to 10 minutes). Place dough in a bowl that has been coated with cooking spray, turning to grease top. Cover and let rise in a warm place (85°), free from drafts, 1½ hours or until doubled in bulk.

Punch dough down, and divide in half. Roll each half into a 9-inch square. Spoon half of reserved fig mixture in a 3-inch strip down center of dough square. Make 3-inch cuts toward center at 1-inch intervals on both sides of dough. Fold strips to center, alternating and overlapping ends. Repeat procedure with remaining dough square and fig mixture. Place loaves on a baking sheet that has been coated with cooking spray. Cover and let rise in a warm place (85°), free from drafts, 45 minutes or until doubled in bulk. Bake at 375° for 20 minutes or until golden brown. Remove from baking sheet, and let cool on wire racks. Yield: 36 servings (114 calories per ½-inch slice).

PROTEIN 2.3 / FAT 1.7 / CARBOHYDRATE 23.1 / CHOLESTEROL 8 / IRON 0.8 / SODIUM 38 / CALCIUM 28

PEANUTTY CINNAMON TWIST

1 package dry yeast
¼ cup warm water (105° to 115°)
1 teaspoon sugar
¼ cup sugar, divided
1 teaspoon ground cinnamon, divided
½ teaspoon salt
3 tablespoons no-sugar-added chunky peanut
  butter
½ cup skim milk
1 tablespoon unsalted margarine
2 eggs
3 cups all-purpose flour
Vegetable cooking spray
2 tablespoons finely chopped, dry-roasted unsalted
  peanuts

Dissolve yeast in warm water; add 1 teaspoon sugar, and let stand 5 minutes.

Combine 2 tablespoons sugar, ¼ teaspoon cinnamon, salt, and peanut butter in a large bowl; set aside. Combine milk and margarine in a small saucepan; heat until margarine melts, stirring occasionally. Cool to 105° to 115°. Add milk mixture to peanut butter mixture; stir well. Add yeast mixture, eggs, and 2 cups flour; stir

well. Add enough remaining flour to make a soft dough. Turn out onto a lightly floured surface; knead until smooth and elastic (about 8 to 10 minutes). Place dough in a large bowl that has been coated with cooking spray, turning to grease top. Cover and let rise in a warm place (85°), free from drafts, 1½ hours or until doubled in bulk.

Punch dough down; divide in half. Divide each half into 3 equal portions. Shape each portion into a 15-inch rope; braid ropes to make 2 loaves. Place loaves on a baking sheet that has been coated with cooking spray. Combine remaining 2 tablespoons sugar, ¾ teaspoon ground cinnamon, and peanuts; sprinkle mixture evenly over loaves. Cover and let rise in a warm place, free from drafts, 45 minutes or until doubled in bulk. Bake at 350° for 20 minutes or until loaves sound hollow when tapped. Remove loaves from baking sheet, and let cool on wire racks. Yield: 30 servings (81 calories per 1-inch slice).

PROTEIN 2.7 / FAT 2.0 / CARBOHYDRATE 13.0 / CHOLESTEROL 18 / IRON 0.6 / SODIUM 47 / CALCIUM 12

RICH OAT BRAN BREAD

2 cups whole wheat flour
1 package dry yeast
½ teaspoon salt
2 cups skim milk
¼ cup molasses
2 tablespoons unsalted margarine
½ cup unprocessed oat bran, uncooked
3 cups all-purpose flour
Vegetable cooking spray
1 egg white, lightly beaten
1 tablespoon unprocessed oat bran, uncooked

Combine whole wheat flour, yeast, and salt in a large mixing bowl; stir well. Set aside.

Combine milk, molasses, and margarine in a small saucepan; cook over medium heat until very warm (120° to 130°). Remove from heat. Gradually add milk mixture to flour mixture, beating at medium speed of an electric mixer 3 minutes. Stir in ½ cup oat bran and enough all-purpose flour to make a soft dough.

Turn dough out onto a lightly floured surface; knead until smooth and elastic (about 8 to 10 minutes). Place in a bowl that has been coated with cooking spray, turning to grease top. Cover and let rise in a warm place (85°), free from drafts, 35 minutes or until doubled in bulk.

Punch dough down; divide into 2 portions. Cover and let dough rest 10 minutes. Shape each portion into a loaf. Place in two 8½- x 4½- x 3-inch loafpans that have been coated with cooking spray. Brush loaves with egg white; sprinkle 1½ teaspoons oat bran over each loaf.

Cover and let rise in a warm place, free from drafts, 30 minutes or until doubled in bulk. Bake at 375° for 20 minutes or until loaves sound hollow when tapped. Remove from pans, and let cool on wire racks. Yield: 34 servings (92 calories per ½-inch slice).

PROTEIN 3.2 / FAT 1.2 / CARBOHYDRATE 17.4 / CHOLESTEROL 0 / IRON 0.8 / SODIUM 45 / CALCIUM 31

CRACKED WHEAT-ZUCCHINI BREAD

½ cup boiling water
½ cup uncooked cracked wheat
1 package dry yeast
¼ cup warm water (105° to 115°)
½ cup skim milk
2 tablespoons unsalted margarine
2 tablespoons brown sugar
1 egg, beaten
½ teaspoon salt
½ teaspoon ground cinnamon
¼ teaspoon ground nutmeg
1 cup whole wheat flour
2 cups shredded zucchini
3½ cups unbleached flour
Vegetable cooking spray

Pour boiling water over cracked wheat in a small bowl; set aside. Dissolve yeast in warm water in a large bowl; let stand 5 minutes.

Combine milk, margarine, and sugar in a small saucepan; cook over medium heat until lukewarm (105° to 115°). Stir in egg, salt, cinnamon, and nutmeg. Add milk mixture to reserved yeast mixture. Add whole wheat flour; beat at low speed of an electric mixer until well blended. Beat an additional 3 minutes at high speed. Stir in reserved cracked wheat mixture, zucchini, and enough unbleached flour to make a soft dough.

Turn dough out onto a lightly floured surface, and knead until dough is smooth and elastic (about 8 to 10 minutes). Place dough in a large bowl that has been coated with cooking spray, turning to grease top. Cover and let rise in a warm place (85°), free from drafts, 1 hour or until doubled in bulk.

Punch dough down; cover and let stand 10 minutes. Shape dough into a round loaf. Place in a 9-inch round cake pan that has been coated with cooking spray. Cover and let rise in a warm place, free from drafts, 30 minutes or until doubled in bulk. Bake at 425° for 10 minutes. Reduce heat to 350°, and bake an additional 30 minutes or until loaf sounds hollow when tapped. Remove from pan, and let cool on a wire rack. Yield: 18 servings (141 calories per 1-inch wedge).

PROTEIN 4.6 / FAT 2.0 / CARBOHYDRATE 26.8 / CHOLESTEROL 15 / IRON 1.5 / SODIUM 75 / CALCIUM 19

MUSTARD-BEER BREAD

2 packages dry yeast
¾ cup warm, flat light beer (105° to 115°)
2 teaspoons brown sugar
2 cups all-purpose flour, divided
¼ cup spicy brown mustard
3 tablespoons margarine, melted
1 teaspoon salt
1⅓ cups whole wheat flour
Vegetable cooking spray

Dissolve yeast in beer; let stand 5 minutes.

Add sugar and 1½ cups all-purpose flour; beat at low speed of an electric mixer until smooth. Cover and let rise in a warm place (85°), free from drafts, 30 minutes or until light and bubbly.

Stir in mustard, margarine, and salt. Add whole wheat flour and stir well. Gradually add enough of remaining ½ cup all-purpose flour to make a soft dough.

Turn dough out onto a lightly floured surface; knead until smooth and elastic (about 8 to 10 minutes). Place in a large bowl that has been coated with cooking spray, turning to grease top. Cover and let rise in a warm place, free from drafts, 1½ hours or until doubled in bulk.

Punch dough down. Turn dough out onto a lightly floured surface; knead until smooth and elastic (about 8 to 10 minutes). Cover and let stand 10 minutes. Shape dough into a loaf. Place in an 8½- x 4½- x 2½-inch loafpan that has been coated with cooking spray. Cover and let rise in a warm place, free from drafts, 30 minutes or until doubled in bulk. Bake at 375° for 30 to 40 minutes or until loaf sounds hollow when tapped. Remove from pan, and let cool on a wire rack. Yield: 17 servings (118 calories per ½-inch slice).

PROTEIN 3.5 / FAT 2.7 / CARBOHYDRATE 19.9 / CHOLESTEROL 0 / IRON 1.0 / SODIUM 211 / CALCIUM 14

PEPPERY GARLIC BAGUETTE

3¾ cups all-purpose flour,
   divided
2 packages dry yeast
1 tablespoon sugar
2 teaspoons salt
1 tablespoon garlic powder
1 teaspoon coarsely ground
   pepper
1 teaspoon dried whole thyme
1¾ cups water
1 tablespoon unsalted margarine
Vegetable cooking spray
1 tablespoon cornmeal
1 egg white, lightly beaten
1 tablespoon cold water

Combine 1½ cups flour, yeast, sugar, salt, garlic powder, pepper, and thyme in a large bowl; stir well. Set aside.

Combine water and margarine in a small saucepan; cook over medium heat until very warm (120° to 130°). Stir water mixture into flour mixture, and beat at medium speed of an electric mixer 2 minutes or until smooth. Add ¾ cup flour; beat an additional 2 minutes at high speed. Stir in enough remaining 1½ cups flour to make a soft dough.

Turn dough out onto a lightly floured surface; knead until smooth and elastic (about 8 to 10 times). Cover and let rest 20 minutes.

Divide dough in half. Roll each half into a 15- x 10-inch rectangle on a lightly floured surface. Roll up jellyroll fashion, starting with long side; pinch ends and seam to seal. Place each loaf, seam side down, on a baking sheet that has been coated with cooking spray and sprinkled with cornmeal. Lightly spray loaves with cooking spray. Cover and chill at least 2 hours.

Uncover, and let stand at room temperature 10 minutes. Using a sharp knife, make diagonal slits about ¼-inch deep down the length of loaves. Bake at 425° for 20 minutes. Combine egg white and water; brush loaves with egg white mixture. Bake an additional 10 minutes or until golden brown. Remove from baking sheets and let cool on wire racks. Yield: 60 servings (36 calories per ½-inch slice).

PROTEIN 1.1 / FAT 0.3 / CARBOHYDRATE 7.1 / CHOLESTEROL 0 /
IRON 0.3 / SODIUM 79 / CALCIUM 3

GARDEN BATTER BREAD

2 cups all-purpose flour
1 package dry yeast
½ teaspoon salt
1 cup water
2 tablespoons vegetable oil
1 tablespoon molasses
1 egg
1 cup whole wheat flour
½ cup wheat germ
1 cup finely shredded carrot
1 medium onion, minced
¼ cup minced fresh parsley
½ teaspoon celery seeds
¼ teaspoon pepper
¼ teaspoon dried whole tarragon
1 clove garlic, minced
Vegetable cooking spray

Combine all purpose flour, yeast, and salt in a large bowl; set aside.

Combine water, oil, and molasses in a saucepan; cook over medium heat until very warm (120° to 130°). Add molasses mixture and egg to flour mixture; beat at low speed of an electric mixer until blended. Beat an additional 3 minutes at high speed. Add whole wheat flour and wheat germ; mix well. Stir in carrot, onion, parsley, celery seeds, pepper, tarragon, and garlic.

Spoon mixture into a 2-quart soufflé dish that has been coated with cooking spray. Cover and let rise in a warm place (85°), free from drafts, 1 hour and 15 minutes or until doubled in bulk. Bake at 350° for 1 hour or until loaf sounds hollow when tapped. Cool on a wire rack. Yield: 14 servings (149 calories per ½-inch wedge).

PROTEIN 5.3 / FAT 3.3 / CARBOHYDRATE 25.6 / CHOLESTEROL 20 /
IRON 1.6 / SODIUM 93 / CALCIUM 23

 ### ADD WHEAT GERM FOR FIBER

Wheat germ, found in the seed of the wheat kernel, is ideal for adding a nutty, robust flavor to foods. It becomes available in the milling process when wheat is converted to refined white flour. In addition to removing fiber, the milling eliminates 18 vitamins and minerals. Adding wheat germ, especially to baked products containing refined flour, returns these essential nutrients.

GLAZED ORANGE-RUM BUNS

3½ cups all-purpose flour, divided
1 package dry yeast
½ teaspoon salt
½ cup skim milk
2 tablespoons sugar
2 tablespoons unsalted margarine
1 egg
½ cup unsweetened orange juice
1½ teaspoons rum extract
Vegetable cooking spray
2 tablespoons unsalted margarine,
  melted
¼ cup sugar
¼ cup raisins, chopped
1 teaspoon grated orange rind
½ cup low-sugar orange marmalade
2 tablespoons unsweetened orange juice
½ teaspoon rum extract

Combine 1 cup flour, yeast, and salt in a large bowl; set aside. Combine milk, 2 tablespoons sugar, and margarine in a small saucepan; cook over low heat, stirring constantly, until mixture reaches 120° to 130°. Stir milk mixture into flour mixture. Add egg and orange juice. Beat at low speed of an electric mixer until well blended. Beat an additional 3 minutes at medium speed. Add remaining 2½ cups flour and 1½ teaspoons rum extract; stir well.

Turn dough out onto a lightly floured surface, and knead until dough is smooth and elastic (about 8 to 10 minutes). Place dough in a large bowl that has been coated with cooking spray, turning to grease top. Cover and let rise in a warm place (85°), free from drafts, 1 hour or until doubled in bulk.

Punch dough down, and divide in half. Turn dough out onto a lightly floured surface. Roll each half into a 12- x 5-inch rectangle. Brush each rectangle with 1 tablespoon melted margarine. Combine ¼ cup sugar, chopped raisins, and grated orange rind; stir well. Sprinkle half of sugar mixture over each rectangle. Roll up jellyroll fashion, starting with long side. Pinch ends and seam to seal, and tuck ends under. Cut each rectangle into 12 (1-inch) slices. Place slices, cut side down, in muffin pans that have been coated with cooking spray. Cover and let rise in a warm place, free from drafts, for 1 hour

or until doubled in bulk. Bake at 400° for 12 minutes or until golden brown. Remove muffin pans from oven.

Combine orange marmalade, 2 tablespoons orange juice, and ½ teaspon rum extract in a small saucepan. Cook over low heat, stirring frequently, until marmalade melts. Remove from heat; let cool 2 to 3 minutes. Spoon marmalade mixture evenly over warm buns. Remove from muffin pans, and let cool on wire racks. Yield: 2 dozen (127 calories each).

PROTEIN 2.7 / FAT 2.6 / CARBOHYDRATE 22.6 / CHOLESTEROL 12 / IRON 0.7 / SODIUM 55 / CALCIUM 13

BLUEBERRY ENGLISH MUFFINS

1 package dry yeast
1 cup warm water (105° to 115°)
3¼ cups all-purpose flour, divided
2 tablespoons honey
2 tablespoons unsalted margarine, melted
½ teaspoon salt
1 cup fresh or frozen blueberries, thawed and
  drained
2 tablespoons cornmeal, divided

Dissolve yeast in warm water in a large bowl; let stand 5 minutes. Add 2 cups flour, honey, margarine, and salt; mix well. Stir in enough remaining 1¼ cups flour to make a soft dough. Gently knead in blueberries.

Turn dough out onto a lightly floured surface; roll to ½-inch thickness. Cut dough into rounds with a 3-inch cutter. Sprinkle 2 baking sheets with 1 tablespoon cornmeal. Transfer dough rounds to baking sheets, placing 2 inches apart. Sprinkle remaining 1 tablespoon cornmeal evenly over tops of muffins. Cover and let rise in a warm place (85°), free from drafts, 1 hour or until doubled in bulk.

Heat an electric skillet at medium heat (350°) until hot. Using a wide spatula, transfer muffins to skillet, 7 at a time. Cook, partially covered, 5 minutes. Turn muffins over. Cook, partially covered, an additional 8 to 10 minutes. Remove from skillet, and let cool on wire racks. Repeat procedure with remaining muffins. Yield: 14 muffins (150 calories each).

PROTEIN 3.7 / FAT 2.0 / CARBOHYDRATE 29.0 / CHOLESTEROL 0 / IRON 1.1 / SODIUM 85 / CALCIUM 7

Angel Biscuits are wonderfully light in texture.

ANGEL BISCUITS

1 package dry yeast
2 tablespoons warm water (105° to 115°)
1 cup nonfat buttermilk
2½ cups all-purpose flour
1½ teaspoons sugar
1 teaspoon baking powder
½ teaspoon salt
¼ teaspoon baking soda
3 tablespoons shortening
Vegetable cooking spray

Dissolve yeast in warm water; let stand 5 minutes. Stir buttermilk into yeast mixture; set aside.

Combine flour and next 4 ingredients in a large bowl; cut in shortening with a pastry blender until mixture resembles coarse meal. Add buttermilk mixture, stirring with a fork until dry ingredients are moistened. Turn dough out onto a lightly floured surface, and knead lightly 3 or 4 times.

Roll dough to ½-inch thickness; cut into rounds with a 2½-inch biscuit cutter. Place biscuits on a baking sheet that has been coated with cooking spray. Cover and let rise in a warm place (85°), free from drafts, for 10 to 15 minutes. Bake at 400° for 10 to 12 minutes or until golden. Yield: 1 dozen (139 calories each).

PROTEIN 3.9 / FAT 3.1 / CARBOHYDRATE 23.5 / CHOLESTEROL 0 / IRON 0.9 / SODIUM 162 / CALCIUM 25

CHEDDAR CHEESE CRESCENT ROLLS

1 package dry yeast
½ cup warm water (105° to 115°)
2 tablespoons unsalted margarine
2 tablespoons sugar
¾ teaspoon ground red pepper
½ teaspoon salt
½ teaspoon garlic powder
½ cup skim milk
¾ cup (3 ounces) finely shredded extra-sharp
    Cheddar cheese
1 egg, beaten
3 cups all-purpose flour, divided
Vegetable cooking spray

Dissolve yeast in warm water, and let stand 5 minutes.

Combine margarine, sugar, pepper, salt, garlic powder, and milk in a small saucepan; heat until margarine melts, stirring constantly. Transfer milk mixture to a large bowl; cool to 105° to 115°. Add yeast mixture, cheese, egg, and 2 cups flour, stirring well. Add enough remaining flour to make a soft dough.

Turn dough out onto a lightly floured surface; knead until dough is smooth and elastic (about 8 to 10 minutes). Place dough in a large bowl that has been coated with cooking spray, turning to grease top. Cover and let rise in a warm place (85°), free from drafts, 1 hour or until doubled in bulk.

Punch dough down; turn onto a lightly floured surface. Cover and let stand 10 minutes. Divide dough in half. Roll each half into a 12-inch circle. Cut each circle into 12 wedges. Roll up each wedge, beginning at wide end. Place wedges, point side down, on baking sheets that have been coated with cooking spray. Cover and let rise in a warm place, free from drafts, 30 minutes or until doubled in bulk. Bake at 425° for 6 minutes or until lightly browned. Yield: 2 dozen (97 calories each).

PROTEIN 3.2 / FAT 2.7 / CARBOHYDRATE 14.6 / CHOLESTEROL 15 / IRON 0.6 / SODIUM 77 / CALCIUM 37

PUMPERNICKEL PITA BREAD

1 package dry yeast
2 cups warm water (105° to 115°)
1 tablespoon plus 1 teaspoon sugar,
    divided
2 tablespoons vegetable oil
1 tablespoon unsweetened cocoa
½ teaspoon salt
½ teaspoon caraway seeds
2 cups rye flour
3½ cups all-purpose flour
Vegetable cooking spray

Dissolve yeast in warm water in a large bowl; add 1 teaspoon sugar, and let stand 5 minutes. Add remaining 1 tablespoon sugar, oil, cocoa, salt, caraway seeds, and rye flour. Beat at low speed of an electric mixer just until blended. Beat an additional 3 minutes at medium speed. Gradually stir in enough all-purpose flour to make a stiff dough.

Turn dough out onto a lightly floured surface; knead until dough is smooth and elastic (about 8 to 10 minutes). Place dough in a large bowl that has been coated with cooking spray, turning to grease top. Cover with heavy-duty plastic wrap and a towel. Let rest 20 minutes.

Punch dough down. Divide into 12 equal pieces. Shape each piece into a smooth ball. Place balls on 2 ungreased baking sheets. Cover and let rise in a warm place (85°), free from drafts, 30 minutes or until doubled in bulk.

Roll each dough ball into a 5-inch circle on a lightly floured surface. Place 6 circles on a large wire rack. Place wire rack directly on middle oven rack. Bake at 500° for 4 to 5 minutes or until puffed and brown. Remove bread and rack from oven, and let bread cool on the wire rack. Repeat procedure with remaining circles. Cut circles in half. Yield: 2 dozen servings (114 calories per serving).

PROTEIN 3.0 / FAT 1.5 / CARBOHYDRATE 21.8 / CHOLESTEROL 0 / IRON 0.8 / SODIUM 49 / CALCIUM 6

POPPY SEED-ONION TWISTS

Vegetable cooking spray
¼ cup minced onion
1 package dry yeast
¼ cup warm water (105° to 115°)
3 tablespoons sugar
3 tablespoons unsalted
  margarine
1 teaspoon cracked pepper
½ teaspoon salt
¾ cup skim milk
1 egg yolk
1 cup whole wheat flour
2¾ cups all-purpose flour,
  divided
¼ cup poppy seeds

Coat a small nonstick skillet with cooking spray; place over medium-high heat until hot. Add onion, and sauté until tender. Remove from heat and set aside.

Dissolve yeast in warm water, and let stand 5 minutes.

Combine sugar, unsalted margarine, cracked pepper, salt, and milk in a small saucepan. Place over medium heat and cook until margarine melts, stirring occasionally. Place milk mixture in a large bowl; cool to 105° to 115°. Add yeast mixture, reserved onion mixture, and egg yolk to milk mixture, stirring well. Gradually add whole wheat flour; stir well. Add 2 cups all-purpose flour to make a soft dough.

Turn dough out onto a lightly floured surface; knead remaining ¾ cup all-purpose flour into dough until smooth and elastic (about 8 to 10 minutes). Place in a large bowl that has been coated with cooking spray, turning to grease top. Cover; let rise in a warm place (85°), free from drafts, 1 hour or until doubled in bulk.

Punch dough down, and divide in half. Roll each half into a 15- x 18-inch rectangle on a lightly floured surface. Lightly spray surface of each rectangle with cooking spray; sprinkle 1 tablespoon poppy seeds over each rectangle. Fold dough in thirds starting with short ends; roll into 15- x 18-inch rectangles. Lightly spray surface of each rectangle with cooking spray; sprinkle 1 tablespoon poppy seeds over each rectangle. Fold dough in thirds starting with short ends; roll into 8-inch squares. Cut dough into 4- x ½-inch strips. Twist strips loosely; place on baking sheets that have been coated with cooking spray. Bake at 400° for 12 minutes or until golden brown. Remove from baking sheets; cool on wire racks. Yield: 5½ dozen (32 calories each).

PROTEIN 0.9 / FAT 1.0 / CARBOHYDRATE 5.0 / CHOLESTEROL 4 / IRON 0.3 / SODIUM 20 / CALCIUM 13

SOURDOUGH STARTER

1 cup warm water (105° to 115°)
¼ cup plain low-fat yogurt
1 cup all-purpose flour
Starter Food

Combine water and yogurt, stir well. Pour into a 2-quart non-metal casserole dish that has been warmed.

Cover loosely with plastic wrap or cheesecloth; let stand in a warm place (85°) for 24 hours. Gradually stir in flour until well blended. Cover and let stand in warm place (85°) for 72 hours, stirring 2 to 3 times daily. Place fermented mixture in refrigerator, and stir once a day. Use within 11 days.

To use starter, remove from refrigerator; let stand at room temperature at least 1 hour.

Stir starter well, and measure amount needed for recipe. Replenish remaining starter with Starter Food, and return to refrigerator. Use starter within 11 days, stirring daily. Yield: 1⅓ cups (25 calories per tablespoon).

Starter Food:

¾ cup all-purpose flour
¾ cup warm water (105° to 115°)

Combine all ingredients; stir into remaining Sourdough Starter. Yield: 1 cup.

PROTEIN 0.8 / FAT 0.1 / CARBOHYDRATE 5.1 / CHOLESTEROL 0 / IRON 0.2 / SODIUM 2 / CALCIUM 6

SOURDOUGH BANANA BREAD

1 cup all-purpose flour
1 cup shreds of wheat bran cereal
½ cup whole wheat flour
⅓ cup sugar
1 teaspoon baking soda
¼ teaspoon salt
¼ teaspoon ground cardamom
½ cup Sourdough Starter (at room temperature)
¼ cup unsalted margarine, melted
3 tablespoons molasses
1 egg, beaten
1 cup mashed ripe banana
Vegetable cooking spray

Combine first 7 ingredients in a large bowl; set aside.

Combine starter and next 3 ingredients; mix well. Add to dry ingredients; stir well. Stir in banana.

Spoon batter into an 8½- x 4½- x 3-inch loafpan that has been coated with cooking spray. Bake at 375° for 55 minutes to 1 hour or until a wooden pick inserted in center comes out clean. Cool in pan 10 minutes. Remove from pan, and let cool on a wire rack. Yield: 16 servings (139 calories per ½-inch slice).

PROTEIN 2.9 / FAT 3.7 / CARBOHYDRATE 25.4 / CHOLESTEROL 17 / IRON 1.3 / SODIUM 124 / CALCIUM 35

SOURDOUGH TOMATO BREAD

1 (28-ounce) can tomatoes, undrained and mashed
1 cup Sourdough Starter (at room temperature)
¼ cup grated Parmesan cheese
2 tablespoons minced fresh chives
2 teaspoons vegetable oil
1 teaspoon garlic powder
½ teaspoon salt
½ teaspoon baking powder
½ teaspoon dried whole oregano
2 packages dry yeast
¼ cup warm water (105° to 115°)
9½ cups whole wheat flour
Vegetable cooking spray

Combine first 9 ingredients in a large bowl; beat at low speed of a heavy-duty electric mixer until well blended. Set aside.

Dissolve yeast in warm water; let stand 5 minutes. Add to tomato mixture; beat well. Gradually add flour, beating until well blended. (Dough will be sticky.)

Turn dough out onto a lightly floured surface; knead until smooth and elastic (about 8 to 10 minutes). Place in a large bowl that has been coated with cooking spray; turn to grease top. Cover and let rise in a warm place (85°), free from drafts, 1 hour or until doubled in bulk.

Punch dough down, and divide in half. Shape each half into a loaf. Place loaves in two 9- x 5- x 3-inch loafpans that have been coated with cooking spray. Cover and let rise in a warm place, free from drafts, 1 hour or until doubled in bulk. Bake at 375° for 40 minutes or until loaves sound hollow when tapped. Remove from pans, and let cool on wire racks. Yield: 36 servings (128 calories per ½-inch slice).

PROTEIN 5.2 / FAT 1.2 / CARBOHYDRATE 25.9 / CHOLESTEROL 0 / IRON 1.3 / SODIUM 85 / CALCIUM 33

STREUSEL PEAR COFFEE CAKE

1 cup all-purpose flour
1 teaspoon baking powder
¼ teaspoon salt
¼ teaspoon ground cinnamon
⅓ cup sugar
⅓ cup firmly packed brown sugar
¼ cup unsalted margarine, melted
1 egg
1 teaspoon vanilla extract
½ cup peeled, chopped pear
Vegetable cooking spray
¼ cup quick-cooking oats, uncooked
3 tablespoons all-purpose flour
2 tablespoons brown sugar
½ teaspoon ground cinnamon
2 tablespoons unsalted margarine, softened

Combine first 4 ingredients in a small bowl; set aside.

Combine sugar, ⅓ cup brown sugar, ¼ cup melted margarine, egg, and vanilla extract in a large bowl; stir well. Add reserved dry ingredients and pear, stirring just until dry ingredients are moistened.

Spoon batter into an 8-inch square pan that has been coated with cooking spray. Combine oats, flour, 2 tablespoons brown sugar, and cinnamon; stir well. Cut in margarine with a pastry blender until mixture resembles coarse meal; sprinkle over top of batter. Bake at 350° for 30 minutes or until a wooden pick inserted in center comes out clean. Cool in pan on a wire rack. Yield: 16 servings (135 calories per serving).

PROTEIN 1.9 / FAT 5.0 / CARBOHYDRATE 20.9 / CHOLESTEROL 17 / IRON 0.8 / SODIUM 62 / CALCIUM 25

FRESH BLUEBERRY-ORANGE BREAD

1 cup fresh blueberries
1½ cups plus 1 tablespoon all-purpose flour, divided
¼ cup plus 2 tablespoons sugar
2 teaspoons baking powder
¼ teaspoon salt
1 egg, beaten
¼ cup water
¼ cup unsweetened orange juice
3 tablespoons margarine, melted
1 tablespoon plus 2 teaspoons grated orange rind, divided
Vegetable cooking spray
2 tablespoons sugar
3 tablespoons chopped pecans

Toss blueberries with 1 tablespoon flour, and set aside.

Combine remaining 1½ cups flour, ¼ cup plus 2 tablespoons sugar, baking powder, and salt in a large mixing bowl; stir well. Combine egg, water, orange juice, margarine, and 1 tablespoon orange rind; add to dry ingredients, stirring well. Gently fold in blueberries.

Spoon batter into a 7½- x 3- x 2-inch loafpan that has been coated with cooking spray. Combine 2 tablespoons sugar, 2 teaspoons orange rind, and pecans. Sprinkle over batter. Bake at 350° for 1 hour or until a wooden pick inserted in center comes out clean. Let cool in pan 10 minutes; remove from pan and let cool on a wire rack. Yield: 14 servings (130 calories per ½-inch slice).

PROTEIN 2.3 / FAT 4.2 / CARBOHYDRATE 21.3 / CHOLESTEROL 20 / IRON 0.6 / SODIUM 119 / CALCIUM 35

SPICED PEACH BREAD

1½ cups all-purpose flour
½ cup whole wheat flour
½ cup wheat germ
¼ cup firmly packed brown sugar
2 teaspoons baking powder
½ teaspoon baking soda
½ teaspoon ground cinnamon
¼ teaspoon salt
¼ teaspoon ground cloves
¼ teaspoon ground allspice
1 egg, beaten
1 (8-ounce) carton lemon low-fat yogurt
⅓ cup skim milk
¼ cup vegetable oil
1 teaspoon vanilla extract
2 cups peeled, sliced fresh peaches
Vegetable cooking spray

Combine first 10 ingredients in a large bowl; stir well. Make a well in center of mixture. Combine egg, yogurt, milk, oil, and vanilla in a small bowl; stir well. Add liquid ingredients to dry ingredients, stirring just until moistened.

Position knife blade in food processor bowl. Add peaches; top with cover, and process until smooth. Fold peaches into flour mixture. Spoon into an 8½- x 4½- x 3-inch loafpan that has been coated with cooking spray. Bake at 350° for 1 hour or until a wooden pick inserted in center comes out clean. Cool in pan 10 minutes; remove from pan and cool on a wire rack. Yield: 16 servings (143 calories per ½-inch slice).

PROTEIN 4.3 / FAT 4.7 / CARBOHYDRATE 22.1 / CHOLESTEROL 18 / IRON 1.0 / SODIUM 124 / CALCIUM 70

OAT BRAN

Research has shown that including oat bran in your diet can lower blood cholesterol, but evidence is inconclusive as to the extent of the reduction. A study by Northwestern University School of Medicine reported that 2 ounces a day of either oatmeal or oat bran—equivalent to 2 cups of hot cereal or 2 muffins—lowered cholesterol by almost 5 percent. However, the oats were accompanied by a low-fat, low-cholesterol diet; the long-term effects of oat bran on a diet high in fat are not yet known.

CRANBERRY-PINEAPPLE MUFFINS

1 cup whole wheat flour
½ cup all-purpose flour
½ cup regular oats, uncooked
¼ cup sugar
2 teaspoons baking powder
¼ teaspoon salt
¼ cup unsalted margarine
1 egg, beaten
1 cup skim milk
1 cup fresh cranberries, coarsely chopped
½ cup unsweetened crushed pineapple, drained
Vegetable cooking spray
1 tablespoon sugar
¼ teaspoon ground cinnamon

Combine first 6 ingredients; stir well. Cut in margarine with a pastry blender until mixture resembles coarse meal. Make a well in center of mixture. Combine beaten egg and milk; add to dry ingredients, stirring just until moistened. Gently fold in cranberries and pineapple.

Spoon batter into muffin pans that have been coated with cooking spray, filling three-fourths full. Combine 1 tablespoon sugar and cinnamon; sprinkle evenly over muffin batter. Bake at 400° for 20 to 25 minutes or until golden brown. Remove from pans immediately. Yield: 1 dozen (147 calories each).

PROTEIN 3.8 / FAT 5.0 / CARBOHYDRATE 22.8 / CHOLESTEROL 23 / IRON 0.8 / SODIUM 116 / CALCIUM 70

BUCKWHEAT-CORN MUFFINS

¾ cup buckwheat flour
½ cup cornmeal
¼ cup all-purpose flour
1 tablespoon brown sugar
2½ teaspoons baking powder
½ teaspoon salt
1⅓ cups skim milk
2 tablespoons vegetable oil
2 eggs, beaten
Vegetable cooking spray

Combine first 6 ingredients in a large bowl; make a well in center of mixture. Combine milk, oil, and eggs; add to dry ingredients, stirring just until moistened.

Spoon batter into muffin pans that have been coated with cooking spray, filling three-fourths full. Bake at 400° for 15 minutes or until lightly browned. Remove from pans immediately. Yield: 1 dozen (99 calories each).

PROTEIN 3.4 / FAT 3.7 / CARBOHYDRATE 13.2 / CHOLESTEROL 46 / IRON 0.6 / SODIUM 187 / CALCIUM 82

SESAME-WHEAT GERM CRACKERS

1 cup whole wheat flour
½ cup wheat germ
2 tablespoons sesame seeds
1 teaspoon baking powder
1 teaspoon sugar
½ teaspoon salt
¼ cup margarine
4 tablespoons cold water

Combine first 6 ingredients; stir well. Cut in margarine with a pastry blender until mixture resembles coarse meal. Sprinkle water (1 tablespoon at a time) over surface; stir until dry ingredients are moistened. Shape into a ball.

Roll dough to ⅛-inch thickness on a lightly floured surface. Cut into 3- x 1½-inch rectangles; place on ungreased baking sheets. Bake at 375° for 10 to 12 minutes or until golden brown. Remove from baking sheets; cool on wire racks. Store in an airtight container. Yield: 3 dozen (31 calories each).

PROTEIN 1.0 / FAT 1.8 / CARBOHYDRATE 3.3 / CHOLESTEROL 0 / IRON 0.3 / SODIUM 56 / CALCIUM 13

FRUIT BITS GRAHAM CRACKERS

1½ cups whole wheat flour
1 cup plus 2 tablespoons all-purpose flour
1 cup dried fruit bits, finely chopped
¾ teaspoon baking soda
¼ teaspoon salt
½ cup unsalted margarine, softened
⅓ cup firmly packed brown sugar
¼ cup honey
1 teaspoon vanilla extract
3 tablespoons apricot nectar
2 tablespoons sugar
1 teaspoon ground cinnamon

Combine first 5 ingredients in a large bowl, stirring well; set aside.

Cream margarine in a large bowl; gradually add brown sugar, beating until light and fluffy. Add honey and vanilla, beating well. Add reserved dry ingredients to creamed mixture alternately with nectar, beginning and ending with flour mixture. Mix well after each addition.

Turn dough out onto a lightly floured surface. (Dough will be soft.) Knead lightly 3 to 5 minutes. Shape dough into a flat rectangle. Cover and chill 3 hours.

Divide chilled dough into 4 equal portions. Roll each portion into a 15- x 5-inch rectangle on a lightly floured surface. Cut each portion into six 5- x 2½-inch rectangles. Lightly score each rectangle in half using the dull side of a knife. Prick surface of each square in 3 parallel rows, using a fork. Place squares 1 inch apart on ungreased baking sheets.

Combine sugar and cinnamon, stirring well. Sprinkle evenly over squares. Bake at 350° for 10 to 12 minutes or until browned. Remove from baking sheets, and cool completely on wire racks. Yield: 4 dozen (64 calories each).

PROTEIN 1.0 / FAT 2.0 / CARBOHYDRATE 10.7 / CHOLESTEROL 0 / IRON 0.3 / SODIUM 28 / CALCIUM 7

APPLE-BUCKWHEAT WAFFLES

1 package dry yeast
½ cup warm water (105° to 115°)
2 cups skim milk
2 cups buckwheat flour
1 cup all-purpose flour
1 teaspoon salt
½ teaspoon ground cinnamon
1 teaspoon baking soda
½ cup hot water
¼ cup plus 2 tablespoons vegetable oil
2 tablespoons molasses
3 eggs, separated
1 cup peeled, finely chopped cooking apples
Vegetable cooking spray

Dissolve yeast in warm water in a large bowl; let stand 5 minutes. Add milk, flours, salt, and cinnamon; beat at medium speed of an electric mixer until mixture is smooth. Cover and chill at least 8 hours.

Dissolve soda in hot water. Add soda mixture, oil, molasses, egg yolks, and apple to chilled flour mixture, stirring until blended at high speed of an electric mixer.

Beat egg whites (at room temperature) until stiff peaks form; carefully fold into batter.

Coat a waffle iron with cooking spray; allow to preheat. Pour 1 cup plus 2 tablespoons batter onto hot waffle iron, spreading batter to edges. Bake 6 minutes or until steaming stops. Repeat procedure with remaining batter. Yield: 24 (4-inch) waffles (107 calories each).

PROTEIN 2.7 / FAT 4.9 / CARBOHYDRATE 13.1 / CHOLESTEROL 35 / IRON 0.6 / SODIUM 152 / CALCIUM 44

THE RDAs DEFINED

The Recommended Dietary Allowances should be thought of as recommendations, not requirements, for good nutrition. They include a margin of safety so that with the exception of calories, an intake of two-thirds of the RDA is often adequate for healthy people.

GOLDEN ORANGE PANCAKES

¾ cup all-purpose flour
¾ cup whole wheat flour
¼ cup wheat germ
2 teaspoons baking powder
1½ teaspoons sugar
½ teaspoon salt
¾ cup skim milk
¾ cup unsweetened orange juice
1 egg, beaten
½ teaspoon grated orange rind
Vegetable cooking spray

Combine first 6 ingredients in a large bowl; make a well in center of mixture. Combine milk, orange juice, egg, and orange rind; add to dry ingredients, stirring just until moistened.

For each pancake, pour ¼ cup batter onto hot griddle or skillet that has been coated with cooking spray. Turn pancakes when tops are covered with bubbles and edges look cooked. Yield: 12 (4-inch) pancakes (85 calories each).

PROTEIN 3.8 / FAT 1.1 / CARBOHYDRATE 15.9 / CHOLESTEROL 23 / IRON 0.8 / SODIUM 162 / CALCIUM 61

WAKE-ME-UP GRITS

Vegetable cooking spray
1 teaspoon unsalted margarine
2 tablespoons minced onion
1 small green pepper, seeded and finely chopped
2 medium tomatoes, peeled and coarsely chopped
2 drops of hot sauce
3 tablespoons chopped lean cooked ham
3 cups water
½ teaspoon salt
¾ cup quick-cooking grits

Coat a medium-sized nonstick skillet with cooking spray; add margarine. Place over medium-high heat until hot; add onion and green pepper, and sauté until tender. Stir in tomatoes and hot sauce. Reduce heat and simmer, uncovered, 20 minutes or until thickened. Set aside.

Coat a small nonstick skillet with cooking spray; place over medium-high heat until hot. Add ham, and sauté 2 minutes or until ham is browned; set aside.

Combine water and salt in a medium saucepan; bring to a boil. Stir in grits. Cover; reduce heat, and simmer 5 minutes or until thickened, stirring occasionally. Remove from heat; stir in reserved tomato mixture. Top each serving with 1 teaspoon reserved ham. Serve immediately. Yield: 9 servings (61 calories per ½-cup serving).

PROTEIN 2.0 / FAT 0.8 / CARBOHYDRATE 11.8 / CHOLESTEROL 2 / IRON 0.6 / SODIUM 172 / CALCIUM 6

GARDEN VEGETABLE COUSCOUS

1 cup peeled, cubed rutabaga
1 teaspoon sugar
1 teaspoon chicken-flavored bouillon granules
Vegetable cooking spray
¼ cup chopped green onions
1 large carrot, scraped and shredded
1 small zucchini, diagonally sliced
1 cup water
1 teaspoon margarine
¼ teaspoon ground cinnamon
¼ teaspoon freshly ground black pepper
⅛ teaspoon ground cumin
⅛ teaspoon ground red pepper
¾ cup uncooked couscous
1 tablespoon chopped fresh parsley

Combine first 3 ingredients in a small Dutch oven; add water to cover, and bring to a boil. Cover, reduce heat, and cook 10 minutes or until rutabaga is tender. Drain and set aside.

Coat a large nonstick skillet with cooking spray; place over medium-high heat until hot. Add onions, carrot, and zucchini, and sauté until crisp-tender. Remove from heat and add rutabaga mixture; set aside.

Combine water, margarine, cinnamon, pepper, cumin, and ground red pepper in a saucepan. Cover and bring to a boil; remove from heat. Add couscous; cover and let stand 5 minutes or until couscous is tender and liquid is absorbed. Add chopped parsley and stir well. Transfer couscous to a serving platter, and top with vegetable mixture. Yield: 8 servings (86 calories per ½-cup serving).

PROTEIN 2.9 / FAT 0.8 / CARBOHYDRATE 17.2 / CHOLESTEROL 0 / IRON 0.7 / SODIUM 116 / CALCIUM 24

TRY COUSCOUS INSTEAD OF RICE

Couscous is growing in popularity. Produced from finely cracked wheat or millet grain, it has been steamed, dried, and refined; this process helps impart a delicate flavor when cooked. Couscous is a rich source of complex carbohydrates and is low in fat and sodium. But like other unenriched, refined grains, it is not a good source of fiber, vitamins, or minerals. A more nutritious alternative is whole wheat couscous, which contains more vitamin B-6, minerals, and fiber.

Add instant couscous to boiling water for a quick, low-fat accompaniment that is especially flavorful when combined with spicy meats or vegetables.

APPLE-SPICED RICE

1⅓ cups water
1 cup unsweetened apple juice
1 cup uncooked long grain rice
1 cup peeled, chopped cooking apple
½ teaspoon salt
¼ teaspoon apple pie spice
2 (3-inch) sticks cinnamon

Combine water and apple juice in a medium saucepan; bring to a boil. Stir in rice and remaining ingredients. Cover, reduce heat, and simmer 20 to 25 minutes or until rice is tender and liquid is absorbed. Remove and discard cinnamon sticks. Yield: 8 servings (99 calories per ½-cup serving).

PROTEIN 1.5 / FAT 0.1 / CARBOHYDRATE 22.3 / CHOLESTEROL 0 / IRON 0.8 / SODIUM 149 / CALCIUM 9

APRICOT-RICE BAKE

Vegetable cooking spray
2 teaspoons margarine
1 cup uncooked long-grain rice
½ cup chopped onion
¼ cup diced, dried apricots
¼ cup diced, dried, pitted prunes
2 cups water
2 teaspoons chicken-flavored bouillon granules
¼ teaspoon ground thyme
2 tablespoons sliced blanched almonds, toasted

Coat a large nonstick skillet with cooking spray; add margarine. Place over medium-high heat until hot; add rice and onion. Sauté until rice is browned and onion is tender.

Spoon rice mixture into a 1½-quart casserole that has been coated with cooking spray. Add apricots and prunes, stirring well. Combine water, bouillon granules, and thyme in a large nonstick skillet; bring mixture to a boil. Pour over rice mixture. Cover and bake at 350° for 20 minutes or until rice is tender and liquid is absorbed. Sprinkle with almonds. Yield: 8 servings (127 calories per ½-cup serving).

PROTEIN 2.3 / FAT 2.4 / CARBOHYDRATE 24.5 / CHOLESTEROL 0 / IRON 1.1 / SODIUM 219 / CALCIUM 17

SPRINGTIME RICE

Vegetable cooking spray
1 tablespoon margarine
1 cup uncooked long-grain rice
¼ cup chopped green onions
¼ cup diced carrot
1 teaspoon dried whole basil
¼ cup fresh or frozen English peas, thawed
2¼ cups water
1 teaspoon chicken-flavored bouillon granules

Coat a large nonstick skillet with cooking spray; add margarine. Place over medium-high heat until hot; add rice, onions, carrot, and basil. Sauté until rice is lightly browned and vegetables are crisp-tender. Spoon rice mixture and peas into a 1½-quart casserole that has been coated with cooking spray.

Combine water and bouillon granules in a saucepan. Bring to a boil. Pour over rice mixture, stirring well. Cover and bake at 350° for 25 to 30 minutes or until rice is tender and liquid is absorbed. Yield: 8 servings (105 calories per ½-cup serving).

PROTEIN 1.9 / FAT 1.8 / CARBOHYDRATE 19.8 / CHOLESTEROL 0 / IRON 0.8 / SODIUM 127 / CALCIUM 11

SOUTH-OF-THE-BORDER RICE DRESSING

⅔ cup uncooked long-grain rice
1⅓ cups water
1 cup cornmeal
½ teaspoon salt
½ teaspoon baking soda
1 cup skim milk
1 (8¾-ounce) can no-salt-added cream-style corn
2 eggs, beaten
½ cup chopped onion
2 tablespoons minced jalapeño pepper
1 tablespoon vegetable oil
Vegetable cooking spray
¾ cup (3 ounces) shredded Monterey Jack cheese with jalapeño peppers

Combine rice and water in a medium saucepan; bring to a boil. Cover, reduce heat, and simmer 20 minutes or until rice is tender and liquid is absorbed. Set aside.

Combine cornmeal, salt, and soda in a large bowl; stir well. Add rice, milk, and next 5 ingredients, stirring well. Pour mixture into a 12- x 8- x 2-inch baking dish that has been coated with cooking spray. Bake, uncovered, at 350° for 45 minutes or until lightly browned. Sprinkle evenly with cheese, and bake an additional 5 minutes or until cheese melts. Yield: 12 servings (150 calories per ½-cup serving).

PROTEIN 5.5 / FAT 4.6 / CARBOHYDRATE 21.7 / CHOLESTEROL 52 / IRON 1.0 / SODIUM 193 / CALCIUM 96

HAWAIIAN RICE RING

1 cup uncooked short-grain rice
¼ teaspoon salt
2 cups water
¼ cup water
¾ cup frozen English peas
Vegetable cooking spray
2 teaspoons unsalted margarine
½ cup chopped onion
½ cup chopped sweet red pepper
3 ounces turkey ham, diced
1 (8-ounce) can unsweetened crushed pineapple,
  drained
1 tablespoon low-sodium soy sauce
½ teaspoon ground ginger
Spinach leaves
Sweet red pepper strips (optional)
Green onion tops (optional)

Combine first 3 ingredients in a heavy sauce-pan; bring to a boil. Cover, reduce heat, and simmer 15 to 20 minutes or until rice is tender and liquid is absorbed. Set aside.

Bring ¼ cup water to a boil in a saucepan. Add peas. Cover, reduce heat, and simmer 5 minutes or until tender. Drain; set aside.

Coat a small nonstick skillet with cooking spray. Add margarine; place over medium-high heat until hot. Add chopped onion and sweet red pepper, and sauté until tender. Combine reserved rice, peas, sautéed vegetables, ham, pineapple, soy sauce, and ginger, stirring until blended. Pack hot rice mixture into a 5-cup ring mold that has been coated with cooking spray. Invert onto a spinach leaf-lined serving plate. If desired, garnish with red pepper strips tied with green onion tops. Yield: 8 servings (141 calories per ½-cup serving).

PROTEIN 4.8 / FAT 1.9 / CARBOHYDRATE 25.8 / CHOLESTEROL 6 / IRON 1.5 / SODIUM 239 / CALCIUM 16

WILD SPANISH RICE

1 (14½-ounce) can no-salt-added whole tomatoes,
  undrained
Vegetable cooking spray
¼ cup chopped onion
3 tablespoons chopped green pepper
1 stalk celery, chopped
⅔ cup uncooked wild rice
1 teaspoon beef-flavored bouillon granules
¼ teaspoon prepared mustard

Drain tomatoes, reserving liquid. Coarsely chop tomatoes. Add enough water to reserved liquid to measure 1¼ cups. Set aside.

Coat a large nonstick skillet with cooking spray; place over medium-high heat until hot. Add onion, green pepper, and celery, and sauté until tender. Wash wild rice in 3 changes of hot water; drain. Add rice, reserved tomatoes and liquid, bouillon, and mustard to sautéed vegetable mixture; bring to a boil. Cover, reduce heat, and simmer 1 hour or until rice is tender and liquid is absorbed. Yield: 6 servings (84 calories per ½-cup serving).

PROTEIN 3.2 / FAT 0.4 / CARBOHYDRATE 17.6 / CHOLESTEROL 0 / IRON 1.1 / SODIUM 179 / CALCIUM 32

LABEL LANGUAGE

The words "made with vegetable oil" or "contains no cholesterol" are no guarantee that the fat is polyunsaturated. Unlike oils from other vegetables, palm and coconut oil are saturated fats. While they do not contain cholesterol, they stimulate the body to manufacture it. In fact, tests show that these oils can increase cholesterol levels more than the saturated fat from beef or pork. In 1987, the National Academy of Sciences showed that coconut oil contains 91 percent saturated fat and palm oil 47 percent, which exceeds or equals the 47 percent found in beef tallow.

Many manufacturers use palm and coconut oils because they are more stable than the less saturated varieties. Also, these tropical oils are usually cheaper. Read labels closely as crackers, cookies, non-dairy creamers, cake mixes, and a variety of other snack foods generally are made with palm or coconut oil.

Hawaiian Rice Ring will be a flavorful complement to all types of entrées.

VEGETABLE GARDEN-PASTA MEDLEY

1 small zucchini, cut into julienne strips
1 pint cherry tomatoes, halved
¼ cup sliced pitted ripe olives
2 cloves garlic, minced
½ teaspoon dried whole oregano
½ teaspoon dried whole basil
¼ cup chopped fresh parsley
¼ teaspoon salt
⅛ teaspoon coarsely ground pepper
½ cup plain low-fat yogurt
1 tablespoon plus 1½ teaspoons olive oil
6 ounces corkscrew pasta, uncooked

Combine all ingredients except pasta in a large bowl, tossing well. Cover and let stand at room temperature 1 hour.

Cook pasta according to package directions, omitting salt and fat; drain. Combine pasta and vegetable mixture in a large saucepan. Cook over medium heat 5 minutes or until thoroughly heated. Serve immediately. Yield: 12 servings (86 calories per 1-cup serving).

PROTEIN 2.8 / FAT 2.4 / CARBOHYDRATE 13.7 / CHOLESTEROL 1 / IRON 0.8 / SODIUM 80 / CALCIUM 32

JALAPEÑO MACARONI AND CHEESE

1 (8-ounce) package elbow macaroni, uncooked
1 cup evaporated skimmed milk
1 tablespoon cornstarch
¾ cup (3 ounces) shredded Monterey Jack cheese with jalapeño peppers
2 green onions, finely chopped
2 tablespoons diced green pepper
¼ teaspoon salt
1 (2-ounce) jar diced pimiento, drained
1 tablespoon chopped fresh parsley

Cook macaroni according to package directions, omitting salt and fat. Drain and set aside.

Combine milk and cornstarch in a medium saucepan; stir with a wire whisk until smooth. Cook over medium heat until thickened, stirring frequently. Stir in cheese and next 4 ingredients.

Combine macaroni and cheese mixture, stirring well. Transfer mixture to a serving dish; sprinkle with parsley. Serve immediately. Yield: 8 servings (176 calories per ½-cup serving).

PROTEIN 8.7 / FAT 3.7 / CARBOHYDRATE 26.5 / CHOLESTEROL 10 / IRON 1.2 / SODIUM 169 / CALCIUM 183

Colorful Crab-Broccoli Macaroni is made with surimi—an economical imitation crabmeat.

COLORFUL CRAB-BROCCOLI MACARONI

1 (8-ounce) package medium shell macaroni, uncooked
Vegetable cooking spray
⅓ cup chopped green onions
3 cloves garlic, minced
2 teaspoons unsalted margarine
1 tablespoon all-purpose flour
½ cup Chablis or other dry white wine
¼ cup skim milk
¾ teaspoon dried whole basil
½ teaspoon dried whole dillweed
1 small sweet yellow pepper, seeded and cut into ½-inch pieces
½ pound fresh broccoli, coarsely chopped
½ (1-pound) package frozen imitation crabmeat, thawed, rinsed, and drained
Fresh basil sprigs (optional)

Cook macaroni according to package directions, omitting salt and fat. Drain; set aside.

Coat a large nonstick skillet with cooking spray; place over medium-high heat until hot. Add onions and garlic, and sauté until crisp-tender. Remove from skillet, and set aside.

Melt margarine in skillet. Add flour; cook over medium heat, stirring constantly, 1 minute. Gradually stir in wine; cook over medium heat, stirring constantly, until mixture is thickened and bubbly. Remove from heat; gradually stir in milk, basil, and dillweed.

Add onion mixture, pepper, broccoli, and crabmeat to sauce. Simmer 5 minutes or until vegetables are crisp-tender. Combine pasta and broccoli mixture; toss gently. Garnish with fresh basil sprigs, if desired. Yield: 6 servings (218 calories per 1-cup serving).

PROTEIN 11.1 / FAT 2.4 / CARBOHYDRATE 38.3 / CHOLESTEROL 0 / IRON 2.2 / SODIUM 335 / CALCIUM 163

SURIMI—SEAFOOD IN DISGUISE

Have you enjoyed a seafood salad or seafood dinner lately? Was it really crab that you savored? Surimi can imitate many types of seafood, depending on the flavors added. The growth of the surimi industry is impressive, and manufacturers predict it to continue over the next few years.

The modern process of transforming low-cost fish into other seafood products is similar to the ancient Japanese technique of fish preservation. The fish is made into a paste, combined with flavors, and molded into the desired shape.

Although low in price and rich in protein, surimi is not the perfect substitute for fresh seafood. When it is processed, it loses niacin and potassium and in some instances, calories may be added with sweeteners or starch. In addition, it is not a good choice for those who are watching their sodium intake for its sodium content is often six to ten times that of fresh seafood.

But surimi products do have many desirable aspects. For example, they are generally low in fat and cholesterol in addition to being fully cooked and ready to eat when purchased. The fish, commonly white pollack, and the manufacturing process are relatively inexpensive, enabling the price to be much lower than that of the "real" seafood products.

Look in the supermarket for "sea legs" or "imitation crab meat" and enjoy the high-price flavor at a much lower cost.

CREAMY SEAFOOD CASSEROLE

2 cups shell macaroni, uncooked
3 ounces Neufchâtel cheese, softened
½ cup plain low-fat yogurt
½ cup lemon low-fat yogurt
1 cup part-skim ricotta cheese
⅓ cup chopped green onions
1 teaspoon dried whole basil
¼ teaspoon garlic powder
1 (2-ounce) jar diced pimiento,
  undrained
Vegetable cooking spray
1 pound fresh lump crabmeat,
  drained and flaked
½ cup (2 ounces) shredded Monterey
  Jack cheese

Cook macaroni according to package directions, omitting salt and fat. Drain and set aside.

Combine Neufchâtel cheese and next 7 ingredients; stirring well.

Coat a 2-quart baking dish with cooking spray. Place half of macaroni in baking dish. Sprinkle half of crabmeat over macaroni. Spoon half of cheese mixture over crabmeat. Repeat layers with remaining ingredients. Bake at 350° for 30 minutes. Sprinkle with shredded Monterey Jack cheese and bake an additional 5 minutes or until cheese melts. Let stand 10 minutes before serving. Yield: 6 servings (316 calories per 1-cup serving).

PROTEIN 25.6 / FAT 11.7 / CARBOHYDRATE 25.7 / CHOLESTEROL 104 / IRON 1.8 / SODIUM 344 / CALCIUM 299

SKILLET PORK AND NOODLES

1 pound boneless pork center loin,
  cut into thin strips
Vegetable cooking spray
¾ cup chopped onion
2 cloves garlic, minced
1 (16-ounce) can whole tomatoes,
  undrained and coarsely chopped
½ cup Burgundy or other dry red
  wine
2 teaspoons dried whole basil
½ teaspoon dried whole thyme
¼ teaspoon pepper
2 large carrots, scraped and sliced
2 cups hot cooked medium egg
  noodles (cooked without salt or fat)
1 tablespoon minced fresh
  parsley

Cook pork in a large nonstick skillet that has been coated with cooking spray over medium heat until browned. Drain and pat dry with paper towels. Wipe pan drippings from skillet with a paper towel.

Coat skillet with cooking spray. Add chopped onion and garlic; sauté until tender. Return pork strips to skillet. Stir in tomatoes, wine, basil, thyme, and pepper; bring to a boil. Cover, reduce heat, and simmer 25 minutes. Stir in carrot; simmer until tender.

Serve pork mixture over noodles. Sprinkle with parsley. Yield: 4 servings (349 calories per 1 cup mixture and ½ cup noodles).

PROTEIN 31.3 / FAT 10.5 / CARBOHYDRATE 31.5 / CHOLESTEROL 105 / IRON 2.9 / SODIUM 266 / CALCIUM 76

CHICKEN-NOODLE PARMESAN

1 (8-ounce) package medium egg noodles,
  uncooked
¼ cup chopped fresh parsley
Vegetable cooking spray
½ cup chopped onion
2 cloves garlic, minced
1 (28-ounce) can no-salt-added whole tomatoes,
  undrained
1 (8-ounce) can no-salt-added tomato
  sauce
¼ teaspoon ground oregano
¼ teaspoon pepper
⅓ cup fine, dry breadcrumbs
3 tablespoons grated Parmesan cheese
1 egg, beaten
1 tablespoon water
6 (4-ounce) skinned, boned chicken breast halves,
  cut into 1-inch pieces
1 tablespoon vegetable oil
½ cup (2 ounces) shredded part-skim mozzarella
  cheese

Cook noodles according to package directions, omitting salt and fat. Drain; stir in parsley, and set aside.

Coat a large nonstick skillet with cooking spray; place over medium-high heat until hot. Add chopped onion and garlic, and sauté until tender. Set aside.

Drain tomatoes; reserve ½ cup liquid. Coarsely chop tomatoes. Add tomatoes, ½ cup tomato liquid, tomato sauce, oregano, and pepper to reserved onion mixture. Set aside.

Combine breadcrumbs and Parmesan cheese in a small bowl. Combine egg and water in a small bowl. Dip chicken into egg mixture; dredge in breadcrumb mixture.

Coat a large nonstick skillet with cooking spray; add oil. Place over medium-high heat until hot; add chicken, and cook 3 to 5 minutes or until lightly browned.

Coat a 13- x 9- x 2-inch baking dish with cooking spray. Spoon noodles into dish. Arrange chicken over noodles. Pour reserved tomato mixture over chicken. Sprinkle with mozzarella cheese. Bake, uncovered, at 350° for 25 minutes. Yield: 8 servings (300 calories per serving).

PROTEIN 26.9 / FAT 6.7 / CARBOHYDRATE 31.8 / CHOLESTEROL 104 /
IRON 2.3 / SODIUM 179 / CALCIUM 137

BAKED TURKEY PASTRAMI CASSEROLE

1 (7-ounce) package vermicelli, uncooked
Vegetable cooking spray
1 tablespoon olive oil
1 medium onion, chopped
1 medium-size green pepper, seeded and chopped
½ pound fresh mushrooms, sliced
1 (8-ounce) package turkey pastrami, cut into
  julienne strips
1 (16-ounce) jar no-salt-added meatless spaghetti
  sauce
¾ cup Chablis or other dry white wine
2 teaspoons dried Italian seasoning
1 cup (4 ounces) shredded part-skim mozzarella
  cheese

Cook pasta according to package directions, omitting salt and fat; drain and set aside.

Coat a large nonstick skillet with cooking spray; add oil. Place over medium-high heat until hot; add onion and green pepper, and sauté until tender. Add mushrooms and pastrami; cook over medium heat until thoroughly heated, stirring occasionally. Remove from heat; stir in pasta, spaghetti sauce, wine, and Italian seasoning.

Spoon pasta mixture into a 13- x 9- x 2-inch baking dish that has been coated with cooking spray. Cover and bake at 350° for 25 minutes. Sprinkle with cheese; bake, uncovered, an additional 5 minutes or until cheese melts. Yield: 8 servings (263 calories per serving).

PROTEIN 14.3 / FAT 8.0 / CARBOHYDRATE 34.5 / CHOLESTEROL 8 /
IRON 2.5 / SODIUM 381 / CALCIUM 122

*Seafood Boil (page 129) is a great
way to feast in a casual style.*

Fish & Shellfish

PICANTE BASS FILLETS

Vegetable cooking spray
1 teaspoon vegetable oil
⅓ cup chopped onion
3 large cloves garlic, minced
1 cup water
1 teaspoon chicken-flavored bouillon granules
1 (4-ounce) can chopped green chiles, drained
2 teaspoons chili powder
¼ teaspoon ground cumin
⅔ cup uncooked long-grain rice
6 (4-ounce) bass fillets
½ medium avocado
1 medium tomato, chopped
2 tablespoons plus 2 teaspoons chopped ripe olives
¼ cup plus 2 tablespoons (1½ ounces) shredded
    40% less-fat Cheddar cheese

Coat a nonstick skillet with cooking spray; add oil. Place over medium-high heat until hot. Add onion and garlic; sauté until tender. Add water and next 5 ingredients. Bring to a boil; cover and simmer 10 minutes. Arrange fillets over rice; cover and cook 12 minutes or until fish flakes easily when tested with a fork and rice is tender. Remove from heat.

Combine avocado, tomato, and olives; spoon evenly over fillets. Sprinkle with cheese. Cover, and let stand 2 minutes or until cheese melts. Yield: 6 servings (263 calories per serving).

PROTEIN 25.5 / FAT 7.7 / CARBOHYDRATE 21.6 / CHOLESTEROL 62 / IRON 2.4 / SODIUM 325 / CALCIUM 98

CATFISH CACCIATORE

2 medium zucchini
3 medium-size yellow squash
1 large onion, thinly sliced
1 (16-ounce) can stewed tomatoes, undrained
1 tablespoon chopped fresh basil
Vegetable cooking spray
6 (4-ounce) farm-raised catfish fillets
¼ cup grated Parmesan cheese

Cut zucchini and yellow squash lengthwise into ⅛-inch-thick slices. Cut slices into ⅛-inch strips. Combine squash, onion, tomatoes, and basil in a large skillet; cover and bring to a boil. Reduce heat, and simmer 10 minutes or until

vegetables are tender, stirring occasionally. Drain mixture, reserving liquid. Spoon mixture into a 13- x 9- x 2-inch baking dish that has been coated with cooking spray.

Arrange fish fillets over vegetable mixture. Spoon reserved vegetable liquid over fish fillets. Sprinkle with Parmesan cheese. Bake, covered, at 375° for 15 minutes or until fish flakes easily when tested with a fork. Yield: 6 servings (202 calories per serving).

PROTEIN 24.6 / FAT 5.2 / CARBOHYDRATE 14.4 / CHOLESTEROL 66 / IRON 1.7 / SODIUM 340 / CALCIUM 147

SWEET-AND-SOUR CATFISH

Vegetable cooking spray
1 teaspoon vegetable oil
½ cup chopped onion
¾ cup sliced carrot
2 tablespoons brown sugar
¼ cup rice wine vinegar
3 tablespoons Chablis or other dry white wine
3 tablespoons water
3 tablespoons reduced-calorie catsup
2 teaspoons cornstarch
1½ teaspoons water
¾ cup snow pea pods (2½ ounces)
4 (6-ounce) dressed farm-raised catfish
1 tablespoon lemon juice
1 teaspoon garlic powder

Coat a large nonstick skillet with cooking spray; add oil. Place over medium-high heat until hot. Add onion, and sauté until tender. Add carrot and next 5 ingredients. Bring to a boil; boil 1 minute, stirring constantly. Soften cornstarch in 1½ teaspoons water; stir into onion mixture. Add snow peas; cook, stirring constantly, until vegetables are crisp-tender and mixture is thickened. Set aside and keep warm.

Place fish on rack of a broiler pan that has been coated with cooking spray. Brush with lemon juice and sprinkle with garlic powder. Broil 4 inches from heat 6 minutes. Carefully turn with spatula; broil 5 minutes or until fish flakes easily when tested with a fork. Spoon vegetable mixture over fish. Serve immediately. Yield: 4 servings (269 calories per serving).

PROTEIN 32.1 / FAT 8.8 / CARBOHYDRATE 13.7 / CHOLESTEROL 99 / IRON 2.5 / SODIUM 121 / CALCIUM 94

Offer Grilled Caribbean Grouper with Mango-Avocado Salsa for an unusual but delicious entrée.

GRILLED CARIBBEAN GROUPER WITH MANGO-AVOCADO SALSA

3 grouper fillets (1½ pounds)
¼ cup lime juice
3 tablespoons Chablis or other dry white wine
1 tablespoon Curaçao or other orange-flavored liqueur
1 tablespoon olive oil
1 teaspoon pepper
1 teaspoon grated lime rind
¼ cup chopped mango
¼ cup chopped avocado
2 tablespoons finely chopped sweet red pepper
2 tablespoons lime juice
1½ tablespoons finely chopped purple onion
1 tablespoon coarsely chopped fresh cilantro
1 clove garlic, minced
Vegetable cooking spray
Lemon twists (optional)
Lime twists (optional)
Fresh parsley sprigs (optional)

Place fillets in a 12- x 8- x 2-inch baking dish. Combine lime juice and next 5 ingredients; stir well. Pour marinade over fillets. Cover and marinate in refrigerator 2 hours.

Combine mango and next 6 ingredients; stir gently. Cover; chill thoroughly.

Coat grill rack with cooking spray; place on grill over medium-hot coals. Remove fillets from marinade, reserving marinade. Place fillets on rack, and cook 5 minutes on each side or until fish flakes easily when tested with a fork. Baste frequently with reserved marinade.

Transfer fillets to serving plates; top with salsa mixture. If desired, garnish with lemon and lime twists and fresh parsley. Yield: 6 servings (155 calories per serving).

PROTEIN 22.2 / FAT 3.9 / CARBOHYDRATE 4.9 / CHOLESTEROL 62 / IRON 1.0 / SODIUM 71 / CALCIUM 34

FLOUNDER WITH CAVIAR SAUCE

4 (4-ounce) flounder fillets
Vegetable cooking spray
2 tablespoons lemon juice
1 tablespoon margarine, melted
⅛ teaspoon paprika
¼ cup low-fat sour cream
1 tablespoon water
1 teaspoon lemon juice
⅛ teaspoon ground white pepper
1 tablespoon plus 1 teaspoon red caviar
1 tablespoon plus 1 teaspoon thinly sliced green onion tops

Place fillets in a 13- x 9- x 2-inch baking dish that has been coated with cooking spray. Combine 2 tablespoons lemon juice and margarine; pour over fillets. Sprinkle with paprika. Broil 4 inches from heat 10 minutes or until fish flakes easily when tested with a fork. Set aside.

Combine sour cream and next 3 ingredients in a saucepan. Cook over low heat, stirring constantly, until thoroughly heated (do not boil).

Transfer fillets to serving plates. Spoon 1 tablespoon sauce over each. Top each with 1 teaspoon caviar and 1 teaspoon green onion tops. Yield: 4 servings (172 calories per serving).

PROTEIN 23.9 / FAT 7.1 / CARBOHYDRATE 1.9 / CHOLESTEROL 88 / IRON 1.0 / SODIUM 257 / CALCIUM 51

HADDOCK WITH BROCCOLI-CHEDDAR SAUCE

1 (10-ounce) package frozen chopped broccoli, thawed and drained
3 tablespoons reduced-calorie mayonnaise
3 tablespoons (¾ ounce) shredded sharp Cheddar cheese
1 (2-ounce) jar diced pimiento, drained
1 tablespoon lemon juice
1 clove garlic, crushed
4 (4-ounce) haddock fillets
Vegetable cooking spray

Combine first 6 ingredients in a medium bowl; stir well. Set aside.

Arrange fillets in a 12- x 8- x 2-inch baking dish that has been coated with cooking spray. Spoon reserved broccoli mixture evenly over fillets. Bake, uncovered, at 400° for 15 minutes or until fish flakes easily when tested with a fork. Serve immediately. Yield: 4 servings (174 calories per serving).

PROTEIN 25.0 / FAT 6.0 / CARBOHYDRATE 5.2 / CHOLESTEROL 74 / IRON 1.9 / SODIUM 212 / CALCIUM 118

CREOLE HALIBUT

3 tablespoons hot sauce
3 tablespoons water
1 tablespoon creole mustard
6 (4-ounce) halibut steaks
⅓ cup fine, dry breadcrumbs
1 teaspoon creole seasoning

Combine hot sauce, water, and mustard in a shallow dish; stir well. Add halibut steaks, turning to coat. Cover and marinate in refrigerator 30 minutes.

Combine breadcrumbs and seasoning; toss well. Remove steaks from marinade mixture. Dredge in breadcrumb mixture. Place a large nonstick skillet over medium-high heat until hot. Add steaks, and cook 3 minutes on each side or until fish flakes easily when tested with a fork. Serve immediately. Yield: 6 servings (151 calories per serving).

PROTEIN 24.3 / FAT 3.1 / CARBOHYDRATE 4.3 / CHOLESTEROL 54 / IRON 1.2 / SODIUM 360 / CALCIUM 64

ORANGE ROUGHY FILLETS WITH GRAPEFRUIT BRÛLÉE

1 medium-size red grapefruit
1 tablespoon Grand Marnier or other orange-flavored liqueur
4 (4-ounce) orange roughy fillets
Vegetable cooking spray
2 tablespoons brown sugar
¼ teaspoon ground cinnamon

Peel and section grapefruit, reserving ¼ cup juice. Combine grapefruit sections and liqueur. Cover and let stand 30 minutes.

Arrange orange roughy fillets in a 10- x 6- x 2-inch baking dish that has been coated with cooking spray. Spoon reserved ¼ cup grapefruit juice over fillets. Bake, uncovered, at 400° for 10 to 15 minutes or until fish flakes easily when tested with a fork.

Arrange reserved grapefruit sections over fillets. Combine brown sugar and cinnamon. Sprinkle evenly over grapefruit and fillets. Broil 6 inches from heat for 2 minutes or until sugar begins to caramelize. Serve immediately. Yield: 4 servings (215 calories per serving).

PROTEIN 17.4 / FAT 8.2 / CARBOHYDRATE 15.8 / CHOLESTEROL 23 / IRON 0.8 / SODIUM 73 / CALCIUM 20

 BETA-CAROTENE AND CANCER

Cancer prevention researchers are keeping a close watch on the benefits of beta-carotene, a precursor of vitamin A found in plants. Animal research studies on tumors in the mouth have shown that beta-carotene, when applied directly to the tumor, inhibited tumor development. It is also postulated that beta-carotene enhances the body's immune response against cancer cells. The National Cancer Institute (NCI) is studying beta-carotene effects on humans, but the research will not be complete for a few years.

While a RDA has not been established, a 1985 food survey showed that the average American consumes a great deal less than the NCI recommends.

To increase consumption, include dark-green leafy vegetables and yellow-orange fruits and vegetables such as apricots, broccoli, cantaloupe, carrots, and spinach in as many meals as possible.

OVEN-FRIED PERCH WITH CUCUMBER TARTAR SAUCE

¼ cup peeled, seeded, and finely chopped cucumber
⅓ cup reduced-calorie mayonnaise
2 teaspoons lemon juice
⅛ teaspoon dry mustard
⅛ teaspoon hot sauce
½ cup whole wheat flake cereal, crushed
2 tablespoons grated Parmesan cheese
½ teaspoon dried whole thyme
¼ teaspoon garlic powder
⅛ teaspoon pepper
4 (4-ounce) perch fillets
1 tablespoon olive oil
Vegetable cooking spray
2 tablespoons sliced green onions

Pat cucumber between paper towels to remove excess moisture; set aside. Combine mayonnaise, lemon juice, mustard, and hot sauce; stir in cucumber. Cover and chill 2 hours.

Combine cereal and next 4 ingredients. Brush fillets with oil; dredge in cereal mixture.

Arrange fillets in a single layer in a 12- x 8- x 2-inch baking dish that has been coated with cooking spray. Bake, uncovered, at 500° for 10 minutes or until fish flakes easily when tested with a fork. Serve each fillet with 2 tablespoons reserved sauce; top with 1½ teaspoons onions. Yield: 4 servings (254 calories per serving).

PROTEIN 23.7 / FAT 14.3 / CARBOHYDRATE 7.0 / CHOLESTEROL 71 / IRON 1.4 / SODIUM 291 / CALCIUM 100

GRILLED POMPANO WITH JALAPEÑO PEPPERS

¼ cup lime juice
2 tablespoons pickled jalapeño pepper juice
1 tablespoon vegetable oil
2 teaspoons honey
6 (4-ounce) pompano fillets
Vegetable cooking spray
¼ cup sliced pickled jalapeño peppers
6 lime wedges (optional)
Fresh cilantro sprigs (optional)

Combine first 4 ingredients in a small bowl, stirring well; set aside.

Place fillets in a wire grilling basket that has been coated with cooking spray. Brush lime juice mixture over fish in basket. Grill 6 inches over medium coals 7 minutes on each side or until fish flakes easily when tested with a fork, basting often with lime juice mixture.

To serve, sprinkle 2 teaspoons jalapeño slices over each fillet. If desired, garnish with lime wedges and fresh cilantro sprigs. Yield: 6 servings (220 calories per serving).

PROTEIN 21.1 / FAT 13.2 / CARBOHYDRATE 3.3 / CHOLESTEROL 57 / IRON 0.9 / SODIUM 206 / CALCIUM 42

SALMON STEAK FINGERS WITH DEVILED DIP

¼ cup plus 1 tablespoon plain nonfat yogurt
1 tablespoon spicy brown mustard
1½ teaspoons reduced-calorie mayonnaise
1½ teaspoons lemon juice
¼ teaspoon hot sauce
4 (4-ounce) salmon steaks (½-inch thick)
Vegetable cooking spray

Combine first 5 ingredients, blending well. Cover and chill 1 hour.

Cut each salmon steak in half lengthwise. Place salmon in a wire grilling basket that has been coated with cooking spray. Grill 4 inches over hot coals 5 minutes on each side or until fish flakes easily when tested with a fork. Serve salmon with 2 tablespoons dip per serving. Yield: 4 servings (212 calories per serving).

PROTEIN 25.4 / FAT 10.7 / CARBOHYDRATE 1.9 / CHOLESTEROL 78 / IRON 0.6 / SODIUM 139 / CALCIUM 47

Delicately flavored salmon steaks lie on a bed of zucchini noodles in Poached Salmon Steaks with Zucchini Noodles.

POACHED SALMON STEAKS WITH ZUCCHINI NOODLES

4 (4-ounce) salmon steaks (½-inch thick)
Vegetable cooking spray
½ cup skim milk
2 tablespoons water
¼ teaspoon chicken-flavored bouillon granules
3 medium zucchini (1 pound)
¼ teaspoon salt
¾ teaspoon minced fresh basil
1 teaspoon poppy seeds
Fresh basil sprigs (optional)

Place salmon in a large nonstick skillet that has been coated with cooking spray. Combine milk, water, and bouillon granules; pour over fish. Cover; bring to a boil. Reduce heat; simmer 8 minutes or until fish flakes easily when tested with a fork.

Using a vegetable peeler, cut zucchini lengthwise into thin strips. Coat a large nonstick skillet with cooking spray. Place over medium-high heat until hot. Add zucchini, salt, and basil; sauté until tender. Add poppy seeds; toss gently.

Transfer zucchini to a serving platter. Top with steaks. Garnish with basil sprigs, if desired. Yield: 4 servings (216 calories per serving).

PROTEIN 25.8 / FAT 10.5 / CARBOHYDRATE 3.7 / CHOLESTEROL 77 / IRON 1.0 / SODIUM 221 / CALCIUM 43

BLUE CHEESE SCAMP FILLETS

Vegetable cooking spray
4 (4-ounce) scamp fillets
1 tablespoon margarine, melted
1 tablespoon lemon juice
3 tablespoons crumbled blue cheese
3 tablespoons sliced green onions

Coat a 10- x 6- x 2-inch baking dish with cooking spray; place fillets in dish. Combine margarine and lemon juice; pour over fillets. Cover and bake at 350° for 30 minutes. Sprinkle with cheese and onions. Bake, uncovered, an additional 10 minutes or until fish flakes easily when tested with a fork. Yield: 4 servings (200 calories per serving).

PROTEIN 23.0 / FAT 11.2 / CARBOHYDRATE 0.7 / CHOLESTEROL 72 / IRON 0.5 / SODIUM 166 / CALCIUM 34

RED SNAPPER PROVENÇALE

Vegetable cooking spray
2 teaspoons olive oil
1½ pounds dressed whole red snapper
½ cup Chablis or other dry white wine
¼ teaspoon salt
½ teaspoon chopped fresh thyme
¼ teaspoon pepper
1 bay leaf
1 large tomato, seeded and chopped
⅔ cup sliced fresh mushrooms
⅓ cup coarsely chopped green pepper
⅓ cup coarsely chopped onion
2 tablespoons chopped fresh parsley
1 clove garlic, minced

Coat a large nonstick skillet with cooking spray; add oil. Place over medium-high heat until hot. Add snapper and cook until browned. Add wine, salt, thyme, pepper, and bay leaf; bring to a boil. Reduce heat; cover and simmer 5 to 8 minutes. Add tomato and remaining ingredients; cover and simmer 10 minutes or until fish flakes easily when tested with a fork. Remove and discard bay leaf. Transfer fish and vegetables to a serving platter, using a slotted spoon; keep warm. Simmer liquid in skillet until reduced to ⅓ cup; pour over fish. Serve immediately. Yield: 3 servings (168 calories per serving).

PROTEIN 23.8 / FAT 4.4 / CARBOHYDRATE 7.5 / CHOLESTEROL 62 / IRON 2.1 / SODIUM 280 / CALCIUM 40

ZEROING IN ON NUTRITION CONCERNS

According to a recent survey by the Food Marketing Institute, consumers are not as concerned about the total nutritional content of food as they once were. Instead, they are focusing on specific areas such as cholesterol, saturated fat, and sodium.

Of the consumers surveyed, 54 percent were very concerned about the total content, down 10 percent from a similar survey in 1983. However, consumers are putting their interest in fat and sodium into practice, purchasing more and more skim milk, yogurt, poultry, fresh fish, and seafood. At the same time, sales of calorie- and portion-controlled frozen dinners hit an all-time high in the 1980's, accounting for more than a third of all frozen food sales.

PECAN TROUT WITH DIJON SAUCE

6 (4-ounce) trout fillets
1 tablespoon plus 1½ teaspoons vegetable oil
½ cup fine, dry breadcrumbs
Vegetable cooking spray
¼ cup low-fat sour cream
1 tablespoon Dijon mustard
1 tablespoon lemon juice
3 tablespoons chopped pecans, toasted

Brush fillets with vegetable oil. Dredge in breadcrumbs. Arrange fillets in a single layer in a 12- x 8- x 2-inch baking dish that has been coated with cooking spray. Bake, uncovered, at 500° for 10 minutes or until fish flakes easily when tested with a fork. Transfer fillets to a serving platter, and keep warm.

Combine sour cream, mustard, and lemon juice in a small saucepan. Cook over low heat, stirring constantly, until thoroughly heated (do not boil). Spoon 1 tablespoon sauce over each fillet. Sprinkle 1½ teaspoons pecans over each fillet. Serve immediately. Yield: 6 servings (296 calories per serving).

PROTEIN 22.3 / FAT 19.1 / CARBOHYDRATE 7.6 / CHOLESTEROL 67 / IRON 1.3 / SODIUM 232 / CALCIUM 52

OYSTERS ROCKEFELLER SOUFFLÉ

Vegetable cooking spray
1 cup finely chopped fresh spinach
2 tablespoons finely chopped onion
3 tablespoons unsalted margarine
3 tablespoons all-purpose flour
¾ cup plus 2 tablespoons skim milk
3 egg yolks
¼ cup grated Parmesan cheese
¾ cup (3 ounces) shredded Swiss cheese
⅛ teaspoon pepper
5 egg whites
2 (12-ounce) containers fresh Standard oysters, drained and minced

Coat a small nonstick skillet with cooking spray; place over medium-high heat until hot. Add spinach and onion, and sauté until spinach is wilted, stirring frequently. Set aside.

Melt margarine in a large saucepan over low heat; add flour, stirring until smooth. Cook 1 minute, stirring constantly. Gradually add milk; cook over medium heat, stirring constantly, until mixture is thickened and bubbly. Remove from heat. Beat egg yolks until thick and lemon colored. Gradually stir about one-fourth of hot mixture into yolks; add to remaining mixture. Add reserved spinach mixture, cheeses, and pepper, stirring well. Set aside.

Beat egg whites (at room temperature) in a large bowl at high speed of an electric mixer until stiff but not dry. Gently fold egg whites and oysters into spinach mixture. Spoon mixture into a 1½-quart soufflé dish that has been coated with cooking spray. Place dish in a 13- x 9- x 2-inch baking pan; pour hot water into baking pan to a depth of 1 inch. Bake at 350° for 1 hour or until puffed and golden. Serve immediately. Yield: 6 servings (227 calories per serving).

PROTEIN 14.7 / FAT 14.7 / CARBOHYDRATE 8.4 / CHOLESTEROL 176 / IRON 3.9 / SODIUM 222 / CALCIUM 277

THE CAREER ADVANTAGE

A Gallup survey has revealed that a regular exercise program has yet another benefit— positive effects on your career. According to the survey, exercisers improved their lives in several areas: health, career benefits, and stress control. Regular exercisers were reported to be sick less often than before they started working out. They functioned at a higher, more creative level at work, and had less stress on the job and in their personal lives.

These benefits were more pronounced for those who exercised five or more hours a week. The survey also found that other aspects of their lives were enhanced by the exercise. Overall, exercisers were found to have improved their diets by eating more fruits and vegetables; they stopped smoking; and they generally adopted healthier lifestyles.

Scallops en Papillote may be served in the parchment paper or transferred to attractive serving dishes.

SCALLOPS EN PAPILLOTE

1 (8-ounce) package frozen baby corn
¼ pound fresh asparagus spears
Vegetable cooking spray
1 teaspoon vegetable oil
1 medium-size sweet red pepper, seeded and cut
    into julienne strips
1 pound fresh sea scallops
1 teaspoon lemon juice
1 teaspoon Chablis or other dry white wine
⅛ teaspoon salt
⅛ teaspoon pepper

Cook corn according to package directions, omitting salt. Drain and set aside. Snap off tough ends of asparagus. Remove scales from stalks with a knife or vegetable peeler, if desired. Cut asparagus diagonally into 2-inch slices.

Coat a large nonstick skillet with cooking spray; add oil. Place over medium-high heat until hot. Add asparagus slices and sweet red pepper strips, and sauté until crisp-tender. Stir in corn; set aside.

Cut four 15- x 12-inch pieces of parchment paper or aluminum foil; fold in half lengthwise, creasing firmly. Trim each into a large heart shape. Place parchment hearts on baking sheets. Spoon reserved vegetable mixture evenly over one half of each parchment heart near the crease. Spoon scallops over vegetable mixture; sprinkle evenly with lemon juice, wine, salt, and pepper. Starting with rounded edge of each heart, pleat and crimp edges together to make a seal. Twist end tightly to seal. Bake at 400° for 10 to 15 minutes or until bags are puffed and lightly browned. Yield: 4 servings (134 calories per serving).

PROTEIN 19.6 / FAT 2.4 / CARBOHYDRATE 9.1 / CHOLESTEROL 40 / IRON 2.5 / SODIUM 371 / CALCIUM 37

GRILLED SCALLOP KABOBS

2 pounds fresh sea scallops
½ cup Chablis or other dry white wine
¼ cup lemon juice
3 large cloves garlic, minced
2 tablespoons margarine, melted
1 tablespoon chopped fresh dillweed
1 teaspoon pepper
Vegetable cooking spray

Place scallops in a large shallow dish. Combine next 6 ingredients; stir well. Pour over scallops. Cover and marinate in refrigerator 2 hours.

Remove scallops from marinade, reserving marinade. Thread scallops evenly onto 6 (12-inch) skewers. Brush with marinade. Coat grill rack with cooking spray; place on grill over medium-hot coals. Place kabobs on rack, and cook 10 to 12 minutes or until scallops are done, turning and basting frequently with marinade. Yield: 6 servings (176 calories per serving).

PROTEIN 25.6 / FAT 5.0 / CARBOHYDRATE 6.1 / CHOLESTEROL 50 / IRON 0.7 / SODIUM 290 / CALCIUM 48

SHRIMP AND SWEET PEPPER KABOBS

1 (15¼-ounce) can unsweetened pineapple spears, undrained
¼ cup water
2 tablespoons white wine vinegar
1 tablespoon vegetable oil
2 tablespoons low-sodium soy sauce
½ teaspoon curry powder
1 pound large fresh shrimp, peeled and deveined
1 large green pepper, seeded and cut into 12 (1-inch) squares
1 large sweet red pepper, seeded and cut into 12 (1-inch) squares
Vegetable cooking spray

Drain pineapple, reserving ¼ cup juice. Cut pineapple spears in half crosswise; set aside. Combine reserved pineapple juice, water, and next 4 ingredients in a large bowl; stir well. Add shrimp, tossing gently to coat well. Cover and marinate in refrigerator 2 hours.

Remove shrimp from marinade, reserving marinade. Thread shrimp, pineapple spears, and peppers onto 6 (12-inch) skewers. Coat grill rack with cooking spray; place on grill over medium-hot coals. Place kabobs on rack, and cook 6 to 8 minutes or until done, turning and basting frequently with reserved marinade. Yield: 6 servings (125 calories per serving).

PROTEIN 13.2 / FAT 3.8 / CARBOHYDRATE 9.8 / CHOLESTEROL 93 / IRON 2.1 / SODIUM 293 / CALCIUM 40

SHRIMP-STUFFED ARTICHOKES

4 medium artichokes
Lemon wedge
8 cups water
2½ pounds unpeeled medium-size fresh shrimp
2 eggs, beaten
1 cup soft whole wheat breadcrumbs
½ cup finely chopped green onions
2 tablespoons chopped fresh parsley
1 tablespoon reduced-calorie mayonnaise
2 teaspoons white wine Worcestershire sauce
2 teaspoons creole mustard
2 teaspoons prepared horseradish
⅛ teaspoon hot sauce

Wash artichokes by plunging up and down in cold water. Cut off stem end, and trim about ½ inch from top of each artichoke. Remove any loose bottom leaves. With scissors, trim away about a fourth of each outer leaf. Rub top and edges of leaves with a lemon wedge to prevent discoloration.

Place artichokes in a large Dutch oven; add water to depth of 1 inch. Bring to a boil; cover, reduce heat, and simmer 25 minutes or until almost tender. Spread leaves apart; scrape out the fuzzy thistle center (choke) with a spoon. Set artichokes aside.

Bring 8 cups water to a boil; add shrimp, and cook 3 to 5 minutes. Drain well; rinse with cold water. Chill. Peel and devein shrimp. Combine shrimp, eggs, and remaining ingredients; stir well. Spoon shrimp mixture evenly into artichoke cavities. Arrange artichokes in a 9-inch baking dish. Cover and bake at 350° for 20 minutes or until thoroughly heated. Yield: 4 servings (268 calories per serving).

PROTEIN 26.2 / FAT 6.2 / CARBOHYDRATE 29.9 / CHOLESTEROL 291 / IRON 6.1 / SODIUM 500 / CALCIUM 154

SEAFOOD BOIL

20 black peppercorns
4 large bay leaves
1 teaspoon mustard seeds
1 teaspoon dried whole marjoram
½ teaspoon dried whole basil
¼ teaspoon dried whole thyme
2 quarts plus 2 cups water
3 (12-ounce) cans flat light beer
4 medium onions, halved
6 medium ears fresh corn, halved
Water
Vinegar
6 live blue crabs
1 dozen mussels
8 cloves garlic
3 lemons, quartered
¾ pound unpeeled medium-size fresh shrimp
Dilled Seafood Sauce

Place first 6 ingredients on a doubled piece of cheesecloth; tie ends securely.

Combine spice bag, water, and beer in a very large pot; bring to a boil. Add onion; bring to a boil. Cover, reduce heat, and cook 15 minutes. Add corn; cover and cook 5 minutes.

Combine water and vinegar in equal amounts to a depth of 1 inch in a very large pot; bring to a boil. Place a rack in pot over boiling liquid; arrange crabs on rack. Cover tightly and steam 20 to 25 minutes or until crabs turn bright red. Rinse with cold water, and drain well. Set aside.

Remove beards on mussels, and scrub shells well with a brush. Discard opened or cracked mussels, or heavy ones (they're filled with sand). Add mussels, garlic, lemon, and crabs to pot; cover and cook 10 minutes. Remove from heat, and add shrimp; let stand in water 10 minutes. Drain off water. Arrange boiled seafood and vegetables on a large serving platter. Serve with 3 tablespoons Dilled Seafood Sauce per serving. Yield: 6 servings (347 calories per serving).

Dilled Seafood Sauce:

1 cup plus 2 tablespoons reduced-calorie catsup
¼ teaspoon grated lime rind
1 tablespoon lime juice
2 teaspoons hot sauce
2 teaspoons prepared horseradish
½ teaspoon dried whole dillweed

Combine all ingredients; stir well. Cover and chill thoroughly. Yield: 1 cup plus 2 tablespoons.

PROTEIN 39.2 / FAT 4.5 / CARBOHYDRATE 36.1 / CHOLESTEROL 181 / IRON 3.9 / SODIUM 531 / CALCIUM 201

HOW TO CRACK A CRAB

Seafood Boil offers a variety of seafood in just one dish. For the crab, follow these directions to get to the meat. You will then be ready to twist off the claws and legs, crack them with a seafood cracker or nutcracker, remove the meat with a cocktail fork, and enjoy the succulent flavor.

To get to the crab meat, pry off the apron or tail flap.

Lift off the top shell, holding the crab in the space that is left when the apron is removed.

Pull out and discard the feathery gills and internal organs located beneath the top shell.

ONE-DISH SEAFOOD SUPPER

Vegetable cooking spray
1 teaspoon olive oil
1 medium eggplant, cut into ¾-inch cubes
½ cup finely chopped onion
½ cup finely chopped celery
¼ cup finely chopped green pepper
¼ cup finely chopped sweet red pepper
1 clove garlic, minced
½ pound medium-size fresh shrimp, peeled and deveined
½ pound fresh lump crabmeat, drained and flaked
1 teaspoon chopped fresh basil
½ teaspoon hot sauce
½ cup (2 ounces) shredded extra-sharp Cheddar cheese

Coat a large nonstick skillet with cooking spray; add oil. Place over medium-high heat until hot. Add eggplant and next 5 ingredients; sauté until tender. Add shrimp, crab, basil, and hot sauce; cook 5 minutes or until shrimp turn pink. Remove from heat. Sprinkle with cheese; cover and let stand until cheese melts. Yield: 4 servings (221 calories per serving).

PROTEIN 25.8 / FAT 7.9 / CARBOHYDRATE 12.1 / CHOLESTEROL 115 / IRON 2.8 / SODIUM 788 / CALCIUM 220

SEAFOOD TACOS WITH CILANTRO-JALAPEÑO SAUCE

1 tablespoon margarine
1 tablespoon all-purpose flour
1 cup skim milk
3 tablespoons (1½ ounces) shredded Monterey Jack cheese with jalapeño peppers
1 tablespoon minced fresh cilantro
½ pound flounder or sole fillets
1 tablespoon lime juice
¼ teaspoon ground red pepper
Vegetable cooking spray
¼ pound frozen tiny shrimp, thawed
¼ cup canned black beans, rinsed and drained
¼ cup finely chopped green onions
1 tablespoon minced fresh cilantro
1 tablespoon chopped sweet red pepper
1 tablespoon chopped sweet yellow pepper
4 (6-inch) flour tortillas

Melt margarine in a small saucepan over low heat; add flour, stirring until smooth. Cook 1 minute, stirring constantly. Gradually add milk; cook over medium heat, stirring constantly, until mixture is thickened and bubbly. Stir in shredded cheese and 1 tablespoon cilantro; cook until cheese melts, stirring constantly. Set aside and keep warm.

Sprinkle fillets with 1 tablespoon lime juice and ground red pepper. Cover and marinate in refrigerator 15 minutes.

Coat a large nonstick skillet with cooking spray; place over medium-high heat until hot. Add shrimp, and sauté until done. Set aside.

Recoat the skillet with cooking spray; place over medium-high heat until hot. Add fillets and cook until fish flakes easily when tested with a fork. Cut fillets into strips.

Combine reserved cheese mixture, shrimp, beans, and next 4 ingredients in a large bowl; set aside. Wrap tortillas in aluminum foil, and bake at 325° for 15 minutes. Unwrap and spoon shrimp mixture evenly over half of each tortilla. Top shrimp mixture with fish strips, and fold tortillas in half. Serve immediately. Yield: 4 servings (290 calories per serving).

PROTEIN 22.9 / FAT 9.5 / CARBOHYDRATE 29.5 / CHOLESTEROL 80 / IRON 2.4 / SODIUM 208 / CALCIUM 217

Garden Medley Pizza with Oatmeal Crust (page 135) contains a bevy of garden-fresh vegetables and two types of cheese.

Meatless Main

SUMMER SQUASH FRITTATA

Vegetable cooking spray
1 cup shredded yellow squash
1 cup shredded zucchini
½ cup chopped onion
2 cloves garlic, minced
¼ cup grated Parmesan cheese
2 tablespoons chopped fresh parsley
½ teaspoon dried whole basil
¼ teaspoon salt
¼ teaspoon pepper
3 egg whites
1 (2-ounce) jar sliced pimiento,
    drained
6 eggs, beaten

Coat an ovenproof 10-inch skillet with cooking spray; place over medium-high heat until hot. Add squash, zucchini, chopped onion, and garlic, and sauté until vegetables are tender. Stir in cheese, chopped parsley, basil, salt, and pepper; set mixture aside.

Beat egg whites (at room temperature) at high speed of an electric mixer until stiff peaks form. Gently fold egg whites and pimiento into beaten eggs. Pour over reserved vegetable mixture. Cover and cook over medium heat 4 to 6 minutes or until egg mixture is almost set. Broil 6 inches from heating element 2 minutes or until lightly browned. Cut into wedges and serve immediately. Yield: 6 servings (120 calories per serving).

PROTEIN 10.1 / FAT 6.8 / CARBOHYDRATE 4.5 / CHOLESTEROL 277 / IRON 1.6 / SODIUM 258 / CALCIUM 94

CHEESY PICANTE OMELET

Vegetable cooking spray
¼ cup chopped sweet red pepper
¼ cup chopped green onions
¼ cup sliced fresh mushrooms
¼ cup commercial picante sauce
6 eggs, separated
¼ cup skim milk
2 tablespoons reduced-calorie mayonnaise
¼ teaspoon coarsely ground pepper
¾ cup (3 ounces) finely shredded 40% less-fat
    Cheddar cheese

Coat a large nonstick skillet with cooking spray; place over medium-high heat until hot. Add red pepper, onions, and sliced mushrooms, and sauté until tender. Stir in picante sauce, and set aside.

Beat egg whites (at room temperature) at high speed of an electric mixer until stiff peaks form; set aside.

Combine egg yolks, milk, mayonnaise, and pepper; stir well. Fold egg whites into egg yolk mixture. Coat an ovenproof 10-inch omelet pan or heavy skillet with cooking spray; place over medium heat until hot enough to sizzle a drop of water. Pour egg mixture into skillet, and gently smooth surface. Reduce heat to medium-low, and cook 5 minutes or until puffy and light brown on bottom, gently lifting omelet at edge to judge color.

Bake at 350° for 10 minutes or until a knife inserted in center comes out clean. Spoon reserved vegetable mixture over half of omelet and top with cheese. Loosen omelet with spatula; fold omelet in half. Gently slide omelet onto a warm serving plate. Yield: 6 servings (145 calories per serving).

PROTEIN 10.7 / FAT 9.8 / CARBOHYDRATE 3.1 / CHOLESTEROL 276 / IRON 1.4 / SODIUM 280 / CALCIUM 157

COLORFUL CHEDDAR SOUFFLÉ

2 tablespoons margarine
3 tablespoons all-purpose flour
¾ cup skim milk
1 cup (4 ounces) shredded 40% less-fat Cheddar
    cheese
¼ teaspoon paprika
3 egg yolks, beaten
½ cup shredded zucchini
½ cup shredded carrot
4 egg whites
Vegetable cooking spray

Melt margarine in a medium saucepan over low heat; add flour, stirring until smooth. Cook 1 minute, stirring constantly (mixture will be dry). Gradually add milk; cook over medium heat, stirring constantly, until mixture is thickened and bubbly. Add cheese and paprika, stirring until cheese melts.

Beat egg yolks in a small bowl until thick and lemon colored. Gradually stir one-fourth of hot mixture into yolks; add to remaining hot mixture, stirring constantly. Gently fold zucchini and carrot into egg yolk mixture.

Beat egg whites (at room temperature) at high speed of an electric mixer until stiff peaks form; gently fold egg whites into egg yolk mixture. Pour into a 1½-quart soufflé dish that has been coated on the bottom with cooking spray. Bake at 325° for 55 minutes or until puffed and golden. Serve immediately. Yield: 4 servings (241 calories per serving).

PROTEIN 15.6 / FAT 15.4 / CARBOHYDRATE 9.5 / CHOLESTEROL 205 / IRON 1.2 / SODIUM 342 / CALCIUM 310

FRESH-FROM-THE-GARDEN LASAGNA

Vegetable cooking spray
1 cup chopped onion
⅔ cup chopped green pepper
2 cloves garlic, minced
2 cups coarsely chopped zucchini
1½ cups peeled, chopped tomato
1½ cups sliced fresh mushrooms
½ cup shredded carrot
½ cup chopped celery
1¼ cups no-salt-added tomato sauce
1 (6-ounce) can no-salt-added tomato
   paste
1 tablespoon plus 1½ teaspoons red
   wine vinegar
1 teaspoon dried whole oregano
1 teaspoon dried whole basil
½ teaspoon dried Italian seasoning
½ teaspoon salt
½ teaspoon pepper
¼ teaspoon fennel seeds
1 bay leaf
6 lasagna noodles, uncooked
1½ cups part-skim ricotta cheese
1 cup (4 ounces) shredded part-skim
   mozzarella cheese, divided
1 tablespoon grated Parmesan
   cheese

Coat a large Dutch oven with cooking spray; place over medium-high heat until hot. Add onion, green pepper, and garlic, and sauté until

tender. Add zucchini and next 14 ingredients. Cover and bring to a boil; reduce heat and simmer 20 to 30 minutes, stirring occasionally. Remove and discard bay leaf. Set aside.

Cook noodles according to package directions, omitting salt and fat. Drain noodles well, and set aside.

Combine ricotta cheese and ½ cup mozzarella cheese in a small bowl; stir well.

Coat an 11- x 7- x 1½-inch baking dish with cooking spray. Spoon 2 cups reserved vegetable mixture into dish. Layer one-third each of lasagna noodles, cheese mixture, and vegetable mixture; repeat layers twice. Cover and bake at 350° for 25 minutes. Uncover and sprinkle with remaining ½ cup mozzarella cheese and Parmesan cheese. Bake an additional 10 minutes. Let lasagna stand 10 minutes before serving. Yield: 8 servings (246 calories per serving).

PROTEIN 14.3 / FAT 6.9 / CARBOHYDRATE 32.9 / CHOLESTEROL 23 / IRON 2.2 / SODIUM 313 / CALCIUM 270

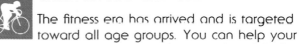 ## CHILDREN AND EXERCISE

The fitness era has arrived and is targeted toward all age groups. You can help your child develop a positive attitude towards activity by encouraging simple participation. It is important, however, to consider the child's age to determine the level of play.

Preschoolers, especially those between the ages of 2 and 4, need activities that build self-confidence and enthusiasm. Formal exercise activities that demand finely-tuned coordination and focus on competition are best saved until after age 5. Help your preschooler master activities that build movement skills such as reaching, standing, walking, or throwing repeatedly. These activities encourage involvement and build concentration.

Playing with your child offers more than exercise—it presents an opportunity for touching and nurturing, which provides a child with a sense of security. Include props such as balls, hoops, or foam blocks in the activities. Toys that can be rolled, climbed on, kicked, or thrown help to develop coordination. Create a roomy, safe environment by removing furniture or items with sharp edges, and enjoy starting your child on a lifetime of fitness based on fun rather than on a rigid regimen.

SPINACH FETTUCCINE ITALIENNE

1 (8-ounce) package spinach fettuccine,
  uncooked
¾ cup part-skim ricotta cheese
1 tablespoon grated Parmesan cheese
1 tablespoon water
1 clove garlic, minced
½ teaspoon dried whole basil
¼ teaspoon lemon juice
¼ teaspoon ground white pepper
Vegetable cooking spray
1 teaspoon olive oil
⅓ cup chopped onion
2 cloves garlic, minced
1 (14½-ounce) can no-salt-added
  whole tomatoes
1 (6-ounce) can no-salt-added tomato
  paste
¾ cup water
¼ cup Burgundy or other dry red wine
1 bay leaf
½ teaspoon pepper
¼ teaspoon salt
¼ teaspoon dried whole basil
¼ teaspoon dried whole oregano
¼ teaspoon dried whole thyme
½ pound fresh mushrooms, sliced

Cook spinach fettuccine according to package directions, omitting salt and fat. Drain fettucine, and set aside.

Combine ricotta, Parmesan, water, garlic, basil, lemon juice, and white pepper in a small bowl; beat at medium speed of an electric mixer until smooth. Set mixture aside.

Coat a large nonstick skillet with cooking spray; add oil, and place over medium-high heat until hot. Add onion and garlic, and sauté until tender. Stir in tomatoes and remaining ingredients except mushrooms; bring to a boil. Reduce heat and simmer, uncovered, 20 minutes or until slightly thickened. Stir in mushrooms. Simmer an additional 5 to 10 minutes or until mushrooms are tender.

To serve, place fettuccine on a warm serving platter; spoon tomato mixture over pasta, and top with reserved ricotta mixture. Yield: 6 servings (238 calories per serving).

PROTEIN 11.4 / FAT 5.4 / CARBOHYDRATE 39.7 / CHOLESTEROL 10 /
IRON 2.9 / SODIUM 177 / CALCIUM 155

VEGETABLE-ENCHILADA CASSEROLE

1 small eggplant, peeled and quartered
1 medium zucchini, sliced
½ pound fresh mushrooms, sliced
1 small green pepper, seeded and quartered
Vegetable cooking spray
2 cloves garlic, minced
½ cup chopped green onions
1 (8-ounce) can no-salt-added tomato sauce
1 medium tomato, chopped
1 (4-ounce) can chopped green chiles, drained
1 teaspoon sugar
½ teaspoon chili powder
⅛ teaspoon ground cumin
6 (8-inch) flour tortillas
¾ cup (3 ounces) shredded 40% less-fat Cheddar
  cheese
¾ cup (3 ounces) shredded Monterey Jack cheese
¼ cup sliced ripe olives
2½ cups shredded lettuce
1 medium tomato, chopped
¼ cup chopped green onions
3 tablespoons low-fat sour cream

Position slicing disc in food processor bowl; top with cover. Arrange eggplant in food chute; slice applying medium pressure with food pusher. Repeat procedure with zucchini, mushrooms, and green pepper. Set aside.

Coat a large nonstick skillet with cooking spray; place over medium-high heat until hot. Add garlic and ½ cup onions, and sauté until tender. Add reserved vegetables; cover and cook 5 minutes or until tender, stirring occasionally. Stir in tomato sauce and next 5 ingredients; cover and simmer 30 minutes.

Coat a 13- x 9- x 2-inch baking dish with cooking spray. Arrange half of tortillas in dish; top with vegetable mixture. Arrange remaining tortillas over vegetable mixture. Cover and bake at 350° for 20 to 30 minutes or until thoroughly heated. Sprinkle with shredded cheeses and olives. Bake an additional 5 minutes or until cheese melts. To serve, place shredded lettuce on a large serving platter. Spoon casserole over lettuce. Top with chopped tomato, ¼ cup onions, and 3 tablespoons sour cream. Yield: 6 servings (336 calories per serving).

PROTEIN 14.4 / FAT 12.2 / CARBOHYDRATE 47.6 / CHOLESTEROL 14 /
IRON 3.4 / SODIUM 259 / CALCIUM 313

GARDEN MEDLEY PIZZA WITH OATMEAL CRUST

Vegetable cooking spray
2 teaspoons vegetable oil
2 cups sliced fresh mushrooms
1 cup thinly sliced broccoli flowerets
1 cup thinly sliced broccoli stalks
2 medium-size yellow squash, sliced and quartered
½ cup diagonally sliced green onions
1 small green pepper, seeded and cut into strips
1 small sweet red pepper, seeded and cut into strips
1 (8-ounce) can no-salt-added tomato sauce
1 (6-ounce) can no-salt-added tomato paste
2 tablespoons red wine vinegar
¾ teaspoon dried whole basil
½ teaspoon dried whole oregano
3 cloves garlic, minced
1 package dry yeast
¼ cup warm water (105° to 115°)
2 tablespoons honey
2 cups all-purpose flour
¾ cup regular oats, uncooked
½ teaspoon salt
⅓ cup warm water (105° to 115°)
¾ cup (3 ounces) finely shredded part-skim mozzarella cheese
¾ cup (3 ounces) finely shredded 40% less-fat Cheddar cheese

Coat a large nonstick skillet with cooking spray; add oil. Place over medium-high heat until hot. Add mushrooms and next 6 ingredients, and sauté until crisp-tender. Drain and set aside.

Combine tomato sauce and next 5 ingredients in a medium saucepan. Bring to a boil, stirring constantly. Reduce heat and simmer, uncovered, 15 to 20 minutes or until thickened. Set aside.

Dissolve yeast in ¼ cup warm water; let stand 5 minutes. Stir in honey. Combine flour, oats, and salt in a large bowl. Add yeast mixture and ⅓ cup warm water to flour mixture, mixing until a soft dough forms.

Turn dough out onto a lightly floured surface, and knead until smooth and elastic (about 8 to 10 minutes). Place in a bowl that has been coated with cooking spray, turning to grease top. Cover and let rise in a warm place (85°), free from drafts, 1½ hours or until doubled in bulk. Punch dough down. Pat dough onto a 14-inch pizza pan that has been coated with cooking spray. Spread tomato sauce mixture evenly over pizza crust. Arrange vegetable mixture evenly over sauce. Combine mozzarella cheese and Cheddar cheese, and sprinkle evenly over top of pizza. Bake at 350° for 30 minutes or until crust is golden brown and cheese melts. Yield: 6 servings (350 calories per serving).

PROTEIN 16.8 / FAT 8.2 / CARBOHYDRATE 54.6 / CHOLESTEROL 8 / IRON 3.6 / SODIUM 391 / CALCIUM 262

THREE-CHEESE SPINACH SANDWICH

2 (10-ounce) packages frozen chopped spinach, thawed
½ cup chopped green onions
3 tablespoons reduced-calorie mayonnaise
1 tablespoon minced sweet red pepper
1 tablespoon lemon juice
Vegetable cooking spray
1 teaspoon unsalted margarine
½ pound fresh mushrooms, sliced
6 slices rye bread
¾ cup alfalfa sprouts
1 cup (4 ounces) shredded Provolone cheese
1 cup (4 ounces) shredded 40% less-fat Cheddar cheese
½ cup (2 ounces) shredded Swiss cheese

Drain thawed spinach; squeeze out excess moisture between paper towels. Combine spinach and next 4 ingredients in a large bowl, stirring well. Set aside.

Coat a large nonstick skillet with cooking spray; add margarine. Place over medium-high heat until hot. Add mushrooms, and sauté until tender. Set aside.

Lightly toast bread. Spread spinach mixture evenly over toasted bread. Top evenly with mushrooms and sprouts. Place on an ungreased baking sheet.

Combine cheeses, tossing well. Sprinkle cheese evenly over each sandwich. Broil 6 inches from heating element 1 minute or until cheese melts. Serve immediately. Yield: 6 servings (281 calories per serving).

PROTEIN 19.0 / FAT 14.6 / CARBOHYDRATE 21.5 / CHOLESTEROL 24 / IRON 3.2 / SODIUM 588 / CALCIUM 516

Fresh basil leaves and melted Swiss cheese add flavor appeal to protein-rich Tofu-Broccoli Strata.

TOFU

Help meet your protein requirements by adding tofu to your diet. Tofu is low in fat and sodium and rich in calcium and iron. Tofu, or soybean-curd, is made by a process similar to that of making cottage cheese. After the soybeans are cooked and mashed, the liquid is removed. A coagulant is added to the liquid, causing a curd to form. This curd is then pressed to make tofu.

Two common forms of tofu are available in this country. Chinese-style is firm in texture and is easily cubed, making it an ideal ingredient in baked or stir-fried dishes such as Tofu-Broccoli Strata or Tofu-Zucchini Stroganoff, or it can be crumbled for use as in Vegetarian Pita Sandwiches (page 138).

Japanese-style (soft) is not as common, but it is ideal as a replacement for part of the sour cream or cream cheese in spreads, dips, and dressings.

TOFU-BROCCOLI STRATA

4 (½-inch) slices French bread
Vegetable cooking spray
½ pound firm tofu
2 teaspoons vegetable oil
2 cups broccoli flowerets
½ cup chopped green onions
1 medium carrot, scraped and shredded
4 eggs, beaten
½ cup skim milk
½ teaspoon dried whole basil
¼ teaspoon garlic powder
½ cup (2 ounces) shredded Swiss cheese
Carrot strips (optional)
Fresh basil sprigs (optional)

Arrange bread in an 8-inch square baking dish that has been coated with cooking spray.

Wrap tofu in several layers of cheesecloth or paper towels; press lightly to remove excess moisture. Remove cheesecloth; coarsely chop tofu. Sprinkle tofu over bread slices; set aside.

Coat a nonstick skillet with cooking spray; add oil. Place over medium-high heat until hot. Add broccoli, green onions, and carrot; sauté until crisp-tender. Spoon over tofu.

Combine eggs, milk, basil, and garlic powder; stir well. Pour over vegetable mixture. Cover and chill 1 hour.

Bake, covered, at 350° for 30 to 35 minutes. Sprinkle with cheese. Bake, uncovered, an additional 5 minutes or until cheese melts. Let stand 10 minutes before serving. If desired, garnish with carrot strips and basil sprigs. Yield: 4 servings (275 calories per serving).

PROTEIN 18.8 / FAT 15.3 / CARBOHYDRATE 16.5 / CHOLESTEROL 288 / IRON 5.2 / SODIUM 227 / CALCIUM 303

TOFU-ZUCCHINI STROGANOFF

1 (10½-ounce) package firm tofu
Vegetable cooking spray
1 teaspoon vegetable oil
1 medium zucchini, cut into julienne strips
½ pound fresh mushrooms, sliced
2 cloves garlic, minced
1 medium-size sweet red pepper, cut into julienne strips
1 tablespoon all-purpose flour
1 teaspoon beef-flavored bouillon granules
½ teaspoon dried whole dillweed
⅔ cup skim milk
1 tablespoon Neufchâtel cheese, softened
2 cups hot cooked medium egg noodles (cooked without salt or fat)

Wrap tofu in several layers of cheesecloth or paper towels; press lightly to remove excess moisture. Remove cheesecloth; cut tofu into ½-inch cubes. Set aside.

Spray a large nonstick skillet with cooking spray; add oil. Place over medium-high heat until hot. Sauté tofu 3 to 4 minutes; remove from skillet. Add zucchini, mushrooms, garlic, and pepper to skillet, and sauté until tender. Set aside. Wipe skillet dry with a paper towel.

Combine flour, bouillon granules, dillweed, and milk in a small bowl, stirring until well blended. Add to skillet, and bring to a boil. Cook 1 minute, stirring constantly. Stir in cheese, reserved tofu, and vegetable mixture. Cook over low heat until thoroughly heated, stirring constantly. Serve over hot cooked noodles. Yield: 4 servings (211 calories per serving).

PROTEIN 12.6 / FAT 7.0 / CARBOHYDRATE 26.6 / CHOLESTEROL 22 / IRON 6.1 / SODIUM 276 / CALCIUM 153

VEGETARIAN PITA SANDWICHES

¾ pound firm tofu
1 medium cucumber, shredded
1 medium-size yellow squash, shredded
1 medium tomato, chopped
2 green onions, chopped
3 hard-cooked eggs, chopped
3 tablespoons sliced blanched almonds, toasted
2 tablespoons reduced-calorie creamy Italian
   dressing
5 ounces fresh spinach
6 (6-inch) whole wheat pita bread rounds, halved
½ cup alfalfa sprouts

Wrap tofu in several layers of cheesecloth or paper towels; press lightly to remove excess moisture. Remove cheesecloth; crumble tofu.

Combine tofu and next 7 ingredients; stir well. Remove stems from spinach. Wash leaves; drain well. Line each pita half with 2 spinach leaves. Spoon ⅓ cup tofu mixture into each half; top with alfalfa sprouts. Yield: 6 servings (154 calories per serving).

PROTEIN 10.2 / FAT 8.9 / CARBOHYDRATE 11.6 / CHOLESTEROL 137 / IRON 5.0 / SODIUM 103 / CALCIUM 126

HEARTY VEGETARIAN CHILI

Vegetable cooking spray
1 large carrot, scraped and chopped
1 large green pepper, seeded and chopped
⅔ cup chopped onion
3 cloves garlic, minced
1 (15-ounce) can kidney beans, rinsed and drained
1 (15-ounce) can pinto beans, rinsed and drained
2½ cups boiling water
1 teaspoon beef-flavored bouillon granules
1 cup no-salt-added tomato juice
1 (8-ounce) can no-salt-added tomato sauce
3 tablespoons chili powder
1 fresh jalapeño pepper, seeded and chopped
¾ teaspoon ground cumin
¾ teaspoon dried whole oregano
½ teaspoon ground cinnamon
1 bay leaf
⅛ teaspoon hot sauce
1 cup plus 2 tablespoons (4½ ounces) shredded
   40% less-fat Cheddar cheese
¼ cup plus 2 tablespoons low-fat sour cream

Coat a large nonstick skillet with cooking spray; place over medium-high heat until hot. Add carrot, pepper, onion, and garlic, and sauté until crisp-tender. Set aside.

Place beans in a large Dutch oven; add water to cover. Bring to a boil. Add reserved vegetable mixture to bean mixture. Combine water and bouillon granules, stirring well. Add bouillon and next 9 ingredients to Dutch oven. Bring mixture to a boil; reduce heat, and simmer, uncovered, 45 minutes. Remove and discard bay leaf. Ladle hot chili into serving bowls; top each serving with 3 tablespoons shredded cheese and 1 tablespoon sour cream. Yield: 6 servings (235 calories per serving).

PROTEIN 11.9 / FAT 6.7 / CARBOHYDRATE 36.1 / CHOLESTEROL 6 / IRON 2.9 / SODIUM 531 / CALCIUM 229

CHICK PEA-FETTUCCINE TOSS

Vegetable cooking spray
1 small zucchini, cut into julienne strips
1 small yellow squash, cut into julienne strips
1 medium carrot, scraped and thinly sliced
1 cup sliced fresh mushrooms
3 green onions, chopped
1 clove garlic, minced
1 (19-ounce) can chick peas, rinsed and drained
½ teaspoon dried whole basil
½ teaspoon pepper
1 (8-ounce) package spinach fettuccine, uncooked
¼ cup grated Parmesan cheese
1½ cups (6 ounces) shredded part-skim mozzarella
   cheese
2 tablespoons chopped fresh parsley

Coat a large nonstick skillet with cooking spray; place over medium-high heat until hot. Add zucchini and next 5 ingredients, and sauté until crisp-tender. Stir in chick peas, basil, and pepper; set aside.

Cook fettuccine in a large Dutch oven according to package directions, omitting salt and fat. Drain and return to Dutch oven.

Add vegetable mixture, cheeses, and parsley to Dutch oven, tossing gently. Cook over low heat until cheese melts. Serve immediately. Yield: 10 servings (183 calories per serving).

PROTEIN 10.2 / FAT 4.9 / CARBOHYDRATE 26.2 / CHOLESTEROL 11 / IRON 1.7 / SODIUM 221 / CALCIUM 170

Southern-style Spicy Red Beans and Chunky Rice makes a hearty, satisfying vegetarian meal.

SPICY RED BEANS AND CHUNKY RICE

¾ pound dried red kidney beans
2 cups water
Vegetable cooking spray
1 tablespoon plus 1½ teaspoons vegetable oil
1¼ cups chopped onion
2 cloves garlic, minced
2½ cups water
2 bay leaves
1 tablespoon beef-flavored bouillon granules
½ teaspoon dried whole oregano
½ teaspoon hot sauce
1 tablespoon honey
Chunky Rice
Fresh oregano sprigs (optional)

Sort and wash beans. Place beans and 2 cups water in a medium saucepan; bring to a boil. Cover, remove from heat, and let stand 1 hour. Drain beans and set aside.

Coat a large Dutch oven with cooking spray; add oil. Place over medium-high heat until hot. Add onion and garlic, and sauté until tender. Add beans, 2½ cups water, and next 5 ingredients; bring to a boil. Cover, reduce heat, and simmer 2 hours, or until beans are tender. Remove and discard bay leaves. Serve over Chunky Rice. Garnish with oregano sprigs, if desired. Yield: 8 servings (323 calories per serving).

Chunky Rice:

Vegetable cooking spray
1 cup chopped onion
1 cup finely chopped carrot
1 cup finely chopped celery
¾ cup finely chopped sweet red pepper
½ cup finely chopped green pepper
2 cloves garlic, minced
1⅓ cups uncooked long-grain rice
1 teaspoon cajun seasoning
2 tablespoons chopped fresh parsley

Coat a large nonstick skillet with cooking spray; place over medium-high heat until hot. Add onion and next 5 ingredients, and sauté until tender. Set aside.

Cook rice according to package directions, omitting salt and fat and adding 1 teaspoon cajun seasoning.

Toss vegetable mixture, rice, and parsley. Yield: 4 cups.

PROTEIN 13.2 / FAT 3.9 / CARBOHYDRATE 59.8 / CHOLESTEROL 0 / IRON 5.1 / SODIUM 417 / CALCIUM 98

ZUCCHINI AND BEAN BURRITOS

1 (15-ounce) can pinto beans, rinsed and drained
1 medium zucchini, chopped
¼ cup chopped green onions
2 tablespoons sliced ripe olives
1 teaspoon chili powder
⅛ teaspoon garlic powder
⅛ teaspoon onion powder
1 (8-ounce) can no-salt-added tomato sauce
1 (4-ounce) can chopped green chiles, drained
6 (10-inch) flour tortillas
¾ cup chopped tomato
1½ cups shredded lettuce
1 cup (4 ounces) shredded 40% less-fat Cheddar cheese

Mash beans with a potato masher. Combine beans and next 8 ingredients in a medium saucepan. Cook, uncovered, over medium heat until thoroughly heated, stirring frequently.

Wrap tortillas in aluminum foil, and bake at 325° for 15 minutes. Unwrap, and spread ½ cup bean mixture over each tortilla. Top evenly with tomato, lettuce, and cheese. Yield: 6 servings (304 calories per serving).

PROTEIN 12.8 / FAT 7.7 / CARBOHYDRATE 49.2 / CHOLESTEROL 0 / IRON 2.3 / SODIUM 186 / CALCIUM 224

SPICY BEAN CHALUPAS

1½ cups dried pinto beans
4 cups water
1 (4-ounce) can chopped green chiles, undrained
⅓ cup chopped green onions
1½ teaspoons ground cumin
½ teaspoon salt
½ teaspoon dried whole oregano
½ teaspoon dried Italian seasoning
6 (6-inch) corn tortillas
3 cups shredded lettuce
1 small tomato, chopped
1 cup (4 ounces) shredded Monterey Jack cheese with jalapeño peppers
¼ cup plus 2 tablespoons plain low-fat yogurt
2 tablespoons sliced ripe olives

Sort and wash pinto beans; place in a large Dutch oven. Add water to cover, and let beans soak overnight.

Drain beans; return to Dutch oven and add 4 cups water. Add green chiles and next 5 ingredients, stirring well. Bring to a boil; cover, reduce heat, and simmer 1½ hours. Pour 1 cup of bean mixture into container of an electric blender or food processor; top with cover, and process until smooth. Return pureed bean mixture to Dutch oven. Cover and simmer 30 minutes. Uncover and simmer an additional 15 to 20 minutes or until mixture is thickened and liquid is absorbed; stir frequently.

Wrap tortillas in aluminum foil. Bake at 350° for 10 minutes or until thoroughly heated. Unwrap, and spread ½ cup bean mixture over each tortilla. To serve, place each tortilla on ½ cup shredded lettuce. Sprinkle chopped tomato and cheese evenly over top of tortillas. Top each serving with 1 tablespoon yogurt and 1 teaspoon sliced olives. Serve immediately. Yield: 6 servings (299 calories per serving).

PROTEIN 17.4 / FAT 7.7 / CARBOHYDRATE 42.1 / CHOLESTEROL 16 / IRON 4.8 / SODIUM 371 / CALCIUM 274

Cumin-Scented Tenderloins (page 151) are marinated in a flavorful mixture of lime juice, white wine, jalapeño pepper, cilantro, garlic, and cumin.

Meats

CRACKED PEPPER ROAST

1 (3-pound) beef eye-of-round roast
⅓ cup black peppercorns, crushed
Vegetable cooking spray

Trim fat from roast. Press pepper over entire surface of meat. Place roast on rack of broiler pan that has been coated with cooking spray. Insert meat thermometer into thickest part of roast; cover with aluminum foil, and bake at 450° for 20 minutes. Uncover, and bake an additional 1 hour or until meat thermometer registers 140° (rare) or 160° (medium).

Let stand 15 minutes before slicing diagonally across grain into thin slices. Yield: 12 servings (161 calories per serving).

PROTEIN 24.2 / FAT 5.5 / CARBOHYDRATE 2.7 / CHOLESTEROL 56 / IRON 2.8 / SODIUM 53 / CALCIUM 22

SAVORY ORANGE ROAST BEEF

1 (4-pound) lean boneless rump roast
¾ cup unsweetened orange juice
½ cup Burgundy or other dry red wine
2 teaspoons grated orange rind
1 teaspoon dried whole thyme
½ teaspoon paprika
¼ teaspoon garlic powder
¼ cup plus 3 tablespoons unsweetened orange juice
¼ cup plus 3 tablespoons low-sugar orange marmalade
Orange slices (optional)
Fresh thyme sprigs (optional)

Trim fat from roast. Place roast in a large shallow dish. Combine ¾ cup unsweetened orange juice and next 5 ingredients, stirring well. Pour over roast. Cover and marinate in refrigerator 8 hours, turning occasionally.

Place roast and marinade in a large Dutch oven. Cover and bake at 350° for 2½ hours or until meat is tender.

Remove roast to a serving platter; keep warm. Combine ¼ cup plus 3 tablespoons unsweetened orange juice and orange marmalade in a nonaluminum saucepan. Cook over low heat, stirring constantly, until marmalade melts and mixture is thoroughly heated. Spoon 1 tablespoon orange juice mixture over each serving of meat. If desired, garnish with orange slices and fresh thyme sprigs. Yield: 14 servings (212 calories per serving).

PROTEIN 27.1 / FAT 8.2 / CARBOHYDRATE 5.8 / CHOLESTEROL 82 / IRON 3.1 / SODIUM 44 / CALCIUM 9

SIRLOIN STEAK WITH HERBED WINE SAUCE

Vegetable cooking spray
¼ pound fresh mushrooms, sliced
3 tablespoons chopped green onions
¾ cup Burgundy or other dry red wine
¾ cup water
2 tablespoons tomato paste
1 teaspoon dried whole tarragon
¾ teaspoon beef-flavored bouillon granules
1 tablespoon plus 1½ teaspoons chopped fresh parsley
1 (1-pound) lean boneless beef sirloin steak (¾-inch thick)

Spray a large nonstick skillet with cooking spray; place over medium-high heat until hot. Add sliced mushrooms and green onions, and sauté until tender. Add wine, water, tomato paste, tarragon, and bouillon granules. Bring to a boil; reduce heat to medium. Cook 10 minutes or until liquid is reduced by half. Stir in chopped parsley; keep warm.

Trim fat from steak. Coat a broiler pan with cooking spray. Broil 4 to 6 inches from heating element for 6 to 8 minutes on each side or to desired degree of doneness.

Cut steak into four equal portions. Spoon ¼ cup sauce over each serving of steak. Yield: 4 servings (215 calories per serving).

PROTEIN 28.3 / FAT 8.6 / CARBOHYDRATE 5.1 / CHOLESTEROL 80 / IRON 4.0 / SODIUM 246 / CALCIUM 24

A flavorful orange sauce made with low-sugar marmalade is spooned over tender slices of roast beef in Savory Orange Roast Beef.

GRILLED GARLIC FLANK STEAK

1 (1½-pound) lean flank steak
¼ cup lime juice
¼ cup tequila
¼ cup minced fresh cilantro
3 cloves garlic, minced
2 teaspoons coarsely ground pepper
Vegetable cooking spray

Trim fat from steak, and place in a large shallow dish. Combine lime juice and next 4 ingredients; pour over steak. Cover and marinate in refrigerator 24 hours, turning occasionally.

Remove steak from marinade; discard marinade. Coat grill rack with cooking spray; place on grill over medium-hot coals. Cook steak 6 to 7 minutes on each side or to desired degree of doneness. Slice steak diagonally across grain into ¼-inch-thick slices. Serve immediately. Yield: 6 servings (223 calories per serving).

PROTEIN 22.3 / FAT 13.2 / CARBOHYDRATE 0.7 / CHOLESTEROL 61 / IRON 2.3 / SODIUM 73 / CALCIUM 9

PREPARING BEEF FOR STIR-FRYING

Start with a lean cut of beef, and trim away visible fat to reduce the calorie and fat content. Arrange the beef on a freezer-proof platter, and place in the freezer until the meat is partially frozen. Remove from the freezer, placing the meat on a cutting board. Slice each piece into thin strips, cutting across the grain.

TERIYAKI STEAK ROLLS

2 (1-pound) lean flank steaks
2 tablespoons brown sugar
1 tablespoon teriyaki sauce
3 tablespoons unsweetened pineapple juice
1 tablespoon vegetable oil
1½ teaspoons minced fresh gingerroot
1 clove garlic, minced
Vegetable cooking spray

Trim fat from steaks; partially freeze steaks. Slice diagonally across grain into ¼-inch strips. Place in a 13- x 9- x 2-inch baking dish.

Combine sugar and remaining ingredients except cooking spray; pour over meat. Cover and marinate in refrigerator 8 hours.

Remove meat from marinade, discarding marinade. Thread meat ribbon-style on 8 (12-inch) skewers. Coat grill rack with cooking spray; place on grill over medium-hot coals. Place meat on rack, and cook 10 to 12 minutes or to desired degree of doneness, turning often. Yield: 8 servings (248 calories per serving).

PROTEIN 22.4 / FAT 14.9 / CARBOHYDRATE 4.7 / CHOLESTEROL 61 / IRON 2.4 / SODIUM 160 / CALCIUM 10

TEXAS STEAK WITH GRAVY

1½ pounds lean round steak
½ teaspoon pepper
¼ teaspoon salt
Vegetable cooking spray
1 teaspoon vegetable oil
⅓ cup evaporated skimmed milk
⅓ cup water
1 tablespoon all-purpose flour
2 tablespoons strong brewed coffee
¼ teaspoon pepper
⅛ teaspoon salt

Trim fat from steak. Place steak between 2 sheets of wax paper; flatten to ½-inch thickness. Cut steak into 6 equal pieces. Combine ½ teaspoon pepper and ¼ teaspoon salt, stirring well. Sprinkle evenly over steak pieces.

Coat a large nonstick skillet with cooking spray; add oil. Place over medium-high heat until hot. Add steak, and cook 3 minutes on each side or until browned. Remove steak; drain and pat dry with paper towels. Place steak on a serving platter, and keep warm. Wipe pan drippings from skillet with a paper towel.

Combine milk, water, and flour; stir until smooth. Add to skillet. Cook over low heat until thickened, stirring constantly. Stir in remaining ingredients. Cook over low heat until thoroughly heated. Pour over steak, and serve. Yield: 6 servings (192 calories per serving).

PROTEIN 25.8 / FAT 7.8 / CARBOHYDRATE 2.9 / CHOLESTEROL 71 / IRON 2.5 / SODIUM 218 / CALCIUM 48

QUICK CUBED STEAKS

4 (4-ounce) lean cubed sirloin steaks
⅛ teaspoon pepper
Vegetable cooking spray
½ pound fresh mushrooms, sliced
2 green onions, sliced
3 tablespoons lemon juice
2 tablespoons water
2 tablespoons Dijon mustard
½ teaspoon dried whole chervil

Sprinkle steak with pepper. Coat a large non-stick skillet with cooking spray; place over medium-high heat until hot. Add steak; cook 5 minutes on each side or until browned. Drain and pat dry with paper towels. Wipe pan drippings from skillet with a paper towel.

Coat skillet with cooking spray; place over medium-high heat until hot. Add mushrooms and onion, and sauté until tender. Stir in lemon juice and remaining ingredients. Return steak to skillet; cover and simmer 6 minutes. Yield: 4 servings (218 calories per serving).

PROTEIN 28.6 / FAT 8.9 / CARBOHYDRATE 4.6 / CHOLESTEROL 80 / IRON 3.9 / SODIUM 285 / CALCIUM 19

STUFFED ONIONS IN GUACAMOLE SAUCE

4 medium onions
½ pound ground chuck
¼ cup chopped green pepper
½ teaspoon pepper
¼ teaspoon salt
¼ teaspoon chili powder
¼ teaspoon ground cumin
1 small avocado, coarsely chopped
½ cup (2 ounces) shredded
  Monterey Jack cheese
¼ cup plus 2 tablespoons skim milk
2 tablespoons low-fat sour cream
1 tablespoon lemon juice
1 teaspoon minced fresh cilantro
⅛ teaspoon garlic powder
⅛ teaspoon Worcestershire sauce

Peel onions; cut a thin slice from top of each. Place onions in a vegetable steamer over boil-ing water. Cover and steam 5 minutes or until tender. Let cool. Scoop out centers, leaving ¼-inch-thick shells. Set aside.

Combine ground chuck and next 5 ingredients; stir well. Cook ground chuck mixture in a large nonstick skillet over medium heat until browned, stirring to crumble. Drain and pat dry with paper towels. Spoon mixture evenly into reserved onion shells; place in a shallow baking dish. Bake at 350° for 10 minutes.

Combine avocado and remaining ingredients in container of an electric blender; top with cover, and process until smooth. Place onions on 4 individual serving plates. Spoon ¼ cup sauce around each onion. Serve immediately. Yield: 4 servings (290 calories per serving).

PROTEIN 17.1 / FAT 18.4 / CARBOHYDRATE 15.5 / CHOLESTEROL 48 / IRON 2.2 / SODIUM 271 / CALCIUM 190

LIVER ITALIANO

1½ cups no-salt-added tomato juice
½ cup finely chopped onion
1¼ cups sliced fresh mushrooms
¾ cup chopped green pepper
½ teaspoon minced fresh basil
½ teaspoon minced fresh oregano
1 clove garlic, minced
¼ teaspoon pepper
Vegetable cooking spray
6 slices beef liver (1¾ pounds)
2 tablespoons grated Parmesan cheese

Combine the first 8 ingredients in a saucepan; bring to a boil. Reduce heat, and simmer, uncovered, for 30 minutes. Set aside, and keep warm.

Coat a large nonstick skillet with cooking spray; place over medium-high heat until hot. Add liver, and cook 5 to 7 minutes on each side or until browned.

Transfer liver to serving plates. Spoon ⅓ cup reserved sauce over each serving. Sprinkle 1 teaspoon Parmesan cheese over each serving. Serve immediately. Yield: 6 servings (193 calories per serving).

PROTEIN 25.8 / FAT 5.6 / CARBOHYDRATE 9.5 / CHOLESTEROL 382 / IRON 7.2 / SODIUM 108 / CALCIUM 39

VEAL CHOPS WITH ARTICHOKES

4 (6-ounce) loin veal chops (1-inch thick)
¼ teaspoon garlic powder
¼ teaspoon cracked pepper
Vegetable cooking spray
¼ cup water
2 tablespoons dry vermouth
2 large tomatoes, peeled, seeded, and chopped
¼ teaspoon chicken-flavored bouillon granules
¼ teaspoon dried whole oregano
¼ teaspoon dried whole thyme
1 (14½-ounce) can artichoke hearts, drained and quartered
1 cup sliced fresh mushrooms

Trim fat from chops; sprinkle with garlic powder and pepper. Coat a large nonstick skillet with cooking spray; place over medium-high heat until hot. Add veal to skillet, and cook 3 to 4 minutes on each side or until browned. Remove veal from skillet. Drain and pat dry with paper towels. Wipe pan drippings from skillet with a paper towel.

Add water and next 5 ingredients. Bring to a boil; reduce heat, and simmer 5 minutes. Gently stir in artichoke hearts.

Place veal chops in a 12- x 8- x 2-inch baking dish that has been coated with cooking spray. Pour tomato mixture over chops; sprinkle with mushrooms. Cover and bake at 350° for 25 minutes or until veal chops are tender. Yield: 4 servings (221 calories per serving).

PROTEIN 28.2 / FAT 7.3 / CARBOHYDRATE 10.9 / CHOLESTEROL 127 / IRON 2.5 / SODIUM 167 / CALCIUM 34

LEMON-PEPPER VEAL CHOPS

⅓ cup lemon juice
1 tablespoon vegetable oil
⅛ teaspoon hot sauce
⅛ teaspoon ground white pepper
4 (6-ounce) lean loin veal chops (¾-inch thick)
Vegetable cooking spray
Lemon slices (optional)

Combine lemon juice, oil, hot sauce, and pepper, stirring well. Trim fat from chops; brush with lemon juice mixture. Set chops and lemon juice mixture aside.

Coat grill rack with cooking spray; place on grill over medium-hot coals. Place veal on rack, and cook 4 minutes on each side or to desired degree of doneness, turning and basting frequently with reserved lemon juice mixture. Transfer to a serving platter. Garnish with lemon slices, if desired. Yield: 4 servings (207 calories per serving).

PROTEIN 25.9 / FAT 10.2 / CARBOHYDRATE 1.8 / CHOLESTEROL 127 / IRON 1.0 / SODIUM 71 / CALCIUM 2

BRANDIED VEAL SCALLOPINI

1 pound veal cutlets (½-inch thick)
2 tablespoons all-purpose flour
½ teaspoon lemon-pepper seasoning
Vegetable cooking spray
1 teaspoon olive oil
½ cup frozen whole small onions, thawed
1½ cups sliced fresh mushrooms
3 tablespoons brandy
2 tablespoons water
1 tablespoon lemon juice
1 teaspoon Worcestershire sauce
½ teaspoon hot sauce
¼ cup chopped fresh parsley

Trim fat from cutlets. Place cutlets between 2 sheets of wax paper; flatten to ¼-inch thickness, using a meat mallet or rolling pin. Combine flour and lemon-pepper seasoning in a shallow dish; dredge veal cutlets in flour mixture. Coat a large nonstick skillet with cooking spray; add olive oil. Place over medium-high heat until hot. Add veal cutlets, and cook 4 minutes on each side or until browned. Transfer to a serving platter, and keep warm.

Add onion and mushrooms to skillet; sauté until tender. Spoon onion mixture over veal. Add brandy, water, lemon juice, Worcestershire sauce, and hot sauce to skillet; bring to a boil, scraping browned bits from bottom of pan. Spoon over veal; sprinkle with parsley. Yield: 4 servings (273 calories per serving).

PROTEIN 23.0 / FAT 13.9 / CARBOHYDRATE 6.5 / CHOLESTEROL 116 / IRON 4.0 / SODIUM 165 / CALCIUM 25

Tucked inside almond-crusted Veal-Fontina Pockets is melted Fontina cheese.

VEAL-FONTINA POCKETS

1 pound veal cutlets (¼-inch thick)
¼ teaspoon pepper
8 fresh sage leaves, minced
2 (½-ounce) slices Fontina cheese
3 tablespoons fine, dry breadcrumbs
1 tablespoon ground blanched almonds
2 tablespoons all-purpose flour
1 egg, lightly beaten
Vegetable cooking spray
2 teaspoons unsalted margarine
8 lemon wedges
Plum tomatoes (optional)
Fresh sage leaves (optional)

Trim fat from cutlets; cut into 4 serving-size pieces. Place cutlets between 2 sheets of wax paper; flatten to ⅛-inch thickness, using a meat mallet or rolling pin. Sprinkle cutlets with pepper and minced sage. Cut cheese slices in half. Top

each cutlet with ½ slice cheese. Fold cutlets in half; pound edges to seal.

Combine breadcrumbs and almonds in a small bowl; set aside.

Place flour in a shallow dish. Dredge sealed cutlets in flour. Carefully dip in egg, and coat with breadcrumb mixture. Coat a large nonstick skillet with cooking spray; add margarine. Place over medium-high heat until hot. Add veal cutlets and cook 2 minutes on each side or until browned. Arrange in a 12- x 8- x 2-inch baking dish that has been coated with cooking spray. Cover and bake at 375° for 15 to 20 minutes. Transfer to a serving platter. Top with lemon wedges. If desired, garnish with plum tomatoes and fresh sage leaves. Yield: 4 servings (298 calories per serving).

PROTEIN 27.6 / FAT 16.6 / CARBOHYDRATE 8.5 / CHOLESTEROL 157 / IRON 4.3 / SODIUM 154 / CALCIUM 78

VEAL STROGANOFF

1 pound veal cutlets (¼-inch thick)
Vegetable cooking spray
2 cups sliced fresh mushrooms
1 cup chopped onion
2 cloves garlic, minced
½ cup water
1 teaspoon beef-flavored bouillon granules
½ teaspoon pepper
¼ teaspoon dry mustard
¼ teaspoon paprika
¾ cup low-fat sour cream
2 cups hot cooked medium egg noodles (cooked
    without salt or fat)
¼ cup minced fresh parsley

Trim fat from cutlets; cut into 1-inch strips. Coat a large nonstick skillet with cooking spray; place over medium-high heat until hot. Add veal; cook until browned. Remove from skillet; drain and pat dry with paper towels. Wipe pan drippings from skillet. Add mushrooms, onion, and garlic to skillet; sauté until tender. Add veal, water, and next 4 ingredients. Cover; simmer 20 minutes or until veal is tender. Add sour cream; cook over low heat until heated. Toss veal mixture and noodles. Sprinkle with parsley. Yield: 6 servings (249 calories per serving).

PROTEIN 22.3 / FAT 9.6 / CARBOHYDRATE 17.5 / CHOLESTEROL 118 / IRON 1.8 / SODIUM 222 / CALCIUM 51

LEG OF LAMB À LA BONNE FEMME

1 (7½-pound) lean leg of lamb
3 cloves garlic, sliced
Vegetable cooking spray
1½ pounds small new potatoes
1¼ pounds small white boiling onions, peeled
1 (12-ounce) package baby carrots, scraped
5 stalks celery, cut into 1-inch pieces
1 teaspoon beef-flavored bouillon granules
1 cup boiling water
8 black peppercorns
2 bay leaves
2 sprigs fresh parsley
1 teaspoon dried whole thyme
½ teaspoon dried whole marjoram
½ teaspoon dried whole sage
Fresh sage leaves (optional)

Trim fat from leg of lamb. Make several small slits on outside of lamb and insert garlic slices. Place lamb in a deep roasting pan that has been coated with cooking spray. Insert meat thermometer, being careful not to touch bone.

Scrub potatoes. Add potatoes, onion, carrot, and celery to pan. Combine bouillon granules and water; pour over lamb. Combine peppercorns and remaining ingredients on a small square of cheesecloth; bring ends together and tie with string. Add to pan 30 minutes before lamb is done. Bake, uncovered, at 325° for 2½ hours or until meat thermometer registers 140° (rare) to 160° (medium), basting frequently with pan drippings.

Remove lamb from oven; discard herb pouch. Let stand 10 minutes before carving. Garnish with fresh sage leaves, if desired. Yield: 15 servings (221 calories per serving).

PROTEIN 26.2 / FAT 6.2 / CARBOHYDRATE 14.3 / CHOLESTEROL 85 / IRON 2.9 / SODIUM 159 / CALCIUM 49

Garlic-studded Leg of Lamb à la Bonne Femme is a hearty me

SPINACH-CROWNED LAMB CHOPS

6 (6-ounce) lean lamb loin chops (1-inch thick)
¼ teaspoon pepper
⅛ teaspoon garlic powder
Vegetable cooking spray
1 teaspoon olive oil
⅓ cup shredded carrot
¼ cup chopped onion
2 cups torn fresh spinach
1 tablespoon pine nuts
1 teaspoon cornstarch
½ cup water
½ teaspoon beef-flavored bouillon
   granules

Trim fat from chops. Sprinkle with pepper and garlic powder. Coat a large nonstick skillet with cooking spray; add oil. Place over medium-high heat until hot. Add chops, and cook 8 minutes on each side or until browned. Remove chops from skillet. Drain and pat dry with paper towels. Wipe pan drippings from skillet with a paper towel.

Coat a large nonstick skillet with cooking spray; place over medium-high heat until hot.

Add carrot and onion to skillet, and sauté until tender. Add spinach and pine nuts. Combine cornstarch and water, stirring well. Add cornstarch mixture to spinach mixture. Stir in bouillon granules. Return chops to skillet; and bring to a boil. Reduce heat, and simmer 5 minutes or until spinach mixture is thickened. Place chops on a serving platter, and top with spinach mixture. Serve immediately. Yield: 6 servings (193 calories per serving).

PROTEIN 24.9 / FAT 7.4 / CARBOHYDRATE 2.7 / CHOLESTEROL 85 / IRON 2.4 / SODIUM 157 / CALCIUM 33

TARRAGON LAMB STEAKS

4 (5-ounce) lean lamb sirloins (¾-inch thick)
Vegetable cooking spray
½ teaspoon salt
⅛ teaspoon pepper
2 tablespoons finely chopped shallots
½ cup Chablis or other dry white wine
¼ cup water
1 teaspoon dried whole tarragon

Trim fat from lamb. Coat a large nonstick skillet with cooking spray; place over medium-high heat until hot. Add lamb, and cook until browned. Sprinkle with salt and pepper. Reduce heat to medium-low; cook, uncovered, 5 minutes on each side or to desired degree of doneness. Remove lamb to a serving platter, and keep warm.

Coat a small nonstick skillet with cooking spray; place over medium-high heat until hot. Add shallots, and sauté until tender. Add wine, water, and tarragon. Cook, uncovered, for 5 minutes. Remove from heat. Spoon tarragon mixture over lamb. Serve immediately. Yield: 4 servings (146 calories per serving).

PROTEIN 18.8 / FAT 6.3 / CARBOHYDRATE 2.2 / CHOLESTEROL 60 / IRON 1.7 / SODIUM 342 / CALCIUM 8

HUNGARIAN LAMB GOULASH

Vegetable cooking spray
1 pound lean boneless lamb, cut into 1-inch cubes
1 large onion, minced
1 tablespoon brown sugar
1 tablespoon sweet paprika
¼ teaspoon dry mustard
1¼ cups water
1 (6-ounce) can no salt added tomato paste
1 tablespoon Worcestershire sauce
1 teaspoon cider vinegar
2 tablespoons all-purpose flour
¼ cup water
4 cups hot cooked medium egg noodles (cooked without salt or fat)

Coat a large Dutch oven with cooking spray; place over medium-high heat until hot. Add lamb, and cook until browned. Drain and pat dry with paper towels. Wipe pan drippings from Dutch oven with a paper towel. Add lamb, onion and next 7 ingredients to Dutch oven. Cover and simmer 1 hour or until lamb is tender.

Combine flour and ¼ cup water, blending until smooth. Stir flour mixture into lamb mixture. Cook, stirring frequently, until thickened.

Spoon lamb mixture over hot cooked noodles; toss gently. Yield: 8 servings (205 calories per serving).

PROTEIN 16.2 / FAT 4.3 / CARBOHYDRATE 25.1 / CHOLESTEROL 63 / IRON 2.2 / SODIUM 60 / CALCIUM 30

HAWAIIAN LAMB KABOBS

1 pound lean ground lamb
½ cup soft whole wheat breadcrumbs
2 tablespoons finely chopped green pepper
2 tablespoons finely chopped onion
2 teaspoons low-sodium soy sauce
⅛ teaspoon pepper
1 (8-ounce) can unsweetened pineapple chunks, undrained
1 large sweet red pepper, seeded and cut into 1-inch squares
6 medium-size fresh mushrooms
Vegetable cooking spray
2 tablespoons low-sodium soy sauce
1 tablespoon vegetable oil
1 teaspoon sugar
½ teaspoon grated fresh gingerroot
⅛ teaspoon garlic powder

Combine first 6 ingredients in a medium bowl; stir well. Shape mixture into 24 balls, using 1 tablespoon lamb mixture for each meatball. Cover and chill at least 1 hour.

Drain pineapple chunks, reserving juice. Alternate meatballs, pineapple chunks, pepper, and mushrooms on 6 (12-inch) skewers. Arrange on a rack of a broiler pan that has been coated with cooking spray.

Combine reserved pineapple juice, 2 tablespoons soy sauce, oil, sugar, gingerroot, and garlic powder; stir well. Brush mixture over kabobs. Broil kabobs 6 inches from heating element for 5 minutes. Turn kabobs; broil an additional 5 minutes or until meatballs are browned, basting with remaining pineapple juice mixture. Yield: 6 servings (167 calories per serving).

PROTEIN 17.5 / FAT 7.0 / CARBOHYDRATE 8.5 / CHOLESTEROL 57 / IRON 2.0 / SODIUM 330 / CALCIUM 21

ITALIAN STUFFED PORK LOIN ROAST

Vegetable cooking spray
2½ cups thinly sliced fresh mushrooms
¼ cup minced onion
1 clove garlic, minced
2 tablespoons Chablis or other dry white wine
2 tablespoons minced fresh parsley
1¾ teaspoons minced fresh oregano, divided
¼ teaspoon salt
1 (2½-pound) lean boneless pork loin roast, rolled and tied
1 tablespoon cracked pepper
¼ cup Chablis or other dry white wine
1 tablespoon low-sugar raspberry spread

Coat a medium nonstick skillet with cooking spray; place over medium-high heat until hot. Add mushrooms, onion, and garlic, and sauté until tender. Reduce heat to medium; stir in 2 tablespoons wine, parsley, 1½ teaspoons oregano, and salt. Cook, uncovered, until liquid is absorbed. Set aside.

Untie roast, and trim fat. Spread mushroom mixture over inside of roast. Retie roast and rub on all sides with pepper. Place on a rack in a roasting pan that has been coated with cooking spray. Insert meat thermometer into thickest part of roast, making sure it does not touch stuffing. Combine ¼ cup wine, remaining ¼ teaspoon oregano, and raspberry spread; stir until well blended. Pour over roast and bake, uncovered, at 325° for 1½ hours or until meat thermometer registers 160° (medium).

Let roast stand 10 minutes. Remove string; cut diagonally across grain into ½-inch slices. Yield: 10 servings (219 calories per serving).

PROTEIN 29.2 / FAT 9.7 / CARBOHYDRATE 2.3 / CHOLESTEROL 88 / IRON 1.1 / SODIUM 130 / CAL 11

BREAKFAST—HOW IMPORTANT IS IT?

After observing a group of 9- to 11-year-olds, researchers at the University of Texas reported that when the children skipped breakfast, their classroom performance was affected negatively. Although not all studies conclude that breakfast is important, experts agree there is no good argument for skipping the meal.

Do not let busy mornings keep you from getting the fuel your body needs. A nutritious breakfast on the go can be as quick as a graham cracker with skim milk, peanut butter on a banana, or fruit with low-fat cottage cheese or plain, nonfat yogurt. Give your day a head start by eating a nutritious low-fat breakfast.

MUSTARD-TOPPED PORK ROAST

1 (3½-pound) lean boneless pork loin roast, rolled and tied
2 cloves garlic, minced
1 teaspoon mustard seeds, crushed
½ teaspoon dry mustard
¼ teaspoon onion powder
¼ teaspoon dried whole thyme
¼ teaspoon freshly ground pepper
Vegetable cooking spray

Unroll roast, and trim excess fat. Retie roast, and set aside.

Combine garlic and next 5 ingredients, stirring well. Rub garlic mixture over entire surface of meat. Place roast on rack of a broiler pan that has been coated with cooking spray. Insert meat thermometer into thickest part of roast. Bake, uncovered, at 350° for 2 hours or until meat thermometer registers 160° (medium).

Let roast stand at room temperature 10 minutes before slicing diagonally across grain into thin sices. Yield: 14 servings (210 calories per serving).

PROTEIN 28.8 / FAT 9.6 / CARBOHYDRATE 0.3 / CHOLESTEROL 88 / IRON 0.8 / SODIUM 70 / CALCIUM 8

CUMIN-SCENTED TENDERLOINS

¼ cup lime juice
2 tablespoons Chablis or other dry white wine
1 small jalapeño pepper, seeded and finely chopped
1 tablespoon minced fresh cilantro
1 teaspoon coarsely ground pepper
¾ teaspoon garlic powder
¼ teaspoon ground cumin
2 (¾-pound) pork tenderloins
Vegetable cooking spray
Lime wedges (optional)
Fresh cilantro sprigs (optional)

Combine first 7 ingredients in a large zip-top heavy-duty plastic bag; seal bag and shake well. Trim fat from pork. Add pork to bag; seal bag and shake until pork is well coated. Marinate in refrigerator 8 hours, shaking bag occasionally.

Remove pork from marinade, reserving mari-nade. Coat rack of a broiler pan with cooking spray. Place pork on rack. Insert meat thermometer into thickest part of pork. Bake at 400° for 45 minutes or until meat thermometer registers 160° (medium), basting frequently with reserved marinade. Let pork stand at room temperature 10 minutes before slicing diagonally across grain into thin slices. If desired, garnish with lime wedges and fresh cilantro sprigs. Yield: 6 servings (157 calories per serving).

PROTEIN 26.0 / FAT 4.5 / CARBOHYDRATE 1.8 / CHOLESTEROL 83 / IRON 1.6 / SODIUM 61 / CALCIUM 13

BOURBON-APPLE PORK CHOPS

4 (6-ounce) lean center-loin pork chops (½-inch thick)
Vegetable cooking spray
½ teaspoon garlic powder
¼ teaspoon pepper
¼ teaspoon ground allspice
¼ cup unsweetened apple juice
¼ cup bourbon
1 teaspoon Worcestershire sauce
2 tablespoons water
1 teaspoon cornstarch
1 medium Granny Smith apple, cored and cut into rings

Trim fat from pork chops; set aside.

Coat a large nonstick skillet with cooking spray; place over medium high heat until hot. Add pork chops, and brown on each side. Sprinkle garlic powder, pepper, and allspice evenly over pork chops. Add apple juice, bourbon, and Worcestershire sauce; bring mixture to a boil. Cover, reduce heat, and simmer 10 minutes or until pork chops are tender.

Transfer chops to a serving platter, and keep warm. Combine water and cornstarch, stirring until smooth. Stir into skillet, and cook until mixture thickens, stirring constantly. Add apple rings to skillet, and cook until thoroughly heated. Remove from heat, and spoon over pork chops. Serve immediately. Yield: 4 servings (237 calories per serving).

PROTEIN 26.8 / FAT 9.0 / CARBOHYDRATE 11.2 / CHOLESTEROL 76 / IRON 1.2 / SODIUM 93 / CALCIUM 14

CRANBERRY PORK CHOPS

4 (6-ounce) lean center-loin pork
   chops (½-inch thick)
½ teaspoon coarsely ground pepper
Vegetable cooking spray
3 tablespoons water
⅔ cup fresh or frozen cranberries,
   thawed
2 tablespoons plus 1½ teaspoons sugar
2 tablespoons unsweetened orange juice
2 tablespoons water
⅛ teaspoon ground cinnamon
⅛ teaspoon ground ginger
Fresh mint sprigs (optional)

Trim fat from chops. Rub chops with pepper. Coat a large nonstick skillet with cooking spray; place over medium-high heat until hot. Add chops, and cook until browned on both sides. Add 3 tablespoons water to skillet. Cover, and cook over medium heat 15 to 20 minutes or until chops are tender.

Combine cranberries and remaining ingredients, except mint, in a medium saucepan. Cook over medium heat until cranberry skins pop and mixture is thickened, stirring frequently. Remove from heat; let cool slightly.

Place chops on a serving platter. Spoon 2 tablespoons cranberry mixture over each serving. Garnish with fresh mint sprigs, if desired. Yield: 4 servings (266 calories per serving).

PROTEIN 30.9 / FAT 10.2 / CARBOHYDRATE 10.9 / CHOLESTEROL 88 / IRON 1.3 / SODIUM 93 / CALCIUM 11

SWEET PEPPER PORK CHOPS

½ cup reduced-calorie apricot preserves
1 tablespoon apricot nectar
1 teaspoon crushed red pepper
6 (6-ounce) lean center-loin pork chops (½-inch
   thick)
Vegetable cooking spray
1 medium-size green pepper, seeded and
   cut into 1-inch pieces
1 medium-size sweet red pepper, seeded
   and cut into 1-inch pieces
1 medium-size sweet yellow pepper, seeded
   and cut into 1-inch pieces

Combine first 3 ingredients in a saucepan. Cook over medium heat until preserves melt, stirring constantly. Remove from heat.

Trim fat from pork chops. Coat a large nonstick skillet with cooking spray; place over medium-high heat until hot. Add chops, and cook until browned on both sides. Drain and pat dry with paper towels. Transfer chops to a 12- x 8- x 2-inch baking dish. Brush chops with reserved apricot glaze, reserving any leftover glaze. Cover and bake at 350° for 30 minutes. Add peppers; bake, uncovered, an additional 15 minutes or until pork chops are tender, brushing frequently with reserved apricot glaze. Yield: 6 servings (295 calories per serving).

PROTEIN 29.2 / FAT 13.5 / CARBOHYDRATE 12.9 / CHOLESTEROL 91 / IRON 1.7 / SODIUM 93 / CALCIUM 11

SPICY GRILLED PORK CHOPS

6 (6-ounce) lean center-loin pork chops (½-inch
   thick)
1¼ cups water
2 tablespoons vinegar
2 tablespoons minced onion
1 tablespoon Worcestershire sauce
2 teaspoons sugar
1¼ teaspoons pepper
1 teaspoon chili powder
½ teaspoon dry mustard
¼ teaspoon garlic powder
¼ teaspoon ground red pepper
¼ teaspoon hot sauce
Vegetable cooking spray

Trim fat from pork chops. Place chops in a shallow dish; set aside.

Combine water and next 10 ingredients in a medium saucepan. Bring to a boil. Pour over chops. Cover and marinate in refrigerator 8 hours, turning occasionally.

Remove chops from marinade, reserving marinade. Coat grill rack with cooking spray; place on grill over medium-hot coals. Cook chops 15 to 20 minutes or until tender, turning and basting frequently with reserved marinade. Yield: 6 servings (217 calories per serving).

PROTEIN 24.3 / FAT 11.4 / CARBOHYDRATE 3.0 / CHOLESTEROL 77 / IRON 1.1 / SODIUM 89 / CALCIUM 12

MANDARIN PORK MEDALLIONS

¼ cup all-purpose flour
2 tablespoons wheat germ
½ teaspoon pepper
1 pound pork medallions
Vegetable cooking spray
2 teaspoons vegetable oil, divided
1 (11-ounce) can unsweetened mandarin oranges, undrained
1 tablespoon Cointreau or other orange-flavored liqueur
1 teaspoon lemon juice
1 teaspoon cornstarch
¼ cup sliced green onions
1 tablespoon finely chopped sweet red pepper

Combine flour, wheat germ, and pepper; stir well. Dredge pork in flour mixture.

Coat a large nonstick skillet with cooking spray; add 1 teaspoon oil. Place over medium-high heat until hot. Add ½ pound pork, and cook 2 minutes on each side or until browned. Transfer to a serving platter, and keep warm. Repeat procedure with remaining 1 teaspoon oil and ½ pound pork.

Drain oranges, reserving juice. Combine reserved juice, Cointreau, lemon juice, and cornstarch in a small skillet; stir well. Add green onions and pepper. Cook over medium heat, stirring constantly, until mixture is thickened. Gently stir in mandarin oranges. Spoon sauce over pork, and serve immediately. Yield: 4 servings (270 calories per serving).

PROTEIN 28.0 / FAT 7.5 / CARBOHYDRATE 21.9 / CHOLESTEROL 83 /
IRON 2.3 / SODIUM 66 / CALCIUM 18

PORK 'N' SUCCOTASH STIR-FRY

1 pound lean boneless pork loin
½ teaspoon chili powder
¼ teaspoon ground cumin
¼ teaspoon pepper
2 teaspoons cornstarch
½ teaspoon chicken-flavored bouillon granules
½ cup water
Vegetable cooking spray
1 purple onion, thinly sliced and separated into rings
1 medium-size sweet red pepper, seeded and diced
1½ cups frozen whole kernel corn, thawed
½ cup frozen baby lima beans, thawed

Partially freeze pork; trim fat from pork. Slice pork diagonally across the grain into 2- x ¼-inch strips. Combine chili powder, cumin, and pepper; sprinkle over pork strips. Toss gently to coat; set aside.

Combine cornstarch, bouillon granules, and water; stir well. Set aside.

Coat a wok or large nonstick skillet with cooking spray; place over medium-high heat until hot. Add pork, and stir-fry 3 minutes or until browned. Remove from skillet. Drain and pat dry with paper towels; set aside.

Add onion and sweet red pepper to skillet; stir-fry 2 minutes. Add corn and lima beans, stir fry 2 minutes. Return pork to skillet. Add reserved cornstarch mixture; bring to a boil. Cook, stirring constantly, until thickened. Yield: 4 servings (190 calories per serving).

PROTEIN 26.3 / FAT 3.6 / CARBOHYDRATE 12.7 / CHOLESTEROL 74 /
IRON 2.6 / SODIUM 187 / CALCIUM 29

 ## TOO MUCH TV—BUILDING FAT INSTEAD OF FITNESS

According to research, children are becoming less fit and more obese due in part to the amount of time spent watching television. When the Office of Disease and Health Promotion surveyed 8,800 young people, they found that only half of the children 6 to 17 years old played or exercised vigorously enough to keep their hearts healthy.

The National Health and Nutrition Examination Survey found that more than 20 percent of adolescents who watched five hours of television each day were obese. This percentage was double that of those who watched only one hour a day.

What to do? Encourage your child to be more active. Suggest after-school activities that offer the benefits of exercise. If possible, join in too, so that you can receive the benefits. If your child is still spending too much time in front of the television, limiting the viewing time may be necessary.

PORK PAPRIKASH

1 pound lean boneless pork loin
Vegetable cooking spray
1 cup chopped onion
2 medium-size green peppers, seeded and diced
1 cup chopped celery
½ (6-ounce) can no-salt-added tomato paste
2 teaspoons paprika
½ teaspoon pepper
1½ cups water
2 cups hot cooked long-grain rice (cooked without salt or fat)

Trim fat from pork; cut pork into ½-inch cubes. Coat a large nonstick skillet with cooking spray; place over medium-high heat until hot. Add pork cubes and onion, and cook 10 minutes or until browned, stirring frequently. Remove from skillet. Drain and pat dry with paper towels. Wipe pan drippings from skillet with a paper towel.

Combine pork mixture, and next 5 ingredients in skillet; add water. Cook, covered, over medium heat 30 minutes. Reduce heat; uncover, and cook an additional 20 minutes or until pork is tender, stirring occasionally. Serve over hot cooked rice. Yield: 4 servings (208 calories per 1 cup mixture plus ½ cup cooked rice).

PROTEIN 30.5 / FAT 5.2 / CARBOHYDRATE 43.4 / CHOLESTEROL 83 / IRON 4.3 / SODIUM 101 / CALCIUM 54

LEMON-HONEY PORK STIR-FRY

¾ pound lean boneless pork loin
2 tablespoons lemon juice
1 tablespoon honey
1 tablespoon low-sodium soy sauce
1 tablespoon cornstarch
½ cup water
Vegetable cooking spray
1 teaspoon vegetable oil
1 large carrot, scraped and diagonally sliced
1 (6-ounce) package frozen snow pea pods, thawed
¼ cup sliced green onions
1 cup fresh bean sprouts, washed and drained
2 cups hot cooked rice noodles (cooked without salt or fat)

Partially freeze pork; trim excess fat from pork. Slice pork diagonally across grain into 2- x ½-inch strips; set aside.

Combine lemon juice, honey, and soy sauce. Combine cornstarch and water, stirring well. Add to honey mixture; set aside.

Coat a wok or a large nonstick skillet with cooking spray; add oil. Place over medium-high heat until hot. Add pork; stir-fry 3 minutes or until browned. Remove from skillet; pat dry with paper towels. Set aside.

Add carrot; stir-fry 3 or 4 minutes or until crisp-tender. Add snow peas, green onions, and bean sprouts; stir-fry 1 minute. Return pork to wok.

Pour reserved lemon juice mixture over pork mixture in wok. Cook, stirring constantly, until thickened. Serve over hot cooked rice noodles. Yield: 4 servings (349 calories per 1 cup mixture and ½ cup noodles).

PROTEIN 24.4 / FAT 8.8 / CARBOHYDRATE 43.0 / CHOLESTEROL 54 / IRON 4.3 / SODIUM 218 / CALCIUM 77

FIESTA BURRITOS

10 (6-inch) flour tortillas
1 pound lean ground pork
1 large onion, chopped
2 cloves garlic, minced
3 tablespoons chopped green chiles
1 teaspoon chili powder, divided
¼ teaspoon ground cumin
¼ teaspoon pepper
3 drops of hot sauce
1¼ cups (5 ounces) shredded 40% less-fat Cheddar cheese
1 large tomato, chopped
Vegetable cooking spray
10 cups shredded iceberg lettuce
¾ cup low-fat sour cream
2 drops of hot sauce
Fresh cilantro sprigs (optional)

Wrap tortillas in aluminum foil, and bake at 325° for 15 minutes or until thoroughly heated.

Combine ground pork, onion, and garlic in a large nonstick skillet; cook over medium heat until browned, stirring to crumble. Drain and pat dry with paper towels. Wipe pan drippings from skillet with a paper towel.

Spicy Fiesta Burritos are served on a bed of shredded lettuce and drizzled with a low-fat sour cream topping.

Return meat mixture to skillet; stir in green chiles, ½ teaspoon chili powder, cumin, pepper, and 3 drops of hot sauce.

Spoon ⅓ cup meat mixture onto each tortilla; top with 2 tablespoons cheese and tomato. Roll up and secure with wooden picks; place seam side up in an 11- x 7- x 2-inch baking dish that has been coated with cooking spray. Cover and bake at 350° for 20 minutes.

To serve, place each burrito on 1 cup lettuce. Combine sour cream, remaining ½ teaspoon chili powder, and 2 drops of hot sauce. Drizzle sour cream mixture over each burrito. Garnish with fresh cilantro sprigs, if desired. Yield: 10 servings (286 calories per serving).

PROTEIN 17.4 / FAT 12.5 / CARBOHYDRATE 27.7 / CHOLESTEROL 39 / IRON 1.7 / SODIUM 144 / CALCIUM 179

ANOTHER ADVANTAGE TO BEING ACTIVE

The positive relationship between regular exercise and cardiovascular fitness is well established. Now, studies suggest that even moderate levels of activity such as walking to work or a weekend tennis game may have more health benefits than previously thought. Researchers at the Centers for Disease Control reviewed studies linking heart disease risk factors and inactivity. They found a sedentary lifestyle to be as much a risk factor as a high cholesterol level, hypertension, or heavy smoking. This news is alarming since the number of sedentary Americans (at least 40 percent) is much higher than the number who have high cholesterol (25 to 40 percent), hypertension (36 percent), or who smoke (30 percent).

BURGUNDY-MUSHROOM MEAT LOAF

¼ cup reduced-calorie catsup
2 tablespoons Burgundy or other dry
  red wine
1½ pounds lean ground pork
1 (4-ounce) can mushroom stems and pieces,
  drained and chopped
1 cup soft whole wheat breadcrumbs
¼ cup finely chopped green pepper
¼ cup minced onion
1 egg, beaten
½ teaspoon dry mustard
½ teaspoon garlic powder
¼ teaspoon coarsely ground pepper
Vegetable cooking spray

Combine catsup and wine; stirring mixture well. Set aside.

Combine ground pork and remaining ingredients, except cooking spray, in a large bowl; stir well. Add 3 tablespoons catsup mixture to pork mixture; stir well. Shape pork mixture into a 10- x 4-inch loaf.

Place loaf on rack of broiler pan that has been coated with cooking spray. Pour remaining catsup mixture over meat loaf, and bake at 350° for 1 hour. Yield: 10 servings (173 calories per serving).

PROTEIN 16.0 / FAT 8.8 / CARBOHYDRATE 6.4 / CHOLESTEROL 76 / IRON 0.9 / SODIUM 100 / CALCIUM 18

THE MYSTERY OF METABOLISM

The body uses calories to turn food into energy for activities such as digestion, breathing, and maintaining muscle tone and heart activity, as well as for exercise. Any excess calories become body fat. Now, researchers report that the body requires more calories to process complex carbohydrates than it does to process fats. For example, if you have consumed 100 more carbohydrate calories than your body needs, the body will burn about 23 calories of the 100 calories to convert them to fat. This leaves a net gain of 77 calories to be stored as fat. But if you have eaten 100 extra calories of fat, the body will use only a very efficient 3 calories to process the food, leaving a full 97 calories to be stored as fat.

In addition, scientists believe that carbohydrates stimulate the metabolism more than fat does. Thus, the body may burn a few more calories even after digestion is complete. For these reasons, you will gain a little less weight from eating 1,000 extra calories of bread, rice, or pasta than from eating 1,000 extra calories of fat.

Baby carrots and a rich wine sauce make Cornish Hens with Mushroom-Wine Sauce (page 164) something special.

Poultry

HONEY-BAKED CHICKEN

1 (3-pound) broiler-fryer, skinned
Vegetable cooking spray
¾ cup shredded yellow squash
¾ cup shredded zucchini
½ cup finely chopped onion
½ cup finely chopped celery
1 clove garlic, crushed
1¼ cups toasted whole wheat breadcrumbs
1 egg, beaten
¼ cup chopped pecans
¼ teaspoon salt
¼ teaspoon pepper
3 tablespoons unsweetened apple juice
2 tablespoons honey

Discard giblets and neck of chicken. Rinse chicken under cold, running water, and pat dry. Set aside.

Coat a large nonstick skillet with cooking spray; place over medium-high heat until hot. Add yellow squash, zucchini, onion, celery, and garlic, and sauté until crisp-tender. Drain. Combine vegetable mixture, breadcrumbs, egg, pecans, salt, and pepper in a medium bowl; stir well. Place chicken, breast side up, on a rack in a roasting pan that has been coated with cooking spray. Stuff lightly with dressing mixture. Truss chicken.

Combine apple juice and honey, stirring well. Brush chicken with half of apple juice-honey mixture. Bake at 350° for 1½ to 2 hours or until drumsticks are easy to move and juices run clear, basting occasionally with remaining apple juice-honey mixture. Yield: 6 servings (266 calories per serving).

PROTEIN 26.8 / FAT 10.8 / CARBOHYDRATE 15.6 / CHOLESTEROL 119 / IRON 1.8 / SODIUM 246 / CALCIUM 45

CRISPY MUSTARD CHICKEN

2 tablespoons reduced-calorie mayonnaise
2 tablespoons prepared mustard
¼ cup wheat germ
⅓ cup fine, dry breadcrumbs
½ teaspoon ground thyme
¼ teaspoon salt
4 (4-ounce) skinned, boned chicken breast halves
Vegetable cooking spray

Combine mayonnaise and mustard in a small bowl; stir well. Combine wheat germ and next 3 ingredients in a shallow bowl. Brush each chicken breast with mustard mixture; dredge in breadcrumb mixture.

Place chicken in a 10- x 6- x 2-inch baking dish that has been coated with cooking spray. Cover and bake at 350° for 40 minutes. Uncover and bake an additional 20 minutes or until chicken is tender. Yield: 4 servings (206 calories per serving).

PROTEIN 29.9 / FAT 5.2 / CARBOHYDRATE 10.0 / CHOLESTEROL 69 / IRON 2.0 / SODIUM 435 / CALCIUM 38

DILLED CHICKEN AND ARTICHOKES

3 tablespoons all-purpose flour
½ teaspoon pepper
½ teaspoon grated lemon rind
6 (4-ounce) skinned, boned chicken breast halves
Vegetable cooking spray
1 tablespoon plus 1½ teaspoons margarine
3 cups sliced fresh mushrooms
1 (9-ounce) package frozen artichoke hearts, thawed and halved
¼ cup Chablis or other dry white wine
1 tablespoon lemon juice
1 teaspoon dried whole dillweed
Lemon slices (optional)
Fresh dillweed sprigs (optional)

Combine flour, pepper, and lemon rind; dredge chicken in flour mixture.

Coat a large nonstick skillet with cooking spray; add margarine. Place over medium-high heat until hot. Add chicken, and cook 5 minutes on each side or until browned. Add mushrooms and artichokes. Cover and cook 3 to 5 minutes, stirring occasionally.

Combine wine, lemon juice, and dillweed, and pour over chicken. Cover, reduce heat, and simmer 5 minutes. Transfer chicken to a serving platter. If desired, garnish with lemon slices and fresh dillweed sprigs. Yield: 6 servings (195 calories per serving).

PROTEIN 28.6 / FAT 4.8 / CARBOHYDRATE 9.1 / CHOLESTEROL 66 / IRON 1.7 / SODIUM 130 / CALCIUM 29

GRILLED LIME CHICKEN

¼ cup chopped fresh parsley
½ teaspoon freshly ground pepper
½ teaspoon grated lime rind
2 tablespoons lime juice
1 cup Chablis or other dry white wine
6 (4-ounce) skinned, boned chicken breast halves
Vegetable cooking spray
Lime slices (optional)

Combine first 5 ingredients in a shallow baking dish. Add chicken, turning to coat. Cover and marinate in refrigerator 1 hour.

Remove chicken from marinade, reserving marinade. Coat grill rack with cooking spray; place on grill over medium-hot coals. Place chicken on rack, and cook 5 minutes on each side or until done, basting with reserved marinade. Garnish with lime slices, if desired. Yield: 6 servings (146 calories per serving).

PROTEIN 25.8 / FAT 2.9 / CARBOHYDRATE 2.4 / CHOLESTEROL 70 / IRON 1.2 / SODIUM 64 / CALCIUM 21

PINEAPPLE-GRILLED CHICKEN

1 (8-ounce) can unsweetened pineapple slices, undrained
½ cup unsweetened apple juice
1 tablespoon honey
1 teaspoon chicken-flavored bouillon granules
2 tablespoons raisins
Vegetable cooking spray
4 (4-ounce) skinned, boned chicken breast halves

Drain pineapple, reserving juice; set pineapple slices aside.

Combine pineapple juice, apple juice, honey, and bouillon granules in a small nonaluminum saucepan. Bring to a boil. Add raisins. Cover; reduce heat, and simmer 5 minutes. Remove raisins with a slotted spoon; set raisins and juice mixture aside.

Coat grill rack with cooking spray; place on grill over medium-hot coals. Place pineapple slices on rack; cook 3 minutes on each side. Set aside. Place chicken on rack; cook 15 minutes or until chicken is tender, turning and basting frequently with reserved juice mixture.

Place chicken on a serving platter. Top each breast half with a grilled pineapple slice. Spoon any remaining juice mixture over pineapple. Sprinkle raisins evenly over pineapple. Yield: 4 servings (221 calories per serving).

PROTEIN 26.0 / FAT 3.6 / CARBOHYDRATE 20.7 / CHOLESTEROL 70 / IRON 1.2 / SODIUM 273 / CALCIUM 17

SPANISH SAFFRON CHICKEN

6 (4-ounce) skinned, boned chicken breast halves
¼ teaspoon freshly ground pepper
Vegetable cooking spray
1 medium onion, sliced
1 clove garlic, minced
½ pound fresh mushrooms, sliced
1 cup water
2 teaspoons paprika
1 teaspoon chicken-flavored bouillon granules
½ teaspoon saffron threads
1 cup frozen English peas
2 tablespoons sliced pitted ripe olives
¼ cup skim milk
1 tablespoon cornstarch
2 tablespoons water
3 cups hot cooked long-grain rice (cooked without salt or fat)

Sprinkle chicken with pepper. Place in a large Dutch oven that has been coated with cooking spray. Cook over medium heat until browned.

Wipe pan drippings from Dutch oven with a paper towel. Coat Dutch oven with cooking spray; place over medium-high heat until hot. Add onion, garlic, and mushrooms; sauté until tender. Add chicken, 1 cup water, and next 3 ingredients. Bring to a boil. Cover, reduce heat, and simmer 25 minutes or until chicken is tender. Remove chicken, and set aside.

Add peas, olives, and milk to Dutch oven. Cover and simmer 5 minutes. Combine cornstarch and 2 tablespoons water; add to vegetable mixture. Bring to a boil. Reduce heat; cook, stirring constantly, until thickened and bubbly. Remove from heat. To serve, place rice on a serving platter. Arrange chicken over rice; top with vegetable mixture. Yield: 6 servings (335 calories per serving).

PROTEIN 31.2 / FAT 4.4 / CARBOHYDRATE 40.7 / CHOLESTEROL 71 / IRON 3.2 / SODIUM 275 / CALCIUM 56

CHICKEN-PEPPER GNOCCHI

Vegetable cooking spray
1½ cups chopped sweet red pepper
½ cup chopped green pepper
1 cup chopped onion
3 cloves garlic, minced
¼ teaspoon ground cumin
¼ teaspoon crushed red pepper
¼ teaspoon salt
1 tablespoon all-purpose flour
1 teaspoon chicken-flavored bouillon granules
½ cup water
½ (16-ounce) package gnocchi pasta, uncooked
4 (4-ounce) skinned, boned chicken breast halves
1 (6-ounce) package frozen snow pea pods

Coat a large nonstick skillet with cooking spray; place over medium-high heat until hot. Add sweet red pepper and next 5 ingredients, and sauté until tender. Stir in salt, flour, and bouillon granules. Gradually add water; bring to a boil, stirring constantly. Remove from heat, and pour into container of an electric blender or food processor; top with cover, and process until smooth. Set aside and keep warm.

Cook pasta according to package directions, omitting salt and fat. Drain and set aside.

Coat a nonstick skillet with cooking spray; place over medium heat until hot. Add chicken; sauté until browned. Add snow peas; cover and cook 1 to 2 minutes. Add chicken and vegetable mixture to pasta; toss gently. Yield: 6 servings (216 calories per serving).

PROTEIN 22.8 / FAT 2.2 / CARBOHYDRATE 25.8 / CHOLESTEROL 44 / IRON 2.6 / SODIUM 294 / CALCIUM 48

SPICY CHICKEN FETTUCCINE

6 ounces fettuccine, uncooked
Vegetable cooking spray
1 tablespoon margarine
4 (4-ounce) skinned, boned chicken breast halves, cut into 1-inch pieces
½ cup chopped green onions
½ cup chopped celery
½ cup chopped sweet red pepper
2 tablespoons chopped fresh parsley
2 teaspoons paprika
1 teaspoon onion powder
1 teaspoon garlic powder
½ teaspoon dried whole thyme
½ teaspoon dried whole oregano
½ teaspoon chicken-flavored bouillon granules
¼ teaspoon ground red pepper
½ cup water
1 tablespoon lemon juice

Cook fettuccine according to package directions, omitting salt and fat. Drain well, and set fettuccine aside.

Coat a large nonstick skillet with cooking spray; add margarine. Place over medium-high heat until hot. Add chicken, and sauté until browned. Add green onions, celery, and sweet red pepper; sauté until crisp-tender. Stir in parsley and remaining ingredients. Cover and simmer 5 minutes. Combine fettuccine and chicken mixture, tossing gently. Serve immediately. Yield: 6 servings (215 calories per serving).

PROTEIN 21.8 / FAT 4.6 / CARBOHYDRATE 22.8 / CHOLESTEROL 44 / IRON 2.3 / SODIUM 153 / CALCIUM 39

WALKING WITH HANDWEIGHTS—ARE THERE ADVANTAGES?

Walking is one of the most popular and enjoyable modes of exercise. It appeals to all ages and plays a vital role in developing cardiovascular fitness and assisting in weight loss.

Recently, attention has been given to using handheld weights while walking. Numerous studies, including several published in the *Journal of the American College of Sports Medicine*, suggest that while there are advantages, precautions are necessary.

Start with a well-established walking program before adding handweights to the routine. Select light weights, one pound each, and gradually build up to weights of as much as three pounds each. If you have high blood pressure, your doctor may discourage the use of hand weights because they may elevate blood pressure to unsafe levels.

Bending the elbows and swinging the arms when using handweights will help tone muscles of the arms, shoulders, and upper back while increasing the calorie expenditure 5 to 10 percent.

Tropical Chicken Kabobs combine the fresh flavors of lime, papaya, and pineapple.

TROPICAL CHICKEN KABOBS

⅓ cup lime juice
1 tablespoon vegetable oil
1 tablespoon honey
6 (4-ounce) skinned, boned chicken breast halves,
  cut into 1½-inch pieces
12 pearl onions, peeled
1 large green pepper, seeded and cut into 2-inch
  pieces
1 papaya, peeled, seeded, and cut into 2-inch
  pieces
1½ cups fresh pineapple chunks
Vegetable cooking spray

Combine lime juice, vegetable oil, and honey in a shallow dish. Add chicken; toss gently. Cover and marinate in refrigerator 8 hours, stirring occasionally. Remove chicken from marinade, reserving marinade. Alternate chicken, onion, pepper, papaya, and pineapple on 6 (12-inch) skewers. Coat grill rack with cooking spray; place on grill over medium-hot coals. Place kabobs on rack, and cook 15 to 20 minutes or until done, turning and basting frequently with reserved marinade. Yield: 6 servings (222 calories per serving).

PROTEIN 26.6 / FAT 5.7 / CARBOHYDRATE 16.4 / CHOLESTEROL 70 / IRON 1.5 / SODIUM 66 / CALCIUM 36

CURRIED CHICKEN DINNER

2½ cups water
1 cup uncooked brown rice
1½ teaspoons chicken-flavored bouillon
    granules
6 (6-ounce) skinned chicken breast
    halves
2½ cups water
½ teaspoon curry powder
¼ teaspoon salt
2 cups unsweetened orange juice
2 tablespoons cornstarch
2 tablespoons dry sherry
1 teaspoon ground ginger
1 teaspoon grated orange rind
Vegetable cooking spray
2 cups diagonally sliced celery
1 large sweet red pepper, seeded and
    cut into julienne strips
1 green pepper, seeded and cut into
    julienne strips

Combine water, rice, and bouillon granules in a medium saucepan; bring to a boil. Cover, reduce heat, and simmer 50 minutes or until liquid is absorbed.

Combine chicken, 2½ cups water, curry, and salt in a large Dutch oven; bring to a boil. Cover, reduce heat, and simmer 30 minutes or until chicken is tender; drain. Bone chicken, and cut into bite-size pieces; set meat aside.

Combine orange juice and next 4 ingredients in a small bowl, stirring until cornstarch is dissolved; set aside.

Coat a large nonstick skillet with cooking spray; place over medium-high heat until hot. Add celery and peppers, and sauté until crisp-tender. Stir in reserved chicken and orange juice mixture; bring to a boil. Cook 1 minute, stirring constantly, until thickened. To serve, spoon chicken mixture over hot cooked rice. Yield: 6 servings (332 calories per serving).

PROTEIN 32.1 / FAT 4.5 / CARBOHYDRATE 39.3 / CHOLESTEROL 78 / IRON 2.2 / SODIUM 409 / CALCIUM 51

CREAMY CHICKEN POPOVERS

2 cups water
3 (6-ounce) skinned chicken breast
    halves
1 large carrot, scraped and sliced
1 small onion, sliced
Vegetable cooking spray
1 small onion, chopped
¼ teaspoon dried whole tarragon
½ cup plain low-fat yogurt
¼ cup Chablis or other dry white wine
½ cup frozen English peas, thawed
2 tablespoons chopped pimiento
1¼ cups all-purpose flour, divided
¼ teaspoon salt
2 eggs
1¾ cups skim milk, divided

Combine water, chicken, carrot, and onion in a large saucepan. Bring to a boil; cover, reduce heat, and simmer 30 minutes. Remove chicken from broth; cool. Bone chicken, and cut meat into 1-inch pieces. Set aside. Strain broth, reserving ¾ cup.

Coat a large nonstick skillet with cooking spray; place over medium-high heat until hot. Add onion, and sauté until tender. Gradually add ¼ cup flour and tarragon, stirring well. Gradually stir in ¾ cup milk, yogurt, wine, and reserved chicken broth. Cook, stirring constantly, until mixture is thickened and bubbly. Stir in peas, pimiento, and reserved chicken. Set aside, and keep warm.

Combine remaining 1 cup flour and salt, stirring well. Add eggs and remaining 1 cup milk; beat with a wire whisk until well blended. Spoon mixture evenly into 6 (6-ounce) custard cups that have been coated with cooking spray. Place 4 inches apart on a baking sheet. Bake at 400° for 45 to 50 minutes or until golden brown. Break open each popover. Spoon ½ cup chicken mixture over each popover. Serve immediately. Yield: 6 servings (276 calories per serving).

PROTEIN 25.4 / FAT 3.9 / CARBOHYDRATE 33.1 / CHOLESTEROL 133 / IRON 2.2 / SODIUM 236 / CALCIUM 162

Chicken-Vegetable Pot Pies make a simple-to-prepare supper with down-home flavor.

CHICKEN-VEGETABLE POT PIES

2 (6-ounce) skinned chicken breast halves
2½ cups water
2 medium baking potatoes, peeled and cut into ½-inch cubes
½ cup chopped celery
1 teaspoon chicken-flavored bouillon granules
1 (10-ounce) package frozen mixed vegetables
2 tablespoons unsalted margarine
2 tablespoons all-purpose flour
1 cup skim milk
1 teaspoon poultry seasoning
1 (4-ounce) can sliced mushrooms, drained
Vegetable cooking spray
1 cup all-purpose flour
1 teaspoon baking powder
¼ teaspoon salt
1 tablespoon plus 1½ teaspoons unsalted margarine
½ cup nonfat buttermilk

Combine chicken and water in a large saucepan. Bring to a boil. Cover, reduce heat, and simmer 30 minutes or until chicken is tender. Remove chicken, reserving broth. Bone chicken, and cut meat into bite-size pieces; set aside.

Add potatoes, celery, and bouillon to broth; bring to a boil. Cover, reduce heat, and simmer 15 to 20 minutes or until potatoes are tender. Stir in mixed vegetables; set aside.

Melt 2 tablespoons unsalted margarine in a heavy saucepan over low heat; add 2 tablespoons flour, stirring until smooth. Cook 1 minute, stirring constantly. Gradually add milk; cook over medium heat, stirring constantly, until mixture is thickened and bubbly. Remove from heat, and stir in poultry seasoning.

Combine reserved chicken, vegetable mixture, white sauce, and mushrooms in a large bowl. Spoon into individual baking dishes that have been coated with cooking spray.

Combine 1 cup flour, baking powder, and salt in a small bowl. Cut in 1 tablespoon plus 1½ teaspoons unsalted margarine with a pastry blender until mixture resembles coarse meal. Stir in buttermilk. Spoon biscuit dough into 6 portions over chicken mixture. Bake at 350° for 1 hour or until biscuits are golden brown. Yield: 6 servings (314 calories per serving).

PROTEIN 18.6 / FAT 8.2 / CARBOHYDRATE 41.0 / CHOLESTEROL 27 / IRON 2.2 / SODIUM 458 / CALCIUM 116

OVEN-FRIED CHICKEN THIGHS

½ cup corn flake crumbs
½ teaspoon paprika
¼ teaspoon onion powder
¼ teaspoon ground oregano
¼ teaspoon dry mustard
¼ cup evaporated skimmed milk
4 (6-ounce) chicken thighs, skinned
Vegetable cooking spray

Combine crumbs and next 4 ingredients in a shallow bowl; stir well. Pour milk into a small shallow bowl. Dip each chicken thigh in milk; dredge in corn flake mixture.

Place chicken in an 8- x 8- x 2-inch baking dish that has been coated with cooking spray. Bake, uncovered, at 350° for 1 hour or until chicken is done. Yield: 4 servings (118 calories per serving).

PROTEIN 13.3 / FAT 2.5 / CARBOHYDRATE 9.9 / CHOLESTEROL 49 / IRON 1.3 / SODIUM 155 / CALCIUM 55

CORNISH HENS WITH MUSHROOM-WINE SAUCE

Vegetable cooking spray
1 teaspoon vegetable oil
½ cup minced green onions
¼ cup minced carrot
1 tablespoon all-purpose flour
¾ cup Chablis or other dry white wine
¾ cup water
½ teaspoon chicken-flavored bouillon granules
½ teaspoon dried whole rosemary
¼ teaspoon dried whole thyme
¼ teaspoon garlic powder
1 bay leaf
½ pound fresh mushrooms, halved
4 (1½-pound) Cornish hens, skinned
1 teaspoon coarsely ground pepper
1 (12-ounce) package baby carrots, scraped
2 stalks celery, cut diagonally into 1-inch pieces
Fresh thyme sprigs (optional)

Coat a large nonstick skillet with cooking spray; add oil. Place over medium-high heat until hot. Add onions and carrot; sauté until crisp-tender. Stir in flour. Cook over medium

heat 1 minute, stirring constantly. Stir in wine and next 7 ingredients. Bring to a boil. Reduce heat; simmer 5 to 10 minutes, stirring often.

Remove giblets from hens; reserve for other uses. Rinse hens with cold, running water, and pat dry. Split each hen in half lengthwise, using an electric knife. Sprinkle with pepper.

Coat a roasting pan with cooking spray. Place hens, cut side down, in pan. Spoon mushroom sauce over top. Cover and bake at 350° for 45 minutes, basting frequently. Add baby carrots and celery. Cover and bake an additional 20 minutes or until vegetables are crisp-tender and hens are done. Remove and discard bay leaf. Garnish with fresh thyme sprigs, if desired. Yield: 8 servings (240 calories per serving).

PROTEIN 36.3 / FAT 6.1 / CARBOHYDRATE 8.7 / CHOLESTEROL 114 / IRON 2.4 / SODIUM 204 / CALCIUM 46

SOUTHERN STUFFED TURKEY BREAST

½ cup cornmeal
¼ cup all-purpose flour
1 teaspoon baking powder
½ teaspoon poultry seasoning
¼ teaspoon baking soda
¼ teaspoon salt
¼ teaspoon rubbed sage
½ cup nonfat buttermilk
1 egg, beaten
Vegetable cooking spray
¼ cup finely chopped celery
3 tablespoons chopped onion
1 (8-ounce) can sliced water chestnuts, drained and chopped
1 egg, slightly beaten
¾ teaspoon chicken-flavored bouillon granules
¼ teaspoon pepper
1 (3-pound) boneless turkey breast, skinned
1 tablespoon margarine, melted
1 tablespoon honey
Baby corn (optional)
Fresh sage leaves (optional)
Fresh celery leaves (optional)

Combine first 7 ingredients in a medium bowl; make a well in center of mixture. Combine buttermilk and egg; add to dry ingredients, stirring

Southern Stuffed Turkey Breast is a flavorful way to enjoy turkey throughout the year.

just until moistened. Spoon cornbread mixture into a preheated 6-inch cast-iron skillet that has been coated with cooking spray. Bake at 400° for 16 to 18 minutes or until browned. Let cool.

Coat a small nonstick skillet with cooking spray; place over medium-high heat until hot. Add celery and onion, and sauté until tender.

Crumble cornbread into a large bowl. Add sautéed celery and onion, water chestnuts, egg, bouillon granules, and pepper; stir well.

Lay turkey breast flat on wax paper, skin side down. Remove tendons, skin, and fat, keeping meat intact. From center, slice horizontally (parallel with skin) through thickest part of each side of breast almost to outer edge; flip cut piece and breast fillets over to enlarge breast. Pound breast to ½-inch thickness.

Spoon stuffing mixture in center of turkey breast, leaving a 2-inch border at sides. Roll up turkey breast over filling, starting from bottom. Tie turkey breast securely at 2-inch intervals with string. Place seam side down on a rack in a shallow roasting pan that has been coated with cooking spray. Insert meat thermometer. Bake, covered, at 325° for 30 minutes.

Combine margarine and honey; brush over turkey. Bake, uncovered, 1½ hours or until meat thermometer registers 185°. Transfer turkey to a cutting board; remove string. Let stand 10 minutes before slicing. If desired, garnish with baby corn and fresh sage and celery leaves. Yield: 10 servings (210 calories per serving).

PROTEIN 29.9 / FAT 3.4 / CARBOHYDRATE 13.1 / CHOLESTEROL 130 / IRON 2.0 / SODIUM 274 / CALCIUM 46

SWEET-AND-SOUR TURKEY MEATBALLS

1 (20-ounce) can unsweetened pineapple
  chunks, undrained
1 (1-pound) package frozen raw
  ground turkey, thawed
1 egg, lightly beaten
1 cup soft breadcrumbs
½ teaspoon salt
½ teaspoon ground ginger
Vegetable cooking spray
3 green onions, cut into 1-inch pieces
1 large clove garlic, minced
2 teaspoons cornstarch
2 tablespoons cider vinegar
1 tablespoon brown sugar
1 (6-ounce) package frozen snow
  pea pods, thawed

Drain pineapple chunks, reserving ¼ cup juice; set aside.

Combine ground turkey, beaten egg, breadcrumbs, salt, and ground ginger in a large bowl; stir well. Shape turkey mixture into 1¼-inch meatballs.

Coat a large nonstick skillet with cooking spray; place over medium-high heat until hot. Add meatballs, and cook until lightly browned. Remove meatballs from skillet; set aside and keep warm. Add onions and garlic to skillet, and sauté until tender. Remove from heat.

Combine reserved pineapple juice and cornstarch in a small bowl, stirring until smooth. Add cornstarch mixture, cider vinegar, and sugar to skillet. Bring to a boil, stirring constantly. Boil 1 minute or until slightly thickened. Add reserved turkey meatballs, pineapple chunks, and snow peas to skillet. Cook 3 to 5 minutes or until snow peas are crisp-tender. Yield: 6 servings (184 calories per serving).

PROTEIN 19.3 / FAT 3.8 / CARBOHYDRATE 18.0 / CHOLESTEROL 95 /
IRON 2.4 / SODIUM 305 / CALCIUM 45

ROSEMARY TURKEY PATTIES

1 (1-pound) package frozen raw ground
  turkey, thawed
¼ cup soft whole wheat breadcrumbs
1 egg, slightly beaten
3 tablespoons finely minced onion
2 tablespoons chopped fresh parsley
½ teaspoon salt
½ teaspoon dried whole thyme
¼ teaspoon dried whole rosemary, crushed
Vegetable cooking spray
Rosemary Sauce
Chopped fresh parsley (optional)

Combine turkey and next 7 ingredients, stirring well. Shape into 6 patties.

Place patties in a 12- x 8- x 2-inch baking dish that has been coated with cooking spray. Bake, uncovered, at 350° for 30 to 45 minutes, or until done, turning once. Spoon Rosemary Sauce evenly over patties. Sprinkle with parsley, if desired. Yield: 6 servings (149 calories per serving).

Rosemary Sauce:

1 tablespoon margarine
½ cup chopped onion
1 clove garlic, minced
1 tablespoon all-purpose flour
½ teaspoon dried whole rosemary, crushed
½ teaspoon chicken-flavored bouillon granules
¼ cup plus 2 tablespoons water
¼ cup plus 2 tablespoons skim milk

Melt margarine in a small saucepan. Add onion and garlic; sauté until tender. Add flour and rosemary; cook, stirring constantly, 1 minute. Gradually add bouillon granules, water, and milk. Cook over medium heat, stirring constantly, until thickened. Yield: ¾ cup.

PROTEIN 18.8 / FAT 5.4 / CARBOHYDRATE 5.3 / CHOLESTEROL 95 /
IRON 1.7 / SODIUM 376 / CALCIUM 51

*Creamy Shrimp-Asparagus Salad
(page 177) is a shrimp-lover's
delight.*

Salads & Salad Dressings

BRANDIED FRUIT MOLDS

1 cup diced fresh nectarines
1 cup diced fresh plums
3 tablespoons brandy
2½ cups unsweetened pineapple juice
⅓ cup unsweetened orange juice
½ teaspoon whole cloves
½ teaspoon whole allspice
2 (2-inch) sticks cinnamon
½ cup unsweetened pineapple juice, chilled
2 envelopes unflavored gelatin
Vegetable cooking spray
Lettuce leaves (optional)

Combine nectarines and plums in a small bowl; sprinkle with brandy. Cover and let stand 1 hour at room temperature.

Combine 2½ cups pineapple juice and next 4 ingredients in a saucepan; bring to a boil. Cover, reduce heat, and simmer 10 minutes. Strain into a large bowl.

Sprinkle unflavored gelatin over ½ cup chilled pineapple juice; let stand 1 minute.

Combine hot pineapple juice mixture and gelatin mixture, stirring until gelatin dissolves. Chill until the consistency of unbeaten egg whites.

Fold in reserved fruit mixture. Pour into individual ½-cup molds that have been coated with cooking spray. Cover and chill until set. Unmold on lettuce-lined salad plates, if desired. Yield: 10 servings (79 calories per ½-cup serving).

PROTEIN 1.8 / FAT 0.5 / CARBOHYDRATE 15.2 / CHOLESTEROL 0 / IRON 0.2 / SODIUM 3 / CALCIUM 15

TROPICAL LAYERED SALAD

¼ cup plain low-fat yogurt
½ cup low-fat cottage cheese
1 medium banana, mashed
2 teaspoons lemon juice
½ teaspoon rum extract
¼ pound fresh spinach
2 cups cubed fresh pineapple
1 papaya, peeled, seeded, and cubed
2 medium bananas, sliced
2 oranges, peeled and thinly sliced
2 tablespoons unsweetened grated coconut,
    toasted

Combine yogurt, cottage cheese, banana, lemon juice, and rum extract in container of an electric blender; top with cover, and process until smooth. Set yogurt mixture aside.

Remove stems from spinach; wash leaves thoroughly, and pat dry. Tear into bite-size pieces.

In a large glass serving bowl, layer spinach, pineapple, papaya, sliced banana, and oranges. Top with yogurt mixture. Sprinkle with coconut. Serve immediately. Yield: 10 servings (93 calories per 1-cup serving).

PROTEIN 3.2 / FAT 1.4 / CARBOHYDRATE 19.0 / CHOLESTEROL 1 / IRON 0.8 / SODIUM 65 / CALCIUM 55

SEVEN-FRUIT SALAD

1 (6-ounce) can frozen limeade concentrate
3 tablespoons sugar
1 tablespoon all-purpose flour
1 egg, beaten
2 tablespoons dry sherry
1 (11-ounce) can unsweetened mandarin
    oranges, drained
1 medium mango, peeled, seeded,
    and cubed
1½ cups diced fresh pineapple
1 cup pitted fresh sweet cherries
½ cup chopped jicama
3 fresh apricots, pitted and sliced
2 fresh plums, pitted and sliced
1 tablespoon sesame seeds, toasted

Prepare limeade concentrate according to package directions. Set aside.

Combine sugar and flour in a saucepan; stir well. Stir in egg. Add ¾ cup reserved limeade and sherry, stirring well. (Reserve remaining limeade for use in other recipes.) Cook over low heat, stirring constantly, until mixture is thickened. Cover and chill thoroughly.

Combine oranges, cubed mango, pineapple, cherries, chopped jicama, apricots, and plums in a large bowl; toss gently. Pour chilled limeade mixture over fruit mixture; toss gently. Sprinkle with toasted sesame seeds. Yield: 10 servings (89 calories per ½-cup serving).

PROTEIN 1.6 / FAT 1.5 / CARBOHYDRATE 18.6 / CHOLESTEROL 27 / IRON 0.5 / SODIUM 10 / CALCIUM 13

In Berry-Melon Salad, cantaloupe rings hold honeydew balls and fresh strawberries drizzled with poppy seed dressing.

BERRY-MELON SALAD

½ cup unsweetened orange juice
⅓ cup unsweetened grapefruit juice
3 tablespoons lemon juice
1 tablespoon cornstarch
2 teaspoons vegetable oil
2 teaspoons honey
1 teaspoon poppy seeds
2 medium cantaloupes
2 cups sliced fresh strawberries
2 cups honeydew melon balls
Fresh mint sprigs (optional)

Combine juices, cornstarch, vegetable oil, and honey in a saucepan, stirring well. Cook over medium heat, stirring constantly, until thickened and bubbly. Stir in poppy seeds. Cover and chill thoroughly.

Peel cantaloupe, and cut each melon into four ¾-inch slices. Place slices on individual salad plates. Combine strawberries and honeydew balls. Spoon ½ cup strawberry mixture over each cantaloupe slice. Spoon poppy seed mixture evenly over fruit. Garnish with fresh mint sprigs, if desired. Yield: 8 servings (111 calories per serving).

PROTEIN 1.9 / FAT 1.9 / CARBOHYDRATE 24.3 / CHOLESTEROL 0 / IRON 0.7 / SODIUM 18 / CALCIUM 32

PEACHY BULGUR SALAD

2 cups boiling water
1 cup bulgur wheat
1 cup diced fresh peaches
3 tablespoons unsweetened orange juice
1 tablespoon vegetable oil
1 tablespoon lime juice
½ teaspoon grated lime rind
½ teaspoon grated fresh gingerroot
¼ teaspoon crushed red pepper
⅛ teaspoon ground cinnamon
⅛ teaspoon ground cumin
2 cups fresh spinach leaves, cut into thin strips
1 medium-size fresh peach, peeled and cut into 8 slices

Pour water over bulgur in a large bowl. Add diced peaches, tossing gently. Combine orange juice and next 7 ingredients in a small bowl; stir well. Pour orange juice mixture over bulgur mixture; toss gently. Cover and chill thoroughly.

To serve, place spinach strips on a serving plate; spoon bulgar mixture over spinach, and top with peach slices. Yield: 8 servings (113 calories per ½-cup serving).

PROTEIN 3.1 / FAT 2.1 / CARBOHYDRATE 21.6 / CHOLESTEROL 0 / IRON 1.3 / SODIUM 12 / CALCIUM 24

MINTY APPLE-CUCUMBER SALAD

¼ cup plain low-fat yogurt
1 tablespoon lemon juice
1 tablespoon minced fresh mint leaves
1 large cucumber, peeled, seeded, and diced
1 medium Granny Smith apple, cored and cut into julienne strips
1 small Red Delicious apple, cored and cut into julienne strips
1 tablespoon plus 1½ teaspoons unsalted sunflower kernels, toasted

Combine first 3 ingredients in a large bowl; stir well. Cover and chill 1 hour.

Add diced cucumber, apple strips, and sunflower kernels to yogurt mixture; toss gently. Cover and chill thoroughly. Yield: 8 servings (33 calories per ½-cup serving).

PROTEIN 1.0 / FAT 1.1 / CARBOHYDRATE 5.7 / CHOLESTEROL 0 / IRON 0.3 / SODIUM 7 / CALCIUM 23

FRESH SPINACH-APPLE SALAD

1 pound fresh spinach
1 cup chopped apple
½ cup chopped celery
1 tablespoon lemon juice
¼ cup cider vinegar
¼ cup vegetable oil
2 teaspoons sugar
1 teaspoon caraway seeds
¼ teaspoon ground white pepper

Remove stems from spinach; wash leaves thoroughly, and pat dry. Tear into bite-size pieces.

Combine spinach, apple, and celery in a large bowl. Sprinkle with lemon juice; toss well. Combine vinegar and remaining ingredients in a small saucepan; bring to a boil. Pour over spinach mixture, and toss well. Serve immediately. Yield: 12 servings (70 calories per 1-cup serving).

PROTEIN 1.6 / FAT 4.8 / CARBOHYDRATE 6.6 / CHOLESTEROL 0 / IRON 1.5 / SODIUM 45 / CALCIUM 56

SPICED BEET AND PINEAPPLE SALAD

⅓ cup plus 2 tablespoons plain low-fat yogurt
1 tablespoon white wine vinegar
1 teaspoon sugar
¼ teaspoon ground cinnamon
¼ teaspoon ground cloves
1 (15¼-ounce) can sliced beets, rinsed and drained
1 cup unsweetened pineapple tidbits, drained
Lettuce leaves
2 tablespoons coarsely chopped walnuts

Combine yogurt and next 4 ingredients; stir well. Cover and chill thoroughly.

Combine beets and pineapple and arrange on a lettuce-lined serving platter. Spoon chilled yogurt mixture over beets. Sprinkle walnuts over top of salad. Serve immediately. Yield: 4 servings (95 calories per ½-cup serving).

PROTEIN 3.4 / FAT 3.0 / CARBOHYDRATE 15.6 / CHOLESTEROL 2 / IRON 0.8 / SODIUM 188 / CALCIUM 68

GARLICKY GREEN SALAD

1 cup nonfat buttermilk
3 cloves garlic, minced
2 tablespoons minced fresh parsley
2 tablespoons reduced-calorie mayonnaise
1 teaspoon cracked pepper
1 (14-ounce) can artichoke hearts, drained and quartered
1 (14-ounce) can hearts of palm, drained and sliced into ½-inch pieces
3 cups shredded Boston lettuce
2 cups shredded fresh spinach
1 cup shredded curly endive
1 cup torn fresh watercress
½ cup chopped celery
1 tablespoon chopped fresh chives

Combine buttermilk, garlic, parsley, mayonnaise, and pepper in a jar, cover tightly, and shake vigorously. Cover and chill 2 hours.

Combine artichoke hearts and remaining ingredients in a large serving bowl. Shake chilled dressing mixture and pour over salad. Toss salad lightly. Yield: 10 servings (57 calories per 1-cup serving).

PROTEIN 2.7 / FAT 1.0 / CARBOHYDRATE 11.0 / CHOLESTEROL 1 / IRON 0.8 / SODIUM 80 / CALCIUM 32

CALIFORNIA GREEN SALAD

½ cup plus 1 tablespoon low-fat cottage cheese
3 tablespoons skim milk
2 tablespoons chili sauce
1 teaspoon prepared mustard
½ teaspoon paprika
¼ teaspoon salt
1 tablespoon sweet pickle relish
2 teaspoons minced fresh parsley
1 teaspoon finely minced onion
4 cups shredded red leaf lettuce
4 cups shredded leaf lettuce
½ cup alfalfa sprouts
¼ cup raisins, coarsely chopped
2 tablespoons unsalted sunflower kernels

Combine first 6 ingredients in container of an electric blender; top with cover, and process

until smooth. Add relish, parsley, and onion; stir well. Cover and chill thoroughly.

Combine lettuce and alfalfa sprouts in a large bowl; toss gently. Arrange lettuce mixture on 8 serving plates. Top each serving with 2 tablespoons cottage cheese mixture. Top each serving with 1½ teaspoons raisins and ¾ teaspoon sunflower kernels. Yield: 8 servings (55 calories per ½-cup serving).

PROTEIN 3.4 / FAT 1.5 / CARBOHYDRATE 8.0 / CHOLESTEROL 1 / IRON 0.6 / SODIUM 222 / CALCIUM 33

CAESAR SALAD

2 slices thinly sliced white bread
Vegetable cooking spray
½ teaspoon garlic powder
1 clove garlic, halved
4 cups shredded romaine lettuce
2 eggs
¼ teaspoon dry mustard
3 tablespoons lemon juice
2 tablespoons water
2 teaspoons olive oil
2 teaspoons Worcestershire sauce
2 tablespoons grated Parmesan cheese
½ teaspoon cracked pepper

Coat bread lightly with cooking spray. Sprinkle with garlic powder. Place on an ungreased baking sheet. Bake at 300° for 20 minutes or until bread is golden brown. Cut bread into cubes, and set aside.

Rub inside of a large bowl with garlic halves; discard garlic. Place lettuce in bowl.

Pour water to a depth of 2 inches in a medium saucepan; bring water to a boil, and turn off heat. Carefully lower eggs into water using a slotted spoon; let stand 1 minute. Remove eggs from water and let cool.

Combine eggs, dry mustard, lemon juice, water, oil, and Worcestershire sauce, stirring well. Drizzle egg mixture over lettuce in bowl. Sprinkle with Parmesan cheese and pepper; toss lightly. Top evenly with reserved bread cubes. Yield: 8 servings (62 calories per ½-cup serving).

PROTEIN 3.2 / FAT 3.3 / CARBOHYDRATE 5.1 / CHOLESTEROL 70 / IRON 0.8 / SODIUM 87 / CALCIUM 42

SESAME SLAW

5 cups shredded cabbage (1 pound)
1 cup shredded carrot
½ cup thinly sliced radishes
2 tablespoons vinegar
2 tablespoons vegetable oil
1 teaspoon sesame oil
1 teaspoon spicy brown mustard
2 tablespoons sesame seeds, toasted

Combine cabbage, carrot, and radishes in a large bowl. Combine vinegar, oils, and mustard in a small bowl; stir with a wire whisk until well blended. Pour over cabbage mixture; toss lightly. Cover and refrigerate 8 hours. To serve, add sesame seeds; toss gently. Yield: 12 servings (45 calories per ½-cup serving).

PROTEIN 0.9 / FAT 3.6 / CARBOHYDRATE 3.0 / CHOLESTEROL 0 / IRON 0.4 / SODIUM 16 / CALCIUM 20

LEMONY FENNEL-GREEN BEAN SALAD

1½ pounds fennel
½ pound fresh green beans
6 ounces small fresh mushrooms, quartered
2 (2½- x ½-inch) strips lemon rind
¼ cup balsamic vinegar
2 tablespoons lemon juice
⅛ teaspoon salt
¼ cup water
2 tablespoons olive oil

Wash fennel; trim off leaves, reserving leaves. Mince leaves, reserving 3 tablespoons. Trim off tough outer stalks and discard. Cut bulb in half lengthwise and remove core. Cut crosswise into ⅛-inch slices. Set aside.

Wash beans and remove strings. Cut beans into 1-inch pieces. Cook in a small amount of boiling water 1 to 2 minutes or until crisp-tender; drain.

Combine reserved fennel slices, green beans, and mushrooms in a large bowl; toss gently. Cut lemon rind into very thin strips. Add to fennel mixture.

Place vinegar, lemon juice, salt, water, and olive oil in a small bowl; stir with a wire whisk until well blended. Stir in reserved minced fennel leaves. Pour dressing mixture over vegetables; toss gently. Cover and chill thoroughly. Serve with a slotted spoon. Yield: 12 servings (36 calories per ½-cup serving).

PROTEIN 1.2 / FAT 2.4 / CARBOHYDRATE 3.3 / CHOLESTEROL 0 / IRON 1.0 / SODIUM 28 / CALCIUM 30

FENNEL FINESSE

Enjoy the delicate flavor of fennel in Lemony Fennel-Green Bean Salad. To prepare the fennel, peel stems and cut out the core in the base of the bulb. Trim off the leaves and save to sprinkle over casseroles or salads.

To prepare for sautéing or stir-frying, thinly slice across the bulb on a diagonal. The core will help hold the slices together.

Store fennel in the refrigerator because the stalks stay fresh only 3 to 4 days before drying out and losing their unique flavor.

Fennel, which has only 13 calories per ½ cup, is a fair source of vitamin A, niacin, calcium, and iron.

MEXICAN BEAN SALAD

1 (16-ounce) can no-salt-added cut green beans, drained
1 (16-ounce) can wax beans, drained
1 (16-ounce) can kidney beans, rinsed and drained
1 (17-ounce) can no-salt-added whole kernel corn, drained
1 (4-ounce) can diced green chiles, drained
1 medium tomato, diced
½ cup thinly sliced green onions
2 tablespoons minced fresh parsley
2 tablespoons minced fresh cilantro
2 tablespoons vegetable oil
3 tablespoons red wine vinegar
2 teaspoons chili powder
1 teaspoon garlic powder
½ teaspoon hot sauce
¼ teaspoon pepper

Combine first 9 ingredients in a large bowl; toss gently.

Combine oil, red wine vinegar, chili powder, garlic powder, hot sauce, and pepper in a jar; cover tightly, and shake vigorously. Pour over vegetable mixture, and toss gently. Cover and chill 8 hours. Yield: 16 servings (65 calories per ½-cup serving).

PROTEIN 2.6 / FAT 1.9 / CARBOHYDRATE 10.6 / CHOLESTEROL 0 / IRON 1.1 / SODIUM 62 / CALCIUM 21

TANGY BROCCOLI-POTATO SALAD

½ pound new potatoes, peeled and
cut into ½-inch cubes
1 pound fresh broccoli
¼ cup white wine vinegar
2 tablespoons vegetable oil
2 tablespoons minced fresh
parsley
1 clove garlic, minced
1 teaspoon Worcestershire sauce
1 teaspoon prepared horseradish
2 green onions, thinly sliced
3 drops of hot sauce
1 hard-cooked egg, sliced

Cook potatoes in boiling water to cover until almost tender (about 10 minutes); drain. Set aside and keep warm.

Trim off large leaves of broccoli, and remove tough ends of lower stalks. Wash broccoli thoroughly. Cut away tops, and set aside. Cut stalks into ¼-inch slices. Cook broccoli tops and stalks in a small amount of boiling water 6 to 8 minutes or until crisp-tender; drain. Set aside and keep warm.

Combine white wine vinegar, vegetable oil, parsley, garlic, Worcestershire sauce, and horseradish in a small saucepan; bring to a boil. Remove from heat; stir in green onions and hot sauce. Arrange reserved potatoes and broccoli on a serving platter; pour hot vinegar mixture over vegetables. Top with egg slices. Serve immediately. Yield: 8 servings (81 calories per ½-cup serving).

PROTEIN 3.0 / FAT 4.3 / CARBOHYDRATE 8.6 / CHOLESTEROL 34 / IRON 0.9 / SODIUM 33 / CALCIUM 34

DILLED POTATO SALAD

4 medium baking potatoes
2 tablespoons lemon juice
1 teaspoon minced fresh dillweed
1 cucumber, peeled, seeded, and diced
1 medium-size green pepper, seeded and diced
1 medium tomato, seeded and diced
½ cup commercial reduced-calorie creamy Italian
dressing

Cook potatoes in boiling water to cover for 30 minutes or until tender. Drain and cool slightly. Peel and dice potatoes; place in a large bowl.

Combine lemon juice and dillweed, stirring well. Pour lemon juice mixture over potatoes, tossing gently. Add cucumber and remaining 3 ingredients to potato mixture; toss gently. Cover and chill thoroughly. Yield: 12 servings (81 calories per ½-cup serving).

PROTEIN 2.1 / FAT 0.2 / CARBOHYDRATE 18.5 / CHOLESTEROL 0 / IRON 0.9 / SODIUM 98 / CALCIUM 11

SPICY ZUCCHINI TOSS

1 pound fresh broccoli
1 medium zucchini, cut into julienne strips
2 carrots, scraped and cut into julienne strips
2 shallots, minced
2 cloves garlic, crushed
2 tablespoons minced fresh cilantro
¾ teaspoon crushed red pepper
¼ cup water
¼ cup lemon juice
2 tablespoons vegetable oil
2 green onions, finely chopped

Trim off large leaves of broccoli, and remove tough ends of lower stalks. Wash broccoli thoroughly. Cut away tops, and set aside. Cut stalks into ¼-inch slices. Combine broccoli tops and stalks, zucchini, and carrot in a large bowl. Set broccoli mixture aside.

Combine shallots, garlic, cilantro, and pepper; stir well. Add shallot mixture, water, lemon juice, and oil to broccoli mixture, tossing gently. Top with green onions. Yield: 8 servings (68 calories per 1-cup serving).

PROTEIN 2.5 / FAT 3.7 / CARBOHYDRATE 8.3 / CHOLESTEROL 0 / IRON 0.9 / SODIUM 26 / CALCIUM 44

CRUNCHY BROWN RICE SALAD

1 cup frozen English peas
2 cups cooked brown rice (cooked without salt or fat)
1 cup diced tomato
1 cup shredded carrot
½ cup diced Jerusalem artichokes
½ cup fresh bean sprouts, washed and drained
½ cup sliced green onions
¼ cup crumbled blue cheese
1 tablespoon plus 1½ teaspoons lemon juice
1 tablespoon vegetable oil
2 teaspoons Dijon mustard
½ teaspoon sugar
¼ teaspoon salt
¼ teaspoon ground white pepper
⅛ teaspoon ground red pepper

Cook peas according to package directions, omitting salt. Drain. Combine peas, rice, and next 6 ingredients in a large bowl. Set aside.

Combine lemon juice and remaining ingredients in a jar; cover tightly and shake vigorously. Pour over rice mixture, and toss well. Cover and chill 3 hours. Yield: 10 servings (93 calories per ½-cup serving).

PROTEIN 2.8 / FAT 2.6 / CARBOHYDRATE 14.9 / CHOLESTEROL 2 / IRON 0.9 / SODIUM 151 / CALCIUM 31

PEPPERY PASTA SALAD

2 cups penne pasta, uncooked
2 medium-size sweet red peppers, seeded and chopped
½ cup pepperocini, drained
¼ cup plus 2 teaspoons cider vinegar
2 tablespoons water
1 tablespoon vegetable oil
2 teaspoons minced fresh basil
1 teaspoon dried whole oregano
1 teaspoon garlic powder
2 tablespoons grated Parmesan cheese

Cook pasta according to package directions, omitting salt and fat; drain. Rinse with cold water; drain. Combine pasta, pepper, and pepperocini in a large bowl. Set aside.

Combine vinegar and next 5 ingredients in a small bowl; stir with a wire whisk until well blended. Pour vinegar mixture over pasta mixture; toss gently. Cover and chill 3 hours. Sprinkle with cheese before serving. Yield: 12 servings (78 calories per ½-cup serving).

PROTEIN 2.5 / FAT 1.7 / CARBOHYDRATE 13.3 / CHOLESTEROL 1 / IRON 0.9 / SODIUM 103 / CALCIUM 22

MARINATED MOZZARELLA SALAD

1 cup (4 ounces) part-skim mozzarella cheese, cut into ½-inch cubes
2 medium tomatoes, diced
1 medium cucumber, peeled and cubed
1 medium-size green pepper, seeded and chopped
6 radishes, sliced
½ cup chopped onion
½ cup white wine vinegar
2 tablespoons minced fresh parsley
2 tablespoons vegetable oil
1 tablespoon minced fresh basil
¼ teaspoon garlic powder
¼ teaspoon ground white pepper
4 drops of hot sauce

Combine first 6 ingredients in a large shallow dish; toss gently. Set aside.

Combine remaining ingredients; stir well, and pour mixture over vegetables. Toss gently. Cover and marinate in refrigerator 8 hours. Serve using a slotted spoon. Yield: 8 servings (87 calories per ½-cup serving).

PROTEIN 4.2 / FAT 5.9 / CARBOHYDRATE 4.5 / CHOLESTEROL 8 / IRON 0.6 / SODIUM 75 / CALCIUM 105

PASTA'S POPULAR—AND FOR GOOD REASON

Pasta, like most other complex carbohydrates, helps the body maintain a high energy level and provides a feeling of fullness. Yet, pasta is low in calories and fat. A half cup of plain cooked pasta has only 105 calories and little sodium.

Instead of drenching pasta in a rich cream sauce, try tossing it with reduced-calorie salad dressing and fresh vegetables. Mushrooms, onions, broccoli, and peppers make an eye-pleasing, nutritious dish. For a hearty main dish, add seafood or chicken. Try spicy Peppery Pasta Salad for a nutritious addition to almost any meal.

Warm Fajita Salad with Salsa is a spicy, satisfying main-dish salad

WARM FAJITA SALAD WITH SALSA

1 (1-pound) lean flank steak
¼ cup Burgundy or other dry red wine
¼ cup lime juice
½ teaspoon garlic powder
½ teaspoon ground cumin
2 cups seeded, diced tomato
1 small green pepper, seeded and diced
1 jalapeño pepper, seeded and diced
2 tablespoons diced purple onion
1 tablespoon minced fresh cilantro
2 teaspoons red wine vinegar
Vegetable cooking spray
6 cups torn romaine lettuce
½ cup (2 ounces) shredded extra-sharp Cheddar
   cheese

Trim fat from steak, and place in a large shallow dish. Combine red wine, lime juice, garlic powder, and cumin, stirring well; pour over steak. Cover and marinate in refrigerator 24 hours, turning steak occasionally.

Combine tomato and next 5 ingredients, stirring well. Set aside.

Remove steak from marinade; discard marinade. Place steak on rack in a broiler pan that has been coated with cooking spray. Broil steak 4 inches from heating element 12 to 17 minutes or to desired degree of doneness, turning once. Cut diagonally across grain into thin slices. Combine steak, lettuce, and cheese in a large bowl; toss gently. Spoon ⅓ cup salsa mixture over each serving. Serve warm. Yield: 6 servings (210 calories per serving).

PROTEIN 18.8 / FAT 12.2 / CARBOHYDRATE 5.7 / CHOLESTEROL 51 /
IRON 2.7 / SODIUM 117 / CALCIUM 100

FIRE-AND-ICE CHICKEN SALAD

½ teaspoon ground white pepper
½ teaspoon ground red pepper
½ teaspoon pepper
½ teaspoon garlic powder
4 (4-ounce) skinned, boned chicken breast halves
Vegetable cooking spray
2 cups finely shredded lettuce
1 medium-size sweet red pepper, seeded and diced
2 tablespoons reduced-calorie mayonnaise
2 tablespoons plain low-fat yogurt
1 tablespoon prepared horseradish

Combine first 4 ingredients in a small bowl. Rub pepper mixture evenly on chicken breast halves. Cover and chill 8 hours.

Coat a cast-iron skillet with cooking spray; place over medium-high heat until hot. Add chicken to skillet, and cook 6 minutes on each side or until done. Remove chicken; cover and chill 2 hours. Slice chicken across grain into ½-inch strips.

Combine lettuce and sweet red pepper; divide evenly among 4 individual serving plates. Arrange chicken evenly over salad mixture. Combine mayonnaise, yogurt, and horseradish in a small bowl, stirring well. Top each salad with 1 tablespoon of mayonnaise mixture. Yield: 4 servings (181 calories per serving).

PROTEIN 27.0 / FAT 5.5 / CARBOHYDRATE 4.6 / CHOLESTEROL 73 / IRON 1.6 / SODIUM 131 / CALCIUM 41

BAKED CHICKEN SALAD IN ARTICHOKES

4 medium artichokes
Lemon wedge
2 cups diced cooked chicken breast (skinned before cooking and cooked without salt)
½ cup chopped celery
2 tablespoons slivered blanched almonds, toasted
1 tablespoon chopped pimiento
1 cup plain low-fat yogurt
1 tablespoon minced onion
½ teaspoon garlic powder
¼ teaspoon pepper

Wash artichokes by plunging up and down in cold water. Cut off stem end, and trim about ½-inch from top of each artichoke. Remove any loose bottom leaves. With scissors, trim away about one-fourth of each outer leaf. Rub top and edges of leaves with lemon wedge to prevent discoloration.

Place artichokes in a Dutch oven; add water to a depth of 2 inches. Cover and bring to a boil; reduce heat, and simmer 30 minutes or until tender. Spread leaves apart; scrape out the fuzzy thistle center (choke) with a spoon; discard. Carefully scrape artichoke heart with a spoon, and remove as much pulp as possible. Chop pulp.

Combine chicken, celery, almonds, pimiento, and artichoke pulp in a bowl; stir well. Set aside.

Combine yogurt, minced onion, garlic powder, and pepper, stirring well; reserve ¼ cup yogurt mixture. Pour remaining yogurt mixture over chicken mixture; toss well.

Spoon chicken mixture into prepared artichokes. Place in a baking dish, and add water in dish to a depth of ¼ inch. Bake, uncovered, at 450° for 15 minutes or until thoroughly heated.

Arrange artichokes on serving plates. Top each serving with 1 tablespoon yogurt mixture. Yield: 4 servings (247 calories per serving).

PROTEIN 29.2 / FAT 5.9 / CARBOHYDRATE 21.4 / CHOLESTEROL 63 / IRON 3.2 / SODIUM 209 / CALCIUM 195

TURKEY SAUSAGE-MACARONI SALAD

1⅓ cups corkscrew macaroni, uncooked
1 pound smoked turkey sausage, cut into ½-inch slices
1 medium-size green pepper, seeded and thinly sliced
1 small purple onion, thinly sliced and separated into rings
1⅓ cups canned kidney beans, rinsed and drained
2 tablespoons minced fresh parsley
2 tablespoons olive oil
¼ cup red wine vinegar
1 tablespoon Dijon mustard
½ teaspoon mustard seeds, crushed
½ teaspoon cracked pepper
⅛ teaspoon hot sauce

Cook macaroni according to package directions, omitting salt and fat; drain. Rinse with cold water and drain well.

Cook sausage in a large nonstick skillet over medium heat until browned. Drain and pat dry with paper towels.

Combine sausage, macaroni, green pepper, onion rings, kidney beans, and parsley in a large bowl; toss well.

Combine olive oil and remaining ingredients in a jar; cover tightly, and shake vigorously. Pour over macaroni mixture; toss well. Cover and chill thoroughly. Yield: 8 servings (252 calories per 1-cup serving).

PROTEIN 10.0 / FAT 14.2 / CARBOHYDRATE 20.8 / CHOLESTEROL 24 / IRON 2.1 / SODIUM 521 / CALCIUM 70

CREAMY SHRIMP-ASPARAGUS SALAD

6 ounces bow-tie pasta, uncooked
½ pound fresh asparagus spears
½ cup plain low-fat yogurt
⅓ cup commercial reduced-calorie creamy Italian dressing
1 clove garlic, minced
2 pounds large fresh shrimp, peeled and deveined
12 cherry tomatoes, halved
1 medium cucumber, sliced
1 cup shredded carrot
2 green onions, chopped

Cook bow-tie pasta according to package directions, omitting salt and fat; drain. Rinse with cold water; drain.

Snap off tough ends of asparagus. Remove scales using a knife or vegetable peeler, if desired. Cut asparagus into 1-inch pieces. Cook asparagus, covered, in a small amount of boiling water 2 minutes or until crisp-tender. Drain.

Combine yogurt, dressing, and garlic; stir well. Combine pasta, asparagus, and dressing mixture in a large bowl; toss gently. Set aside.

Bring 1½ quarts water to a boil; add shrimp, and cook 3 to 5 minutes. Drain well; rinse with cold water, and drain again. Add shrimp to reserved pasta mixture. Stir in cherry tomatoes, cucumber, carrot, and onions. Cover and chill thoroughly. Yield: 12 servings (126 calories per 1-cup serving).

PROTEIN 13.4 / FAT 0.9 / CARBOHYDRATE 15.7 / CHOLESTEROL 86 / IRON 1.6 / SODIUM 152 / CALCIUM 68

COLORFUL SALMON-PASTA SALAD

1½ cups tri-color pasta, uncooked
1 (15½-ounce) can salmon, drained and flaked
¼ cup chopped green pepper
4 green onions, chopped
2 medium carrots, scraped and thinly sliced
1 small zucchini, thinly sliced
3 tablespoons white wine Worcestershire sauce
⅓ cup reduced-calorie mayonnaise
Lettuce leaves

Cook pasta according to package directions, omitting salt and fat; drain. Rinse with cold water; drain. Combine pasta, salmon, and next 4 ingredients; toss gently. Combine Worcestershire sauce and mayonnaise; stir well. Pour over pasta; toss gently. Spoon onto a lettuce-lined serving platter. Yield: 6 servings (239 calories per 1-cup serving).

PROTEIN 17.6 / FAT 10.7 / CARBOHYDRATE 17.0 / CHOLESTEROL 30 / IRON 1.8 / SODIUM 227 / CALCIUM 218

APPLESAUCE-BANANA DRESSING

1 (8-ounce) carton banana low-fat yogurt
½ cup unsweetened applesauce
⅛ teaspoon ground cardamom

Combine all ingredients in container of an electric blender; top with cover, and process until smooth. Cover and chill thoroughly. Serve over fresh fruit. Yield: 1½ cups (12 calories per tablespoon).

PROTEIN 0.4 / FAT 0.1 / CARBOHYDRATE 2.3 / CHOLESTEROL 0 / IRON 0.0 / SODIUM 5 / CALCIUM 13

STRAWBERRY-PINEAPPLE DRESSING

1 (8-ounce) carton strawberry low-fat yogurt
½ cup unsweetened crushed pineapple, drained
3 tablespoons unsweetened pineapple juice

Combine all ingredients in a small bowl; stir with a wire whisk until well blended. Cover and chill thoroughly. Serve over fresh fruit. Yield: 1½ cups (14 calories per tablespoon).

PROTEIN 0.4 / FAT 0.1 / CARBOHYDRATE 2.9 / CHOLESTEROL 0 / IRON 0.0 / SODIUM 5 / CALCIUM 14

RASPBERRY VINAIGRETTE

1½ cups fresh raspberries
1 tablespoon sugar
¼ teaspoon dried whole thyme
¼ teaspoon freshly ground pepper
3 tablespoons white wine vinegar
3 tablespoons water
2 teaspoons vegetable oil
1½ teaspoons reduced-sodium soy sauce

Combine all ingredients in container of an electric blender; top with cover, and process until mixture is smooth. Strain raspberry mixture to remove seeds. Cover and chill thoroughly. Serve with salad greens. Yield: 1 cup (14 calories per tablespoon).

PROTEIN 0.1 / FAT 0.6 / CARBOHYDRATE 2.2 / CHOLESTEROL 0 / IRON 0.1 / SODIUM 19 / CALCIUM 3

CUCUMBER-BUTTERMILK DRESSING

1 cup peeled, seeded, and finely chopped cucumber
⅔ cup nonfat buttermilk
¼ cup reduced-calorie mayonnaise
2 tablespoons minced fresh parsley
½ teaspoon minced fresh chives
⅛ teaspoon salt
⅛ teaspoon garlic powder
⅛ teaspoon pepper

Press chopped cucumber between paper towels to remove excess moisture. Combine cucumber and remaining ingredients in a small mixing bowl, stirring until well blended. Cover and chill dressing thoroughly. Serve dressing with salad greens. Yield: 1½ cups (10 calories per tablespoon).

PROTEIN 0.3 / FAT 0.7 / CARBOHYDRATE 0.7 / CHOLESTEROL 1 / IRON 0.0 / SODIUM 38 / CALCIUM 2

SWEET 'N' SOUR SALAD DRESSING

¾ cup plain low-fat yogurt
¼ cup reduced-calorie mayonnaise
3 tablespoons cider vinegar
2 tablespoons sugar
½ teaspoon paprika
¼ teaspoon dry mustard

Combine all ingredients in a small bowl; stir with a wire whisk until well blended. Cover and chill thoroughly. Serve with salad greens. Yield: 1 cup (23 calories per tablespoon).

PROTEIN 0.6 / FAT 1.2 / CARBOHYDRATE 2.8 / CHOLESTEROL 2 / IRON 0.0 / SODIUM 35 / CALCIUM 20

GREEN GODDESS DRESSING

1 cup loosely packed fresh parsley
¼ cup minced fresh chives
½ teaspoon dried whole tarragon
1 cup low-fat cottage cheese
⅓ cup skim milk
3 tablespoons lemon juice
1 tablespoon tarragon vinegar
½ teaspoon hot sauce

Combine all ingredients in container of an electric blender or food processor; top with cover, and process until mixture is smooth. Cover and chill dressing at least 1 hour. Serve dressing with salad greens. Yield: 1½ cups (9 calories per tablespoon).

PROTEIN 1.4 / FAT 0.1 / CARBOHYDRATE 0.8 / CHOLESTEROL 0 / IRON 0.2 / SODIUM 42 / CALCIUM 14

Creamy Vegetable Garden Salad Dressing has a fresh-from-the-garden flavor.

HERBED GARLIC DRESSING

½ cup low-fat sour cream
½ cup plain low-fat yogurt
2 tablespoons white wine vinegar
1 tablespoon minced fresh parsley
2 cloves garlic, minced
½ teaspoon dried whole rosemary, crushed
¼ teaspoon hot sauce
⅛ teaspoon dried whole thyme

Combine all ingredients in a small bowl, stirring well. Cover and chill thoroughly. Serve dressing with salad greens. Yield: 1 cup (16 calories per tablespoon).

PROTEIN 0.6 / FAT 1.0 / CARBOHYDRATE 1.0 / CHOLESTEROL 3 / IRON 0.1 / SODIUM 9 / CALCIUM 22

VEGETABLE GARDEN SALAD DRESSING

1 (8-ounce) carton plain low-fat yogurt
½ cup low-fat sour cream
¼ cup shredded carrot
¼ cup chopped green onions
¼ cup diced radishes
¼ cup minced fresh parsley
2 tablespoons crumbled blue cheese
¼ teaspoon ground white pepper

Combine all ingredients in a small bowl; stir well. Cover and chill thoroughly. Serve with salad greens. Yield: 2 cups (14 calories per tablespoon).

PROTEIN 0.7 / FAT 0.8 / CARBOHYDRATE 0.9 / CHOLESTEROL 3 / IRON 0.1 / SODIUM 20 / CALCIUM 23

BLUE CHEESE DRESSING

½ cup plain low-fat yogurt
½ cup low-fat sour cream
2 tablespoons crumbled blue cheese
1 teaspoon grated lime rind
2 tablespoons lime juice
¼ teaspoon garlic powder
⅛ teaspoon ground white pepper
2 drops of hot sauce

Combine all ingredients in a small bowl, stirring well. Cover and chill thoroughly. Serve with salad greens. Yield: 1¼ cups (17 calories per tablespoon).

PROTEIN 0.8 / FAT 1.2 / CARBOHYDRATE 0.9 / CHOLESTEROL 4 / IRON 0.0 / SODIUM 26 / CALCIUM 24

CREAMY ONION DRESSING

¾ cup chopped green onions
½ cup plain low-fat yogurt
¼ cup chopped fresh parsley
3 tablespoons white wine vinegar
2 tablespoons reduced-calorie mayonnaise
1 clove garlic, minced
1 teaspoon chopped fresh oregano
½ teaspoon ground white pepper
¼ teaspoon salt

Combine all ingredients in container of an electric blender or food processor; top with cover, and process until smooth. Cover and chill thoroughly. Serve with salad greens. Yield: 1 cup (12 calories per tablespoon).

PROTEIN 0.5 / FAT 0.6 / CARBOHYDRATE 1.1 / CHOLESTEROL 1 / IRON 0.2 / SODIUM 56 / CALCIUM 18

TANGY SOUR CREAM-HORSERADISH DRESSING

1 tablespoon all-purpose flour
¼ teaspoon salt
⅛ teaspoon ground red pepper
¾ cup skim milk
¼ cup prepared horseradish
2 teaspoons prepared mustard
2 egg yolks, beaten
3 tablespoons lemon juice
¾ cup low-fat sour cream

Combine flour, salt, and pepper in a heavy saucepan; gradually add milk, horseradish, and mustard, stirring until smooth. Cook over low heat until thickened and bubbly, stirring constantly. Remove from heat. Gradually stir about one-fourth of hot mixture into yolks; add to remaining hot mixture, stirring constantly. Cook over low heat, stirring constantly, until thickened. Transfer mixture to a small bowl; let cool to room temperature. Stir in lemon juice. Cover and chill thoroughly. Fold sour cream into chilled mixture. Serve with salad greens. Yield: 2¼ cups (14 calories per tablespoon).

PROTEIN 0.5 / FAT 0.9 / CARBOHYDRATE 0.9 / CHOLESTEROL 17 / IRON 0.1 / SODIUM 27 / CALCIUM 14

TOMATO-BASIL VINAIGRETTE

⅔ cup no-salt-added tomato juice
⅓ cup red wine vinegar
2 tablespoons finely minced fresh basil
¼ teaspoon onion powder
⅛ teaspoon salt
⅛ teaspoon garlic powder
3 drops hot sauce

Combine all ingredients in a jar. Cover tightly and shake vigorously. Chill thoroughly. Shake dressing again before serving. Serve with salad greens. Yield: 1 cup (3 calories per tablespoon).

PROTEIN 0.1 / FAT 0.0 / CARBOHYDRATE 0.6 / CHOLESTEROL 0 / IRON 0.0 / SODIUM 20 / CALCIUM 2

A seashell-shaped grill press adds flair to Grilled Tuna-Cheddar Sandwiches (page 185).

Sandwiches & Snacks

(Clockwise from bottom): Carrot Bread Tea Sandwiches with Orange-Pineapple Filling, Salmon Tea Sandwich Triangles, Dainty Cucumber-Watercress Sandwiches, and Shrimp Pinwheel Bites.

CARROT BREAD TEA SANDWICHES

1 cup whole wheat flour
½ cup all-purpose flour
1 teaspoon baking soda
¾ teaspoon ground cinnamon
¼ teaspoon salt
¼ teaspoon ground nutmeg
¼ cup plus 2 tablespoons margarine, melted
⅓ cup sugar
½ cup nonfat buttermilk
2 eggs
1 cup shredded carrot
⅓ cup currants
1 teaspoon vanilla extract
Vegetable cooking spray
Orange-Pineapple Filling

Combine first 6 ingredients, stirring well. Set mixture aside.

Combine margarine, sugar, buttermilk, and eggs in a large bowl; beat at medium speed of an electric mixer just until blended. Add reserved dry ingredients; stir until blended. Fold in carrot, currants, and vanilla.

Pour batter into an 8¼- x 4½- x 3-inch loaf-pan that has been coated with cooking spray. Bake at 350° for 50 to 55 minutes or until a wooden pick inserted in center comes out clean. Cool in pan 10 minutes. Remove from pan, and let cool completely on a wire rack.

Using an electric knife, thinly slice heel ends of loaf, and discard. Slice loaf into 28 (¼-inch-thick) slices. Spread 1 tablespoon of Orange-Pineapple Filling over 14 bread slices. Top with remaining bread slices. Cut each sandwich into 4 triangles, if desired. Yield: 56 servings (39 calories per serving).

Orange-Pineapple Filling:

1 (8-ounce) can unsweetened crushed pineapple, drained
2 tablespoons chopped unsweetened mandarin orange segments
½ (8-ounce) package Neufchâtel cheese, softened
1½ teaspoons sugar

Press pineapple and chopped mandarin orange segments between paper towels to remove excess moisture. Combine pineapple, oranges, cheese, and sugar; stir well. Yield: ¾ cup plus 2 tablespoons.

PROTEIN 0.9 / FAT 1.9 / CARBOHYDRATE 4.8 / CHOLESTEROL 11 / IRON 0.2 / SODIUM 50 / CALCIUM 9

DAINTY CUCUMBER-WATERCRESS SANDWICHES

1 medium cucumber, peeled and cut into 12 ⅛-inch slices
¼ cup low-fat sour cream
1 ounce Neufchâtel cheese, softened
¾ teaspoon dried whole chervil
¼ teaspoon onion powder
8 slices honey-wheat berry bread
¼ cup plus 1 tablespoon minced fresh watercress

Press cucumber slices between layers of paper towels to remove excess moisture; set aside.
Combine sour cream, cheese, chervil, and onion powder, stirring until smooth. Set aside.
Remove crust from bread. Cut three 1½-inch rounds from each bread slice. Spread ½ teaspoon reserved sour cream mixture on 12 bread rounds. Place a cucumber slice on top of sour cream mixture. Top with remaining 12 bread rounds. Frost sides of sandwiches with remaining sour cream mixture. Roll sides of sandwiches in minced watercress. Yield: 12 servings (69 calories per serving).

PROTEIN 2.5 / FAT 2.5 / CARBOHYDRATE 9.6 / CHOLESTEROL 4 / IRON 0.1 / SODIUM 106 / CALCIUM 12

SALMON TEA SANDWICH TRIANGLES

1 (7½-ounce) can red salmon, drained and flaked
½ cup minced celery
¼ teaspoon dried whole dillweed
3 tablespoons reduced-calorie mayonnaise
1 teaspoon lemon juice
7 thin slices whole wheat bread, trimmed
7 thin slices white bread, trimmed

Combine salmon, celery, dillweed, mayonnaise, and lemon juice; stir well. Spread 2 tablespoons salmon mixture onto each whole wheat bread slice; top with white bread slices. Cut each sandwich into 4 triangles. Yield: 28 servings (37 calories per serving).

PROTEIN 2.4 / FAT 1.2 / CARBOHYDRATE 4.2 / CHOLESTEROL 4 / IRON 0.3 / SODIUM 61 / CALCIUM 26

SHRIMP PINWHEEL BITES

8 slices pumpernickel bread, trimmed
1 (4¼-ounce) can shrimp, drained
¼ cup Neufchâtel cheese, softened
2 tablespoons plain nonfat yogurt
1 tablespoon reduced-calorie chili sauce
⅛ teaspoon garlic powder
⅛ teaspoon onion powder

Flatten bread slices with a rolling pin, and set aside.
Combine shrimp, Neufchâtel cheese, yogurt, chili sauce, garlic powder, and onion powder, stirring until mixture is well blended.
Spread 1 tablespoon plus 1½ teaspoons shrimp mixture onto each slice of bread. Roll up jellyroll fashion. Place seam side down on a serving platter; cover and chill thoroughly. Cut into ½-inch slices. Yield: 48 servings (15 calories per serving).

PROTEIN 1.0 / FAT 0.2 / CARBOHYDRATE 2.2 / CHOLESTEROL 5 / IRON 0.2 / SODIUM 29 / CALCIUM 6

MUSHROOM-PECAN PITA SANDWICHES

2 tablespoons vegetable oil
2 tablespoons plus 2 teaspoons lemon juice
2 tablespoons grated Parmesan cheese
2 tablespoons chopped fresh parsley
¾ teaspoon dry mustard
¼ teaspoon pepper
2 cups sliced fresh mushrooms
1 cup thinly sliced celery
1 tablespoon sliced pimiento
¼ cup plus 2 tablespoons chopped pecans, toasted
3 (6-inch) whole wheat pita bread rounds, cut in half crosswise
6 lettuce leaves
1 medium tomato, cut into 6 slices
⅓ cup alfalfa sprouts

Combine first 6 ingredients in a large bowl; stir well. Add mushrooms, celery, and pimiento, tossing gently. Cover and chill at least 1 hour. Stir in pecans.

Line each pita round half with a lettuce leaf and tomato slice. Spoon ½ cup mushroom mixture into each pita half. Top sandwiches evenly with alfalfa sprouts. Yield: 6 servings (210 calories per serving).

PROTEIN 4.3 / FAT 11.1 / CARBOHYDRATE 23.3 / CHOLESTEROL 1 / IRON 2.0 / SODIUM 55 / CALCIUM 74

OPEN-FACED MEAT LOAF SANDWICHES

1 pound ground chuck
⅓ cup chopped green pepper
⅓ cup chopped onion
⅓ cup soft breadcrumbs
¼ cup skim milk
1 egg, beaten
1 tablespoon reduced-calorie catsup
¼ teaspoon garlic powder
¼ teaspoon salt
¼ teaspoon pepper
Vegetable cooking spray
1 (8-ounce) can no-salt-added tomato sauce
¼ teaspoon dried whole oregano
¼ teaspoon dried whole marjoram
6 (½-inch-thick) slices Italian bread, toasted

Combine first 10 ingredients in a medium bowl; stir well. Spoon mixture into a 7½- x 3- x

2-inch loafpan that has been coated with cooking spray. Bake at 350° for 1 hour and 10 minutes. Cool in pan 5 minutes. Remove from pan; drain well on paper towels. Let stand 5 minutes before cutting into 1-inch slices.

Combine tomato sauce, oregano, and marjoram in a small saucepan. Bring mixture to a boil. Cover; reduce heat, and simmer 10 minutes, stirring occasionally.

Place bread slices on serving platter. Top each slice with a meatloaf slice. Spoon 2 tablespoons tomato sauce over each sandwich. Yield: 6 servings (279 calories per serving).

PROTEIN 18.5 / FAT 11.8 / CARBOHYDRATE 23.3 / CHOLESTEROL 90 / IRON 2.3 / SODIUM 343 / CALCIUM 35

 ## EXERCISE FOR THE MOTHER-TO-BE

Exercise during pregnancy may not only be safe, but it can also provide emotional support and improve the expectant mother's self-image. Although pregnancy is not the time to begin a vigorous regimen or train for a competitive event, try participating in exercises that are modified for the body's needs during this special time. Ask your obstetrician about your participation in a pregnancy exercise program.

The best choices are low-impact exercises such as walking, swimming, and stationary cycling. If you were involved in jogging, aerobic dancing, or any other exercise program before your pregnancy, your doctor may allow you to continue, but do not do so without medical consent.

BLUE CHEESE-STUFFED TURKEY BURGERS

1 (1-pound) package frozen raw ground turkey, thawed
1 tablespoon white wine Worcestershire sauce
1 egg, beaten
3 tablespoons crumbled blue cheese
2 tablespoons minced fresh cilantro
Vegetable cooking spray
4 lettuce leaves
2 whole wheat hamburger buns, split and toasted

Combine first 3 ingredients; stir well. Shape turkey mixture into 8 (¼-inch-thick) patties, and set aside.

Combine blue cheese and cilantro. Place 1 tablespoon cheese mixture in center of 4 patties. Top with remaining patties, sealing edges well. Coat grill rack with cooking spray; place on grill over medium-hot coals. Place patties on rack, and cook 6 to 8 minutes on each side or until done.

Place a lettuce leaf and turkey patty on each bun half. Serve immediately. Yield: 4 servings (285 calories per serving).

PROTEIN 31.3 / FAT 10.9 / CARBOHYDRATE 13.7 / CHOLESTEROL 150 / IRON 2.6 / SODIUM 419 / CALCIUM 110

TURKEY PITA SANDWICHES WITH CRANBERRY CHUTNEY

1 cup chopped fresh cranberries
½ cup peeled, chopped Granny Smith apple
2 tablespoons brown sugar
1 tablespoon chopped prunes
1 tablespoon chopped onion
¼ teaspoon ground cinnamon
3 tablespoons reduced-calorie cranberry juice cocktail
2 tablespoons red wine vinegar
2 teaspoons lemon juice
3 (6-inch) whole wheat pita bread rounds, cut in half crosswise
6 lettuce leaves
3 cups chopped cooked turkey breast (skinned before cooking and cooked without salt)

Combine chopped cranberries and next 8 ingredients in a nonaluminum saucepan; bring mixture to a boil. Cover, reduce heat, and simmer 30 minutes, stirring frequently. Uncover, and cook 5 minutes or until mixture is thickened; stirring frequently. Set aside.

Line pita bread halves with lettuce leaves. Add ½ cup chopped turkey to each pita bread half. Top each serving with 2 tablespoons cranberry mixture. Yield: 6 servings (199 calories per serving).

PROTEIN 18.7 / FAT 2.5 / CARBOHYDRATE 23.1 / CHOLESTEROL 39 / IRON 2.2 / SODIUM 40 / CALCIUM 46

HEARTY HERO SANDWICHES

2 tablespoons plain nonfat yogurt
2 tablespoons reduced-calorie mayonnaise
1¼ teaspoons prepared mustard
½ teaspoon prepared horseradish
2 (2½-ounce) French bread rolls, split lengthwise
2 (1-ounce) slices lean cooked ham
2 (1-ounce) slices cooked turkey breast (skinned before cooking and cooked without salt)
4 (1-ounce) slices Swiss cheese
2 red leaf lettuce leaves
½ medium-size purple onion, cut into 6 slices
1 medium tomato, cut into 6 slices
½ medium-size green pepper, cut into 6 rings

Combine yogurt, mayonnaise, mustard, and horseradish; stir well. Spread evenly over cut sides of rolls.

Layer half of ham and remaining ingredients in each roll. Cut each roll in half. Yield: 4 servings (288 calories per serving).

PROTEIN 19.4 / FAT 11.9 / CARBOHYDRATE 24.8 / CHOLESTEROL 48 / IRON 1.5 / SODIUM 573 / CALCIUM 314

GRILLED TUNA-CHEDDAR SANDWICHES

1 (6½-ounce) can 60% less-salt tuna packed in water, drained
¼ cup plus 2 tablespoons (1½ ounces) shredded 40% less-fat Cheddar cheese
⅛ teaspoon pepper
1 tablespoon thinly sliced green onions
2 tablespoons plain nonfat yogurt
2 teaspoons diced pimiento
1 teaspoon Dijon mustard
¼ teaspoon low-sodium Worcestershire sauce
4 slices whole wheat bread
Vegetable cooking spray

Combine tuna and next 7 ingredients; stir well. Spread tuna mixture evenly over 2 slices of bread; top with remaining bread slices. Transfer sandwiches to a sandwich press or hot griddle that has beeen coated with cooking spray. Cook until bread is lightly browned and cheese is slightly melted. Yield: 2 servings (292 calories per serving).

PROTEIN 29.6 / FAT 5.4 / CARBOHYDRATE 34.0 / CHOLESTEROL 2 / IRON 3.7 / SODIUM 421 / CALCIUM 242

MEXICAN PIZZA SNACKS

2 (8-inch) flour tortillas
½ (1-pound) package frozen raw ground turkey, thawed
⅓ cup chopped onion
½ (8-ounce) can no-salt-added tomato sauce
1 (4-ounce) can chopped green chiles, undrained
1¼ teaspoons chili powder
½ teaspoon ground cumin
¾ cup chopped tomato
¾ cup (3 ounces) shredded part-skim mozzarella cheese

Place tortillas on an ungreased baking sheet. Bake at 350° for 4 to 5 minutes or until crisp. Set tortillas aside.

Cook turkey and onion in a large nonstick skillet over medium heat until turkey is browned, stirring to crumble. Drain and pat dry with paper towels. Wipe pan drippings from skillet with a paper towel. Return turkey mixture to skillet. Stir in tomato sauce, green chiles, chili powder, and cumin. Cook over medium heat until mixture is thoroughly heated. Spoon ¾ cup turkey mixture over each tortilla. Sprinkle chopped tomato and cheese evenly over turkey mixture. Broil 4 to 6 inches from heat for 1 minute or until cheese melts. To serve, cut each tortilla into 6 wedges. Yield: 12 servings (75 calories per serving).

PROTEIN 6.8 / FAT 2.4 / CARBOHYDRATE 7.1 / CHOLESTEROL 15 / IRON 0.6 / SODIUM 49 / CALCIUM 59

EAST-WEST WONTON SKINS

2 dozen frozen wonton skins, thawed
¼ cup plus 2 teaspoons water
1 tablespoon plus 1 teaspoon vegetable oil
2 teaspoons chili powder
1 teaspoon garlic powder
1 teaspoon onion powder

Cut each wonton skin into 3 lengthwise strips; lay strips on cutting board. Cut a slit down center of each strip using a sharp knife, cutting to within ½ inch of ends. Invert one end of strip through center slit. Gently straighten the strip, rolling twist to center of strip. Repeat with remaining strips.

Place on ungreased 15- x 10- x 1-inch jellyroll pans. Combine water and remaining ingredients; stir well. Brush oil mixture evenly over wonton strips. Bake at 375° for 6 minutes or until crisp and lightly browned. Remove from jellyroll pans, and let cool completely on wire racks. Store in an airtight container. Yield: 6 dozen (5 calories each).

PROTEIN 0.1 / FAT 0.3 / CARBOHYDRATE 0.5 / CHOLESTEROL 2 / IRON 0.0 / SODIUM 6 / CALCIUM 1

BLUE HAWAII BAGELS

6 frozen blueberry bagels, thawed
1 large banana
1 (8-ounce) package Neufchâtel cheese, softened
1 (8-ounce) carton blueberry low-fat yogurt
1 (8-ounce) can unsweetened crushed pineapple, drained
½ teaspoon coconut extract
2 tablespoons unsweetened flaked coconut, toasted
1 tablespoon finely chopped blanched almonds, toasted

Cut each bagel into 4 slices, using a serated knife; cut each slice in half. Place on an ungreased baking sheet. Bake at 300° for 30 to 35 minutes or until crisp and lightly browned. Set bagels aside.

Place banana in container of an electric blender or food processor; top with cover, and process until smooth.

Beat cheese at medium speed of an electric mixer until fluffy; add pureed banana and yogurt, beating until smooth. Stir in pineapple and extract; cover and chill thoroughly. Top dip mixture with toasted coconut and almonds just before serving. Yield: 48 servings (47 calories per 1 chip and 1 tablespoon dip).

PROTEIN 1.6 / FAT 1.5 / CARBOHYDRATE 6.8 / CHOLESTEROL 4 / IRON 0.0 / SODIUM 53 / CALCIUM 11

BAGEL CHIPS

6 bagels
3 tablespoons reduced-calorie margarine
2 tablespoons reduced-calorie mayonnaise
1 tablespoon Dijon mustard
1 tablespoon poppy seeds
¼ teaspoon garlic powder
¼ teaspoon onion powder

Cut each bagel into 6 (¼-inch) slices using a serated knife; place on an ungreased baking sheet. Set aside.

Combine margarine and remaining ingredients in a small bowl, stirring well. Spread ½ teaspoon margarine mixture over each bagel slice. Bake at 300° for 20 minutes or until crisp and lightly browned. Remove from baking sheets, and let cool on wire racks. Store chips in an airtight container. Yield: 3 dozen (41 calories each).

PROTEIN 1.2 / FAT 1.2 / CARBOHYDRATE 6.2 / CHOLESTEROL 0 / IRON 0.3 / SODIUM 66 / CALCIUM 7

SWEET POTATO CHIPS

2 medium-size sweet potatoes (1 pound)
1 egg white, lightly beaten
2 tablespoons water
⅓ cup grated Parmesan cheese
3 tablespoons minced fresh
  parsley
½ teaspoon garlic powder
Vegetable cooking spray

Slice potatoes crosswise into ⅛-inch slices, and set aside.

Combine egg white and water, stirring well. Set aside. Combine cheese, parsley, and garlic powder. Dip potato slices into egg white mixture, and dredge in cheese mixture. Arrange slices on baking sheets that have been coated with cooking spray. Broil 4 to 5 inches from heat 4 minutes on each side or until crisp. Yield: 6 dozen (9 calories each).

PROTEIN 0.3 / FAT 0.1 / CARBOHYDRATE 1.6 / CHOLESTEROL 0 / IRON 0.1 / SODIUM 8 / CALCIUM 7

Blueberry-flavored bagel slices are toasted for a different kind of chip in Blue Hawaii Bagels.

SUGAR-AND-SPICE CEREAL SNACK

3 tablespoons powdered sugar
1 tablespoon instant unsweetened tea
2 teaspoons grated lemon rind
2 teaspoons grated orange rind
½ teaspoon ground cinnamon
¼ teaspoon mint flakes
1 egg white
3 cups crispy corn cereal squares
Vegetable cooking spray

Combine first 6 ingredients in a small bowl; stir well. Beat egg white (at room temperature) at high speed of an electric mixer in a large bowl until foamy. Gently fold sugar mixture into egg white. Add cereal; stir gently to coat evenly. Spread cereal mixture in a 15- x 10- x 1-inch jellyroll pan that has been coated with cooking spray. Bake at 325° for 15 minutes. Cool in pan. Store in an airtight container. Yield: 3 cups (94 calories per ½-cup serving).

PROTEIN 1.3 / FAT 0.3 / CARBOHYDRATE 21.0 / CHOLESTEROL 0 / IRON 1.3 / SODIUM 155 / CALCIUM 5

A HEALTHY SNACK

For a healthy snack, substitute fruit for traditional snack foods, which have dramatically more calories, fat, and sodium.

Snack	Portion	Calories	Percent Fat
Peanuts	¼ cup	212	76
Potato Chips	10 chips	105	61
Ice Cream	½ cup	134	48
Milk Chocolate	1 ounce	149	48
Watermelon	1 cup	51	0
Strawberries	1 cup	45	0
Apple	1 medium	81	0

For a refreshing snack, try assorted fruits such as bananas, red and green seedless grapes, pineapple, and strawberries. Place the fruit on skewers and freeze until hard. Remove the frozen fruit from freezer; let stand at room temperature to soften slightly, and enjoy this healthy treat.

FROZEN FRUIT KABOBS

1 (15¼-ounce) can unsweetened pineapple chunks, undrained
½ cup unsweetened orange juice
3 tablespoons Triple Sec or other orange-flavored liqueur
1 tablespoon lemon juice
2 small bananas, cut into ½-inch slices
1 cup large seedless red grapes
18 (6-inch) wooden skewers

Drain pineapple and reserve juice. Combine pineapple juice and next 3 ingredients in a shallow baking dish. Add bananas and grapes; cover and marinate in refrigerator 8 hours.
Thread fruit alternately on wooden skewers. Place on a baking sheet and freeze until firm. To store, transfer to freezer bags or containers. Serve kabobs frozen. Yield: 18 servings (33 calories per serving).

PROTEIN 0.3 / FAT 0.1 / CARBOHYDRATE 7.2 / CHOLESTEROL 0 / IRON 0.2 / SODIUM 1 / CALCIUM 6

MOCHA BANANA POPS

1 (8-ounce) carton coffee low-fat yogurt
1 cup 1% low-fat chocolate milk
2 small bananas, cut into 1-inch pieces
½ teaspoon ground cinnamon
8 (3-ounce) paper cups
8 wooden sticks

Combine first 4 ingredients in the container of an electric blender or food processor; top with cover, and process until smooth. Pour into paper cups. Cover tops of cups with aluminum foil, and insert a stick through foil into center of each cup. Freeze until firm. To serve, remove foil and peel paper cup away from pop. Yield: 8 servings (76 calories per serving).

PROTEIN 2.7 / FAT 1.0 / CARBOHYDRATE 15.3 / CHOLESTEROL 2 / IRON 0.2 / SODIUM 51 / CALCIUM 83

Zesty Horseradish Sauce (top, page 192) and Creamy Mustard Spread (page 192) add robust flavor without a lot of calories to any sandwich fixings.

Sauces & Condiments

ZESTY BLUEBERRY-ORANGE SAUCE

1½ cups fresh blueberries
2 tablespoons frozen orange juice
  concentrate
1 tablespoon low-sugar orange marmalade
½ teaspoon grated lemon rind

Combine all ingredients in container of an electric blender; top with cover, and process until smooth. Serve warm or chilled over ice milk or angel food cake. Yield: 1 cup (13 calories per tablespoon).

PROTEIN 0.1 / FAT 0.1 / CARBOHYDRATE 3.2 / CHOLESTEROL 0 / IRON 0.0 / SODIUM 1 / CALCIUM 2

SWEET CHERRY SAUCE

3 tablespoons sugar
2 tablespoons cornstarch
⅛ teaspoon salt
½ cup water
1 (16-ounce) package frozen
  sweet cherries, thawed
½ teaspoon almond
  extract
1 tablespoon margarine

Combine first 3 ingredients in a medium saucepan. Add water, stirring until smooth. Add cherries; cook over medium heat until mixture is thickened and bubbly, stirring often. Add extract and margarine, stirring until margarine melts. Serve warm over ice milk or angel food cake. Yield: 2½ cups (16 calories per tablespoon).

PROTEIN 0.0 / FAT 0.3 / CARBOHYDRATE 3.3 / CHOLESTEROL 0 / IRON 0.0 / SODIUM 11 / CALCIUM 0

FRESH PEACH SAUCE

5 medium-size fresh peaches, peeled and sliced
2 tablespoons sugar
1 tablespoon plus 1½ teaspoons
  cornstarch
1 tablespoon lemon juice
½ cup water
½ teaspoon almond extract

Position knife blade in food processor bowl; add sliced peaches. Top with cover, and process until smooth.

Combine sugar and cornstarch in a medium saucepan. Add lemon juice and water, stirring until mixture is smooth. Add pureed peaches, stirring well. Cook over medium heat until thickened and bubbly, stirring often. Stir in almond extract. Serve warm or chilled over pancakes, waffles, or ice milk. Yield: 2 cups (13 calories per tablespoon).

PROTEIN 0.1 / FAT 0.0 / CARBOHYDRATE 3.3 / CHOLESTEROL 0 / IRON 0.0 / SODIUM 0 / CALCIUM 1

TROPICAL STRAWBERRY-BANANA
SAUCE

2 cups sliced fresh strawberries
1 medium banana, sliced
2 tablespoons rum
1 teaspoon lemon juice

Combine all ingredients in container of an electric blender; top with cover, and process until smooth. Serve chilled over ice milk or angel food cake. Yield: 1¾ cups (11 calories per tablespoon).

PROTEIN 0.1 / FAT 0.1 / CARBOHYDRATE 1.6 / CHOLESTEROL 0 / IRON 0.1 / SODIUM 0 / CALCIUM 2

(Clockwise from top): Tropical Strawberry-Banana Sauce, Sweet Cherry Sauce, Cinnamon-Pear Sauce, Fresh Peach Sauce, and Zesty Blueberry-Orange Sauce.

WHAT SHOULD YOU WEIGH?

An easy way to calculate your desirable body weight is to use your height as a base. Remember, however, this is only an estimate and does not include factors such as the amount of body fat, muscle, bone structure, or your age.

For a female, start with 100 pounds for the first 5 feet in height and add 5 pounds for each additional inch. Therefore, a 5-foot 4-inch female should weigh about 120 pounds. For a male, use 106 pounds for the first 5 feet and add 6 pounds for each additional inch. A 6-foot male should then have a desirable body weight of about 178 pounds.

Calculate your weight with the above equation and see how your weight compares.

CINNAMON-PEAR SAUCE

6 medium-size fresh pears (2 pounds), peeled, cored, and quartered
½ cup unsweetened pineapple juice
½ teaspoon ground cinnamon
⅛ teaspoon ground nutmeg
1 tablespoon sugar

Combine first 4 ingredients in a Dutch oven. Cook over medium-low heat 25 to 30 minutes or until tender, stirring frequently. Mash to desired consistency with a potato masher; stir in sugar. Serve warm or chilled over ice milk. Yield: 2¼ cups (14 calories per tablespoon).

PROTEIN 0.1 / FAT 0.1 / CARBOHYDRATE 3.6 / CHOLESTEROL 0 / IRON 0.1 / SODIUM 0 / CALCIUM 3

GREEN CHILE-AVOCADO SAUCE

3 medium tomatoes, coarsely chopped
1 small green tomato, coarsely chopped
8 green onions, coarsely chopped
1 medium avocado, peeled and coarsely chopped
1 (4-ounce) can chopped green chiles, undrained
3 tablespoons lime juice
2 tablespoons chopped fresh parsley
2 tablespoons vegetable oil
1 teaspoon garlic powder
½ teaspoon salt
½ teaspoon ground cumin
¼ teaspoon hot sauce

Combine all ingredients in container of an electric blender or food processor; top with cover, and process until finely chopped. Transfer mixture to a serving bowl. Cover and chill thoroughly. Serve over chicken, meat, or egg dishes. Yield: 5 cups (8 calories per tablespoon).

PROTEIN 0.2 / FAT 0.6 / CARBOHYDRATE 0.7 / CHOLESTEROL 0 / IRON 0.1 / SODIUM 16 / CALCIUM 2

CREAMY CHIVE SAUCE

1 (8-ounce) carton low-fat cottage cheese
¼ cup skim milk
¼ cup plain low-fat yogurt
¼ cup reduced-calorie mayonnaise
2 tablespoons chopped fresh parsley
2 tablespoons chopped fresh chives

Combine first 4 ingredients in container of an electric blender. Top with cover; process until smooth. Add parsley and chives; process until blended. Serve chilled with vegetables. Yield: 1½ cups (16 calories per tablespoon).

PROTEIN 1.4 / FAT 0.8 / CARBOHYDRATE 0.7 / CHOLESTEROL 1 / IRON 0.0 / SODIUM 60 / CALCIUM 14

ZESTY HORSERADISH SAUCE

1 (8-ounce) carton plain low-fat yogurt
¼ cup plus 2 tablespoons reduced-calorie mayonnaise
3 tablespoons prepared horseradish
1 tablespoon plus 1½ teaspoons spicy brown mustard

Combine all ingredients in a small bowl, stirring well. Cover and chill thoroughly. Serve as a meat or sandwich spread. Yield: 1¾ cups (15 calories per tablespoon).

PROTEIN 0.5 / FAT 1.0 / CARBOHYDRATE 1.0 / CHOLESTEROL 2 / IRON 0.0 / SODIUM 39 / CALCIUM 16

CREAMY MUSTARD SPREAD

1 tablespoon unsalted margarine
¼ cup all-purpose flour
1 cup evaporated skimmed milk
2 tablespoons spicy brown mustard
2 tablespoons diced pimiento
1 teaspoon lemon juice

Melt margarine in a heavy saucepan over low heat. Add flour, stirring until smooth. Cook 1 minute, stirring constantly. Gradually add milk; cook over medium heat, stirring constantly, until mixture is thickened. Remove from heat; cool slightly, and stir in mustard, pimiento, and lemon juice. Cover and chill thoroughly. Serve as a meat or sandwich spread. Yield: 1 cup (39 calories per tablespoon).

PROTEIN 2.1 / FAT 1.2 / CARBOHYDRATE 4.9 / CHOLESTEROL 1 / IRON 0.2 / SODIUM 59 / CALCIUM 66

LEMONY MUSTARD SAUCE

1 tablespoon plus 1½ teaspoons cornstarch
1 cup water
1 teaspoon chicken-flavored bouillon granules
2 tablespoons plus 1½ teaspoons Dijon mustard
1 tablespoon lemon juice
1¼ teaspoons grated lemon rind

Place cornstarch in a small saucepan. Gradually add water, stirring until smooth. Stir in bouillon granules and remaining ingredients. Bring to a boil, and cook until thickened and bubbly, stirring constantly. Remove from heat, and let cool slightly. Serve warm over meat or cooked vegetables. Yield: 1¼ cups (5 calories per tablespoon).

PROTEIN 0.0 / FAT 0.2 / CARBOHYDRATE 0.8 / CHOLESTEROL 0 / IRON 0.0 / SODIUM 97 / CALCIUM 0

DILLED MUSTARD SAUCE

¼ cup reduced-calorie mayonnaise
¼ cup Dijon mustard
1 tablespoon minced fresh dillweed
1 tablespoon minced fresh chives
⅛ teaspoon ground white pepper

Combine all ingredients in a small bowl; stir with a wire whisk until well blended. Cover and chill thoroughly. Serve with fresh vegetables. Yield: ½ cup (30 calories per tablespoon).

PROTEIN 0.1 / FAT 2.5 / CARBOHYDRATE 1.1 / CHOLESTEROL 2 / IRON 0.1 / SODIUM 278 / CALCIUM 3

PIMIENTO CHEESE SAUCE

1 cup water
½ cup instant non-fat dry milk powder
1 tablespoon plus 1½ teaspoons all-purpose flour
¼ teaspoon dry mustard
¼ teaspoon salt
⅛ teaspoon ground white pepper
⅛ teaspoon butter flavoring
¼ cup (1 ounce) shredded Swiss cheese
1 (2-ounce) jar diced pimiento, drained

Combine water, milk powder, and flour in a heavy saucepan, stirring until smooth. Cook over medium heat until thickened and bubbly, stirring constantly. Add dry mustard and next 4 ingredients, stirring until cheese melts. Remove from heat; stir in pimiento. Serve warm over cooked vegetables, egg dishes, or meat. Yield: 1½ cups (16 calories per tablespoon).

PROTEIN 1.3 / FAT 0.4 / CARBOHYDRATE 1.8 / CHOLESTEROL 2 / IRON 0.0 / SODIUM 41 / CALCIUM 43

HERBED SPINACH SAUCE

1 ounce fresh spinach
½ cup chopped fresh parsley
1 tablespoon chopped fresh dillweed
1 clove garlic
3 green onions, cut into 1-inch pieces
½ cup reduced-calorie mayonnaise
½ cup plain low-fat yogurt

Remove stems from spinach; wash leaves thoroughly, and tear into large pieces. Position knife blade in food processor bowl; add spinach and next 4 ingredients. Top with cover, and process until finely chopped.

Combine spinach mixture, mayonnaise, and yogurt, stirring well. Cover and chill thoroughly. Serve with fresh vegetables. Yield: 1¼ cups (21 calories per tablespoon).

PROTEIN 0.5 / FAT 1.7 / CARBOHYDRATE 1.1 / CHOLESTEROL 2 / IRON 0.2 / SODIUM 50 / CALCIUM 17

LOW IN IRON? COOK IN IRON PANS

Iron deficiency is common in America, but poor eating habits aren't always the cause. An otherwise balanced diet may not supply adequate iron for dieters, women in childbearing years, pregnant women, endurance athletes, and vegetarians. But before taking an iron supplement, try an often overlooked way of increasing iron intake—cooking in cast-iron pots and pans. This will increase the iron content of food, especially those high in acid, such as tomatoes, or those simmered for a long time.

SPICY BARBECUE SAUCE

2 teaspoons brown sugar
¾ teaspoon chili powder
¾ teaspoon pepper
1 bay leaf
1 (8-ounce) can no-salt-added tomato sauce
¼ cup red wine vinegar
¼ cup Worcestershire sauce
2 tablespoons grated onion
1 tablespoon unsalted margarine
1 tablespoon liquid smoke
1 clove garlic, minced

Combine all ingredients in a medium saucepan; bring to a boil, stirring frequently. Reduce heat, and simmer 10 minutes. Remove and discard bay leaf. Use sauce to baste pork or chicken during cooking. Yield: 1¼ cups (14 calories per tablespoon).

PROTEIN 0.2 / FAT 0.6 / CARBOHYDRATE 2.0 / CHOLESTEROL 0 / IRON 0.1 / SODIUM 33 / CALCIUM 5

PEANUT STIR-FRY SAUCE

1 cup water
1 tablespoon cornstarch
2 tablespoons no-sugar-added peanut butter
2 tablespoons low-sodium soy sauce
1 teaspoon crushed red pepper
¼ teaspoon minced fresh gingerroot

Combine water and cornstarch in a small bowl, stirring until smooth. Stir in peanut butter and remaining ingredients, stirring until well blended. Add to meat or vegetables while stir-frying; stir-fry an additional 2 minutes or until sauce thickens. Yield: 1¼ cups (12 calories per tablespoon).

PROTEIN 0.6 / FAT 0.8 / CARBOHYDRATE 0.8 / CHOLESTEROL 0 /
IRON 0.1 / SODIUM 61 / CALCIUM 1

TERIYAKI MARINADE

1 cup unsweetened pineapple juice
¼ cup plus 3 tablespoons low-sodium soy sauce
¼ cup white wine Worcestershire sauce
1 tablespoon vegetable oil
½ teaspoon ground ginger
¼ teaspoon onion powder
1 clove garlic, crushed

Combine all ingredients in a small bowl, stirring well. Use to marinate chicken, beef, or pork before cooking; use to baste during cooking. Yield: 1¾ cups (14 calories per tablespoon).

PROTEIN 0.3 / FAT 0.5 / CARBOHYDRATE 2.1 / CHOLESTEROL 0 /
IRON 0.1 / SODIUM 174 / CALCIUM 5

HERB VINEGAR

½ cup chopped fresh thyme
¼ cup chopped fresh parsley
¼ cup chopped fresh rosemary
¼ cup chopped fresh sage
4 green onions, thinly sliced
1 clove garlic, crushed
9 black peppercorns
3¾ cups vinegar (5% acidity)
Additional sprigs of fresh thyme, rosemary, and sage
  (optional)

Place first 7 ingredients in a wide-mouth quart glass jar. Place 3¾ cups vinegar in a medium

nonaluminum saucepan; bring to a boil. Pour vinegar over herbs; cover with lid. Let stand at room temperature 2 weeks.

Strain vinegar into decorative jars, discarding herb residue; add additional sprigs of fresh thyme, rosemary, and sage, if desired. Seal jars with a cork or other airtight lid. Yield: 3 cups (2 calories per tablespoon).

PROTEIN 0.0 / FAT 0.0 / CARBOHYDRATE 0.9 / CHOLESTEROL 0 /
IRON 0.0 / SODIUM 0 / CALCIUM 0

CREOLE SEASONING BLEND

3 tablespoons plus 1 teaspoon dried parsley flakes
1 tablespoon plus 1 teaspoon garlic powder
1 tablespoon plus 1 teaspoon dried whole basil
1 tablespoon onion powder
2 teaspoons dry mustard
2 teaspoons sweet paprika
1 teaspoon ground red pepper
½ teaspoon freshly ground black pepper

Combine all ingredients in a small bowl, stirring well. Store in an airtight container. Use to coat fish, chicken, or beef before cooking. Yield: ½ cup (5 calories per teaspoon).

PROTEIN 0.3 / FAT 0.1 / CARBOHYDRATE 0.9 / CHOLESTEROL 0 /
IRON 0.2 / SODIUM 1 / CALCIUM 5

PICKLED PEARL ONIONS

1¼ pounds pearl onions, peeled
1 medium-size green pepper, seeded and cut into
  strips
8 black peppercorns
4 sprigs fresh dillweed
1¾ cups vinegar (5% acidity)
⅓ cup sugar
¼ teaspoon salt

Place first 4 ingredients in a wide-mouth quart glass jar. Combine vinegar, sugar, and salt in a medium nonaluminum saucepan. Bring to a boil, stirring until sugar dissolves. Pour vinegar mixture into prepared jar; cover with lid and cool. Store in refrigerator for 2 weeks before serving. Yield: 1 quart (31 calories per 1/4-cup serving).

PROTEIN 0.3 / FAT 0.1 / CARBOHYDRATE 8.4 / CHOLESTEROL 0 /
IRON 0.2 / SODIUM 40 / CALCIUM 10

Fresh Pepper Refrigerator Relish makes a colorful side dish that will add a flavorful touch to a variety of entrées.

FRESH PEPPER REFRIGERATOR RELISH

Vegetable cooking spray
¾ cup chopped onion
½ cup chopped green pepper
½ cup chopped sweet red pepper
1 banana pepper, seeded and chopped
1 cup grated carrot
2 tablespoons raisins
2 tablespoons sugar
3 tablespoons cider vinegar
¼ teaspoon salt

Coat a nonaluminum saucepan with cooking spray; place over medium-high heat until hot. Add onion and next 5 ingredients. Cook 5 to 10 minutes or until vegetables are crisp-tender, stirring frequently. Stir in sugar, vinegar, and salt. Simmer, uncovered, 5 minutes. Let cool to room temperature. Store in refrigerator. Yield: 1½ cups (12 calories per tablespoon).

PROTEIN 0.2 / FAT 0.1 / CARBOHYDRATE 3.0 / CHOLESTEROL 0 / IRON 0.2 / SODIUM 27 / CALCIUM 4 .

HOT MEXICAN RELISH

6 green onions, coarsely chopped
2 medium tomatoes, quartered
1 small green pepper, seeded and quartered
1 clove garlic
Vegetable cooking spray
1 (8¾-ounce) can no-salt-added whole kernel corn, drained
1 (4-ounce) can chopped green chiles, drained
3 tablespoons hot chili sauce
1 tablespoon chili powder
1 teaspoon pepper

Position knife blade in food processor bowl; add first 4 ingredients. Top with cover, and process until finely chopped. Coat a large nonstick skillet with cooking spray; place over medium-high heat until hot. Add chopped vegetables, and sauté until tender. Stir in corn and remaining ingredients. Cook over medium heat until thoroughly heated. Serve hot or cold. Yield: 3 cups (7 calories per tablespoon).

PROTEIN 0.2 / FAT 0.1 / CARBOHYDRATE 1.4 / CHOLESTEROL 0 /
IRON 0.2 / SODIUM 19 / CALCIUM 3

COLORFUL CORN REFRIGERATOR RELISH

1 (10-ounce) package frozen whole kernel corn
3 tablespoons chopped green pepper
3 tablespoons chopped green onions
2 tablespoons chopped celery
¼ cup white wine vinegar
1 tablespoon sugar
¼ teaspoon salt
⅛ teaspoon pepper
⅛ teaspoon ground turmeric
1 (2-ounce) jar diced pimiento, drained

Cook corn according to package directions, omitting salt and fat; drain.
Combine corn, green pepper, onions, celery, vinegar, sugar, salt, pepper, and turmeric in a medium nonaluminum saucepan. Cook over medium heat 1 minute. Stir in pimiento. Cover and chill 8 hours. Yield: 2 cups (11 calories per tablespoon).

PROTEIN 0.3 / FAT 0.1 / CARBOHYDRATE 2.4 / CHOLESTEROL 0 /
IRON 0.1 / SODIUM 20 / CALCIUM 1

SPICY PEAR RELISH

2 medium pears, peeled, cored, and shredded
1 small apple, peeled, cored and shredded
1 green onion, minced
¼ cup cider vinegar
2 tablespoons golden raisins
2 tablespoons sugar
¼ teaspoon pumpkin pie spice
⅛ teaspoon salt
⅛ teaspoon dried whole thyme

Combine all ingredients in a medium nonaluminum saucepan; stir until well blended. Cook over medium heat 10 minutes, stirring occasionally. Serve warm or at room temperature. Yield: 2¾ cups (11 calories per tablespoon).

PROTEIN 0.1 / FAT 0.1 / CARBOHYDRATE 3.0 / CHOLESTEROL 0 /
IRON 0.1 / SODIUM 7 / CALCIUM 2

ORANGE-CRANBERRY RELISH

1 medium orange
2 cups fresh cranberries
1 medium pear, peeled, cored, and quartered
1 (8-ounce) can unsweetened pineapple chunks, drained
½ cup sugar

Grate orange rind; set aside. Peel orange, removing white membrane; remove seeds, and section.
Position knife blade in food processor bowl; add orange sections. Top with cover, and process until finely chopped. Add grated orange rind, cranberries, pear, pineapple chunks, and sugar; process until coarsely chopped. Cover and chill mixture thoroughly. Serve as a condiment with poultry or pork. Yield: 3 cups (15 calories per tablespoon).

PROTEIN 0.1 / FAT 0.0 / CARBOHYDRATE 4.1 / CHOLESTEROL 0 /
IRON 0.0 / SODIUM 0 / CALCIUM 3

Zucchini Boats with Vegetable Medley (page 204) and Maple-Fried Corn (page 201) have just-picked flavor.

ARTICHOKE HEART CASSEROLE

Vegetable cooking spray
1 cup chopped fresh mushrooms
1/3 cup chopped sweet red pepper
1/4 cup chopped onion
2 cloves garlic, minced
1 cup part-skim ricotta cheese
1/3 cup (1½ ounces) shredded 40% less-fat Cheddar cheese
1 egg, beaten
1 teaspoon lemon juice
1/4 teaspoon salt
1/8 teaspoon ground red pepper
1 (9-ounce) package frozen artichoke hearts, thawed and chopped
1/4 cup soft, whole wheat breadcrumbs
1 tablespoon minced fresh parsley
1 tablespoon grated Parmesan cheese
1 teaspoon margarine, melted

Coat a large nonstick skillet with cooking spray; place over medium-high heat until hot. Add mushrooms, sweet red pepper, onion, and garlic, and sauté until tender. Set aside.

Combine ricotta cheese, Cheddar cheese, egg, lemon juice, salt, and ground red pepper in a large bowl; stir well. Stir in sautéed vegetable mixture and artichokes. Spoon vegetable mixture into a 1-quart casserole that has been coated with cooking spray.

Combine breadcrumbs, parsley, Parmesan cheese, and margarine; stir well. Sprinkle breadcrumb mixture evenly over casserole. Bake, uncovered, at 350° for 30 minutes. Yield: 6 servings (132 calories per ½-cup serving).

PROTEIN 9.8 / FAT 6.9 / CARBOHYDRATE 8.7 / CHOLESTEROL 59 / IRON 1.0 / SODIUM 264 / CALCIUM 200

ALMOND ASPARAGUS

1½ pounds fresh asparagus spears
Vegetable cooking spray
1 tablespoon margarine
2 tablespoons lime juice
1/4 cup slivered blanched almonds, toasted
1/8 teaspoon salt
1/8 teaspoon coarsely ground pepper

Snap off rough ends of asparagus. Remove scales from stalks with a knife or vegetable peeler, if desired.

Coat a large nonstick skillet with cooking spray; add margarine. Place over medium-high heat until margarine melts. Add asparagus, and sauté 3 to 4 minutes. Add lime juice; cover, and simmer 2 to 3 minutes or until crisp-tender. Add almonds and remaining ingredients, tossing gently. Yield: 6 servings (70 calories per serving).

PROTEIN 3.5 / FAT 5.1 / CARBOHYDRATE 4.5 / CHOLESTEROL 0 / IRON 0.8 / SODIUM 73 / CALCIUM 34

GREEN BEANS WITH BLUE CHEESE

1 pound fresh green beans
1 cup water
1 clove garlic
2 tablespoons crumbled blue cheese
1/4 teaspoon chopped fresh dillweed

Wash beans and remove strings. Cut beans into 1-inch pieces. Combine beans, water, and garlic in a large saucepan; bring to a boil. Cover, reduce heat, and simmer 18 minutes or until tender. Drain. Remove and discard garlic. Add blue cheese and dillweed; toss gently. Serve immediately. Yield: 8 servings (24 calories per ½-cup serving).

PROTEIN 1.4 / FAT 0.6 / CARBOHYDRATE 4.1 / CHOLESTEROL 1 / IRON 0.7 / SODIUM 29 / CALCIUM 35

FRESH BROCCOLI TIMBALES

1¼ cups chopped fresh broccoli
2 teaspoons margarine
1 tablespoon all-purpose flour
1¼ cups skim milk
1 clove garlic
1/8 teaspoon salt
2 eggs, beaten
Vegetable cooking spray
1 small tomato, peeled, seeded, and finely chopped
1/2 teaspoon minced fresh basil
2 tablespoons spicy hot vegetable juice cocktail
1 teaspoon cornstarch
2 teaspoons water
Fresh basil sprigs (optional)

Cook broccoli, covered, in a small amount of

Delicately flavored Fresh Broccoli Timbales are an elegant way to enjoy vitamin-rich broccoli.

boiling water 5 minutes or until tender. Drain broccoli well, and set aside.

Melt margarine in a heavy saucepan over low heat, add flour, stirring until smooth. Cook 1 minute, stirring constantly. Gradually add milk; cook over medium heat, stirring constantly, until mixture is thickened and bubbly.

Combine broccoli, garlic, white sauce mixture, and salt in container of an electric blender or food processor; top with cover, and process until smooth. Pour mixture into saucepan. Gradually stir one-fourth of broccoli mixture into beaten eggs; add to remaining broccoli mixture, stirring constantly. Cook over medium heat until thoroughly heated.

Spoon mixture into 4 (6-ounce) timbale molds or custard cups that have been coated with cooking spray.

Place molds in an 8-inch square baking dish; pour hot water into baking dish to a depth of 1 inch. Bake at 350° for 45 minutes or until set. Remove from water; cool 5 minutes before unmolding. Loosen edge of timbales with a spatula; invert onto serving plate. Set aside and keep warm.

Combine tomato, basil, and juice in a small saucepan. Cook over low heat, stirring constantly, until tomato is soft.

Combine cornstarch and water, stirring to blend. Gradually add cornstarch mixture to tomato mixture; bring to a boil. Reduce heat, and cook 1 minute or until mixture thickens, stirring constantly. To serve, spoon 2 tablespoons tomato sauce over each timbale. Garnish with fresh basil sprigs, if desired. Yield: 4 servings (113 calories per serving).

PROTEIN 7.1 / FAT 5.4 / CARBOHYDRATE 9.3 / CHOLESTEROL 139 / IRON 1.0 / SODIUM 205 / CALCIUM 128

BRUSSELS SPROUTS STIR-FRY

Vegetable cooking spray
1 tablespoon vegetable oil
1 (10-ounce) package frozen brussels sprouts, thawed and cut in half lengthwise
4 green onions, cut diagonally into 1-inch pieces
2 medium carrots, scraped and cut diagonally into ⅛-inch slices
1 small sweet red pepper, seeded and cut into julienne strips
1 small green pepper, seeded and cut into julienne strips
1 clove garlic, minced
1 tablespoon plus 1½ teaspoons low-sodium soy sauce
¾ teaspoon ground ginger

Coat a wok or large nonstick skillet with cooking spray; add oil. Place over medium-high heat until hot. Add brussels sprouts and next 5 ingredients; stir-fry 4 minutes or until crisp-tender. Add soy sauce and ginger, tossing gently. Serve immediately. Yield: 6 servings (53 calories per ½-cup serving).

PROTEIN 2.2 / FAT 2.6 / CARBOHYDRATE 6.4 / CHOLESTEROL 0 / IRON 1.0 / SODIUM 167 / CALCIUM 34

BRUSSELS SPROUTS-TOMATO TOSS

1 pound fresh brussels sprouts
1½ cups water
Vegetable cooking spray
1 tablespoon olive oil
2 cloves garlic, sliced
12 small cherry tomatoes, halved
2 teaspoons lemon juice
1 tablespoon chopped fresh cilantro

Wash brussels sprouts thoroughly, and remove discolored leaves. Cut off stem ends, and slash bottom of each sprout with shallow X.

Place water in a medium saucepan; bring to a boil. Add brussels sprouts; return to a boil. Cover, reduce heat, and simmer 8 minutes or until brussels sprouts are tender. Drain. Cut brussels sprouts in half lengthwise.

Coat a large nonstick skillet with cooking spray; add oil. Place over medium-high heat until hot. Add garlic, and sauté until tender. Add brussels sprouts, tomatoes, and lemon juice; cook, stirring frequently, 2 minutes or until thoroughly heated. Sprinkle with cilantro. Serve immediately. Yield: 6 servings (50 calories per ½-cup serving).

PROTEIN 2.2 / FAT 3.1 / CARBOHYDRATE 5.0 / CHOLESTEROL 0 / IRON 0.6 / SODIUM 17 / CALCIUM 36

CUMIN-SPIKED CABBAGE

Vegetable cooking spray
3 cups thinly sliced cabbage
¼ teaspoon salt
¼ teaspoon ground cumin
⅛ teaspoon chili powder
⅛ teaspoon pepper

Coat a large nonstick skillet with cooking spray. Place over medium-high heat until hot. Add cabbage, and sauté until crisp-tender. Add salt and remaining ingredients; toss well. Serve immediately. Yield: 4 servings (15 calories per ½-cup serving).

PROTEIN 0.7 / FAT 0.3 / CARBOHYDRATE 2.9 / CHOLESTEROL 0 / IRON 0.4 / SODIUM 157 / CALCIUM 27

CARROT AND JICAMA MATCHSTICKS

Vegetable cooking spray
2 teaspoons vegetable oil
1 teaspoon margarine
1 (1¼-pound) jicama, peeled and cut into julienne strips
6 medium carrots, scraped and cut into julienne strips
¼ teaspoon salt
¼ teaspoon pepper
¼ teaspoon dried whole basil
2 tablespoons unsweetened orange juice

Coat a large nonstick skillet with cooking spray; add oil and margarine. Place over medium-high heat until hot. Add jicama strips and remaining ingredients, except orange juice. Sauté, stirring constantly, 8 to 10 minutes or until vegetables are crisp-tender. Sprinkle with orange juice; toss gently. Yield: 8 servings (45 calories per ½-cup serving).

PROTEIN 0.9 / FAT 1.8 / CARBOHYDRATE 6.6 / CHOLESTEROL 0 / IRON 0.4 / SODIUM 88 / CALCIUM 14

MINTED CARROTS AND PINEAPPLE

1 small fresh pineapple
⅓ cup unsweetened pineapple juice
1 tablespoon honey
¼ teaspoon salt
¼ cup minced fresh mint
4 large carrots, scraped and cut diagonally into ½-inch slices

Cut pineapple in half lengthwise; remove core. Cut pineapple pulp into ½-inch cubes. Set aside 2 cups pineapple cubes (reserve remaining pineapple for other uses).

Combine pineapple juice, honey, salt, and fresh mint in a medium saucepan; bring to a boil. Add carrot; cover, reduce heat, and simmer 8 to 10 minutes. Stir in reserved pineapple cubes, and cook an additional 5 minutes or until carrots are tender. Yield: 6 servings (68 calories per ½-cup serving).

PROTEIN 0.8 / FAT 0.3 / CARBOHYDRATE 16.9 / CHOLESTEROL 0 / IRON 0.7 / SODIUM 117 / CALCIUM 24

CREOLE CAULIFLOWER

Vegetable cooking spray
1 teaspoon vegetable oil
½ medium onion, chopped
1 small green pepper, seeded and chopped
1 clove garlic, minced
1 small head cauliflower, broken into flowerets
1 (16-ounce) can stewed tomatoes, undrained and chopped
1 bay leaf
½ teaspoon dried whole thyme
¼ teaspoon hot sauce

Coat a large nonstick skillet with cooking spray; add oil. Place over medium-high heat until hot. Add onion, green pepper, and garlic, and sauté until tender. Add cauliflower and remaining ingredients; simmer 10 to 15 minutes

or until cauliflower is crisp-tender. Remove and discard bay leaf before serving. Yield: 8 servings (51 calories per ½-cup serving).

PROTEIN 2.2 / FAT 1.0 / CARBOHYDRATE 9.6 / CHOLESTEROL 0 / IRON 1.1 / SODIUM 156 / CALCIUM 45

MAPLE-FRIED CORN

Vegetable cooking spray
3 cups fresh corn cut from cob
½ cup chopped onion
⅛ teaspoon ground cinnamon
¼ teaspoon salt
3 tablespoons reduced-calorie maple syrup
3 tablespoons skim milk

Coat a large nonstick skillet with cooking spray; place over medium-high heat until hot. Add corn and onion, and sauté 5 minutes. Combine cinnamon and remaining ingredients. Add to corn in skillet, and cook over medium heat 20 minutes, stirring frequently. Yield: 4 servings (117 calories per ½-cup serving).

PROTEIN 4.4 / FAT 1.6 / CARBOHYDRATE 25.6 / CHOLESTEROL 0 / IRON 0.7 / SODIUM 173 / CALCIUM 24

CHILLED VEGETABLE-STUFFED MUSHROOMS

12 large fresh mushrooms (1 pound)
½ cup commercial reduced-calorie Italian dressing
¼ cup plus 3 tablespoons frozen English peas, thawed
1 tablespoon sliced pimiento

Clean mushrooms with damp paper towels. Remove mushroom stems; reserve stems for other uses. Combine mushroom caps and salad dressing in a large bowl, tossing lightly to coat. Cover and chill 2 hours, stirring occasionally. Drain, reserving 1 tablespoon dressing. Set mushroom caps aside.

Combine peas, pimiento, and reserved dressing; stir well. Spoon vegetable mixture evenly into mushroom caps. Cover and chill thoroughly. Yield: 6 servings (37 calories per serving).

PROTEIN 2.2 / FAT 0.4 / CARBOHYDRATE 7.2 / CHOLESTEROL 0 / IRON 1.2 / SODIUM 197 / CALCIUM 8

LEMON BAKED OKRA

Vegetable cooking spray
1 pound fresh okra
2 tablespoons plus 2 teaspoons water
2 teaspoons margarine, melted
¼ teaspoon salt
1 teaspoon grated lemon rind
1 teaspoon lemon juice

Cut two 12- x 18-inch pieces of heavy-duty aluminum foil. Coat each piece with cooking spray. Place ½ pound okra on each piece of foil.

Combine water, margarine, salt, and lemon rind; spoon evenly over okra. Seal foil securely around okra. Bake at 450° for 20 minutes. Unwrap; sprinkle lemon juice evenly over okra. Serve immediately. Yield: 4 servings (62 calories per ½-cup serving).

PROTEIN 2.3 / FAT 2.2 / CARBOHYDRATE 8.9 / CHOLESTEROL 0 / IRON 0.9 / SODIUM 178 / CALCIUM 94

SAVORY CREAMED PARSNIPS

1¼ pounds parsnips, scraped and thinly sliced
½ cup chopped onion
2 cloves garlic, minced
1 tablespoon margarine
1 tablespoon all-purpose flour
1 cup skim milk
½ teaspoon minced fresh rosemary
¼ teaspoon grated lemon rind
¼ teaspoon ground white pepper
⅛ teaspoon salt

Combine parsnips, onion, and garlic in a medium saucepan; cover with water. Bring to a boil. Cover, reduce heat, and simmer 10 minutes or until parsnips are tender. Remove from heat; drain well.

Melt margarine in a heavy saucepan over low heat; add flour, stirring until smooth. Cook 1 minute, stirring constantly. Gradually add milk; cook over medium heat, stirring constantly, until mixture is thickened and bubbly. Remove from heat; stir in rosemary, lemon rind, pepper, and salt. Add reserved vegetables; toss gently. Serve immediately. Yield: 6 servings (86 calories per ½-cup serving).

PROTEIN 2.5 / FAT 2.2 / CARBOHYDRATE 14.7 / CHOLESTEROL 1 / IRON 0.5 / SODIUM 99 / CALCIUM 78

PEACHY SWEET POTATOES

2 medium-size sweet potatoes
1 cup peeled, chopped fresh peaches
⅓ cup peach nectar
2 tablespoons peach schnapps
⅛ teaspoon salt
Vegetable cooking spray
2 tablespoons honey-crunch wheat germ
1 tablespoon brown sugar
1 tablespoon nutlike cereal nuggets
¼ teaspoon ground cinnamon
¼ teaspoon ground nutmeg

Wash sweet potatoes; bake at 400° for 45 minutes or until done. Allow potatoes to cool to touch. Cut in half. Scoop out pulp, discarding peels. Combine potato pulp, peaches, nectar, schnapps, and salt in a medium bowl, stirring until well blended. Spoon into a 1½-quart casserole that has been coated with cooking spray.

Combine wheat germ, brown sugar, cereal, cinnamon, and nutmeg, stirring well. Sprinkle wheat germ mixture evenly over casserole. Bake, uncovered, at 350° for 20 minutes or until thoroughly heated. Yield: 6 servings (124 calories per ½-cup serving).

PROTEIN 1.7 / FAT 0.4 / CARBOHYDRATE 27.1 / CHOLESTEROL 0 / IRON 0.6 / SODIUM 75 / CALCIUM 21

CHUNKY MASHED RUTABAGAS

1 (2-pound) rutabaga, peeled and diced
2 cups water
¼ cup unsweetened apple cider
1 tablespoon chopped fresh chives
¼ teaspoon salt
¼ teaspoon sugar
¼ teaspoon pepper

Combine rutabaga and water in a large saucepan. Bring to a boil; cover, reduce heat, and simmer 20 to 30 minutes or until tender. Drain well.

Combine rutabaga, cider, and remaining ingredients in a medium bowl. Mash until soft but chunky. Serve immediately. Yield: 8 servings (41 calories per ½-cup serving).

PROTEIN 1.2 / FAT 0.2 / CARBOHYDRATE 9.4 / CHOLESTEROL 0 / IRON 0.6 / SODIUM 94 / CALCIUM 49

Serve Grilled Peppers and Squash at the next cookout.

GRILLED PEPPERS AND SQUASH

¼ teaspoon garlic powder
1 tablespoon olive oil
1 tablespoon balsamic vinegar
4 medium-size yellow squash
1 medium-size sweet red pepper, seeded and cut
　into 2-inch pieces
1 medium-size green pepper, seeded and cut into
　2-inch pieces
Vegetable cooking spray

Combine garlic powder, olive oil, and vinegar; set aside.

Cut squash into ½-inch slices. Thread squash and peppers onto 4 (12-inch) skewers. Brush with oil mixture.

Coat grill rack with cooking spray; place on grill over low coals. Place vegetables on rack and cook 10 to 15 minutes or until done, turning occasionally. Yield: 4 servings (58 calories per 1-cup serving).

PROTEIN 1.1 / FAT 4.1 / CARBOHYDRATE 5.3 / CHOLESTEROL 0 /
IRON 0.9 / SODIUM 3 / CALCIUM 16

SPAGHETTI SQUASH WITH JALAPEÑO PEPPER SAUCE

1 (8-ounce) can tomato sauce
1 medium jalapeño pepper, seeded and minced
2 tablespoons chopped fresh cilantro
2 tablespoons finely chopped onion
1 teaspoon chili powder
1 (4-pound) spaghetti squash
2 tablespoons grated Parmesan cheese

Combine first 5 ingredients in a small saucepan. Bring to a boil; reduce heat, and simmer 15 minutes. Set aside, and keep warm.

Wash squash. Cut in half lengthwise, and discard seeds. Place squash, cut side down, in a large Dutch oven; add water to a depth of 2 inches. Bring water to a boil; cover, reduce heat, and simmer 15 to 20 minutes or until tender.

Drain squash and cool. Using a fork, remove spaghetti-like strands; discard shells. Place squash strands in a bowl; add tomato mixture, and toss gently. Sprinkle cheese evenly over top. Serve immediately. Yield: 6 servings (62 calories per ½-cup serving).

PROTEIN 2.3 / FAT 1.0 / CARBOHYDRATE 12.3 / CHOLESTEROL 1 /
IRON 1.0 / SODIUM 289 / CALCIUM 61

SPAGHETTI SQUASH

Select hard, glossy yellow or cream-colored spaghetti squash. Cut the squash in half, and steam until tender. Then, use a fork to shred the pulp into "spaghetti" strands. Spaghetti squash can be served plain or with pasta sauces, or tossed with a small amount of olive oil and grated cheese.

Cooked and cooled, it can also be added to salads. The stringy but flavorful yellow flesh supplies vitamin A, potassium, beta-carotene, niacin, thiamin, and vitamin B₆. Best of all, spaghetti squash has only 22 calories in a ½-cup serving.

ZUCCHINI BOATS WITH VEGETABLE MEDLEY

2 medium zucchini (¾ pound)
Vegetable cooking spray
½ cup diced yellow squash
½ cup frozen English peas, thawed
½ cup sliced fresh mushrooms
2 tablespoons diced sweet red pepper
½ teaspoon dried whole basil
¼ teaspoon salt

Cut zucchini in half lengthwise, leaving stems intact. Arrange, cut side down, on a steaming rack. Place over boiling water; cover and steam 6 to 8 minutes or until crisp-tender. Remove pulp, leaving ¼-inch-thick shells. Dice pulp and set aside; reserve shells.

Coat a large nonstick skillet with cooking spray. Place over medium-high heat until hot. Add reserved zucchini pulp, yellow squash, and remaining ingredients; sauté 3 to 5 minutes, stirring constantly. Spoon zucchini mixture into reserved shells. Arrange in a 12- x 8- x 2-inch baking dish. Bake at 350° for 15 minutes or until thoroughly heated. Yield: 4 servings (34 calories per serving).

PROTEIN 2.3 / FAT 0.4 / CARBOHYDRATE 6.4 / CHOLESTEROL 0 /
IRON 0.9 / SODIUM 170 / CALCIUM 24

WILTED WATERCRESS AND TOMATOES

Vegetable cooking spray
2 teaspoons olive oil
2 cups torn fresh watercress
1 cup torn arugula
2 medium tomatoes, seeded and coarsely chopped
1 tablespoon lemon juice
¼ teaspoon pepper

Coat a large nonstick skillet with cooking spray; add oil. Place over medium-high heat until hot. Add watercress and arugula, and sauté until wilted, stirring constantly. Add tomatoes, and cook until thoroughly heated. Sprinkle with lemon juice and pepper; toss well. Serve warm. Yield: 4 servings (53 calories per ½-cup serving).

PROTEIN 2.3 / FAT 2.8 / CARBOHYDRATE 6.5 / CHOLESTEROL 0 /
IRON 1.0 / SODIUM 17 / CALCIUM 143

TURNIP-SWISS CHEESE PUREE

1½ pounds turnips, peeled and sliced
½ cup (2 ounces) finely shredded Swiss cheese
2 tablespoons grated Romano cheese
½ cup skim milk
1 clove garlic, crushed

Place turnips in a large saucepan; add water to cover, and bring to a boil. Cover; reduce heat, and simmer 15 minutes or until turnips are tender. Drain.

Position knife blade in food processor bowl. Add turnips, cheeses, and remaining ingredients; top with cover, and process until smooth. Transfer to a serving dish, and serve immediately. Yield: 6 servings (83 calories per ½-cup serving).

PROTEIN 5.1 / FAT 3.4 / CARBOHYDRATE 8.6 / CHOLESTEROL 12 /
IRON 0.4 / SODIUM 140 / CALCIUM 176

CINNAMON-CRUSTED APPLES

4 medium Granny Smith apples
¼ cup firmly packed brown sugar
2 tablespoons all-purpose flour
½ teaspoon ground cinnamon
⅛ teaspoon ground nutmeg
2 tablespoons margarine
1 egg white, beaten
Vegetable cooking spray
¼ cup water

Peel and core apples. Cut apples in half lengthwise. Combine brown sugar, flour, cinnamon, and nutmeg; stir well. Cut in margarine with a pastry blender until mixture resembles coarse meal.

Brush apples with beaten egg white. Dredge in brown sugar mixture. Place apples, cut side down, in an 11- x 7- x 2-inch baking dish that has been coated with cooking spray; add water. Bake, uncovered, at 375° for 35 minutes or until apples are tender. Yield: 8 servings (105 calories per serving).

PROTEIN 0.8 / FAT 3.2 / CARBOHYDRATE 19.5 / CHOLESTEROL 0 /
IRON 0.4 / SODIUM 42 / CALCIUM 12

Black Currant Winter Compote is a cinnamony blend of prunes, dried apricots, pears, and apples.

BLACK CURRANT WINTER COMPOTE

1 cup boiling water
4 black currant herb tea bags
½ cup dried pitted baby prunes
⅓ cup dried apricot halves
2 medium pears, peeled, cored, and
   cut into wedges
2 medium cooking apples, peeled, cored,
   and cut into wedges
1 tablespoon plus 1½ teaspoons brown
   sugar
1 teaspoon ground cinnamon
¼ teaspoon ground nutmeg

Pour 1 cup boiling water over tea bags; cover, and let stand 5 minutes. Remove and discard tea bags.

Combine prunes, apricots, pears, and apples in a 2-quart baking dish or soufflé dish. Combine tea, sugar, cinnamon, and nutmeg; pour over fruit mixture.

Cover and bake at 350° for 40 to 50 minutes or until fruit is tender. Yield: 8 servings (112 calories per ½-cup serving).

PROTEIN 0.8 / FAT 0.7 / CARBOHYDRATE 28.4 / CHOLESTEROL 0 /
IRON 0.9 / SODIUM 7 / CALCIUM 21

HONEYED CITRUS MEDLEY

3 medium oranges
1 medium-size pink grapefruit
2 tablespoons honey
1 tablespoon white wine vinegar
1 teaspoon grated lime rind

Peel, seed, and section oranges and grapefruit over a medium bowl, reserving ½ cup juice. Place fruit sections in a small bowl, and set aside.

Combine reserved juice, honey, vinegar, and lime rind in a small nonaluminum saucepan, bring to a boil. Cover, reduce heat, and simmer 10 minutes, stirring occasionally. Pour hot juice mixture over fruit sections. Cover and chill thoroughly. Yield: 4 servings (88 calories per ½-cup serving).

PROTEIN 1.1 / FAT 0.1 / CARBOHYDRATE 22.5 / CHOLESTEROL 0 /
IRON 0.5 / SODIUM 1 / CALCIUM 30

GLAZED MANGO

Vegetable cooking spray
2 teaspoons margarine
2 tablespoons brown sugar
2 tablespoons lime juice
2 cups coarsely chopped ripe mango

Coat a large nonstick skillet with vegetable cooking spray; add margarine. Place over medium-low heat until margarine melts. Add brown sugar and lime juice, stirring well. Add chopped mango. Cook, stirring constantly, 3 minutes or until thoroughly heated. Yield: 4 servings (102 calories per ½-cup serving).

PROTEIN 0.5 / FAT 2.9 / CARBOHYDRATE 20.7 / CHOLESTEROL 0 /
IRON 0.3 / SODIUM 26 / CALCIUM 14

CURRY-GLAZED PINEAPPLE RINGS

1 medium-size fresh pineapple
Vegetable cooking spray
2 tablespoons unsweetened pineapple juice
1 tablespoon plus 1 teaspoon margarine, melted
1 tablespoon plus 1 teaspoon honey
½ teaspoon curry powder

Peel and trim eyes from pineapple; remove core. Cut pineapple crosswise into four ¾-inch slices. (Reserve remaining pineapple for other uses.) Place pineapple slices in a 9-inch square baking dish that has been coated with cooking spray. Combine pineapple juice and remaining ingredients, stirring well. Pour pineapple mixture over pineapple slices. Cover and bake at 350° for 30 minutes or until thoroughly heated. Yield: 4 servings (108 calories per serving).

PROTEIN 0.5 / FAT 4.4 / CARBOHYDRATE 18.7 / CHOLESTEROL 0 /
IRON 0.5 / SODIUM 46 / CALCIUM 11

WARM SPICED PLUMS

¾ cup unsweetened red grape juice
½ cup water
3 tablespoons brown sugar
1 teaspoon whole cloves
1 (3-inch) stick cinnamon
1¼ pounds small ripe plums, pitted and quartered
¼ teaspoon vanilla extract

Combine first 5 ingredients in a medium-size nonaluminum saucepan, stirring well. Bring to a boil; reduce heat, and simmer 10 minutes. Add plums; cover, and simmer 5 minutes or until tender. Remove and discard cloves and cinnamon before serving. Stir in vanilla. Serve warm. Yield: 6 servings (94 calories per ½-cup serving).

PROTEIN 0.7 / FAT 0.5 / CARBOHYDRATE 23.1 / CHOLESTEROL 0 /
IRON 0.4 / SODIUM 3 / CALCIUM 13

The fresh-from-the-bayou flavor of hearty Louisiana Gumbo (page 217) is sure to satisfy.

Soups & Stews

THREE BERRY DESSERT SOUP

2 cups cran-raspberry drink
1 cup unsweetened orange juice
1 cup water
4 (4- x ½-inch) strips orange rind
2 tablespoons plus 2 teaspoons
 cornstarch
2 tablespoons plus 2 teaspoons water
1¼ cups sliced fresh strawberries
1 cup fresh raspberries
1 cup fresh blueberries
¼ cup raspberry schnapps

Combine first 4 ingredients in a large nonaluminum saucepan; bring mixture to a boil. Boil 2 minutes.

Combine cornstarch and water, blending well. Stir cornstarch mixture into juice mixture; cook, stirring constantly, until mixture is clear and thickened. Remove from heat. Remove and discard orange rind. Stir in berries and schnapps. Pour fruit mixture into a serving bowl; cover and chill thoroughly. Yield: 6 cups (130 calories per 1-cup serving).

PROTEIN 0.9 / FAT 0.4 / CARBOHYDRATE 29.0 / CHOLESTEROL 0 /
IRON 0.4 / SODIUM 7 / CALCIUM 16

ICED CRANBERRY-ORANGE SOUP

2 cups unsweetened orange juice
1 cup cranberry juice cocktail
1 cup port or other sweet red dessert wine
⅓ cup firmly packed brown sugar
3 cups fresh or frozen cranberries, thawed
½ cup water
1 tablespoon cornstarch
¼ cup orange low-fat yogurt

Combine first 4 ingredients in a large saucepan. Bring to a boil. Cover; reduce heat, and simmer 10 minutes. Stir in cranberries. Cover and simmer 25 minutes or until cranberry skins pop, stirring frequently. Remove from heat. Strain cranberry mixture through a sieve. Discard skins and seeds.

Return cranberry mixture to saucepan. Combine water and cornstarch, stirring until smooth. Add cornstarch mixture to cranberry mixture; bring to a boil. Boil 1 minute, stirring constantly. Remove from heat. Cover and chill thoroughly. Ladle into individual soup bowls. Garnish each serving with 1½ teaspoons yogurt. Yield: 4 cups (118 calories per ½-cup serving).

PROTEIN 0.9 / FAT 0.2 / CARBOHYDRATE 29.3 / CHOLESTEROL 0 /
IRON 0.5 / SODIUM 10 / CALCIUM 29

 SOUP-ER DESIGNS

Add an elegant touch to soup by decorating the top of each bowl. The Cream of Parsnip Soup (on left in photo) is garnished with Dilled Tomato Sauce. To create the design, drizzle the tomato sauce in a circle on top of the soup. Draw a wooden pick through the sauce, spoke-fashion at regular intervals, to create a webbed effect.

The Iced Cranberry-Orange Soup is garnished with an attractive floral pattern. Pipe low-fat yogurt in large and small circles on each bowl of soup. Draw a wooden pick through yogurt, pulling from the edge of the bowl towards the center. Continue the pattern around the bowl, creating a floral design.

CHILLED HONEYDEW SOUP

1 medium honeydew melon, peeled, seeded, and
 cut into chunks
¾ cup unsweetened orange juice
2 tablespoons lime juice
1½ teaspoons powdered sugar
1 cup skim milk
½ cup fresh blueberries

Combine honeydew, orange juice, lime juice, and powdered sugar in container of an electric blender or food processor; top with cover, and process until smooth. Stir in milk. Cover and chill thoroughly. Stir before serving. Top each serving with 1 tablespoon blueberries. Yield: 8 cups (80 calories per 1-cup serving).

PROTEIN 1.9 / FAT 0.2 / CARBOHYDRATE 19.4 / CHOLESTEROL 1 /
IRON 0.2 / SODIUM 31 / CALCIUM 49

CAESAR CONSOMMÉ

4 cups water
1 tablespoon red wine vinegar
1½ teaspoons chicken-flavored bouillon granules
1 teaspoon lemon juice
1 teaspoon Worcestershire sauce
¼ teaspoon pepper
¼ teaspoon anchovy paste
2½ cups chopped romaine lettuce
¼ cup grated Parmesan cheese
¼ cup croutons

Combine first 7 ingredients in a large saucepan. Cover, and bring to a boil. Reduce heat, and simmer 15 minutes. Stir in chopped lettuce. Cook until soup is thoroughly heated. Ladle soup into individual bowls. Top each serving with 1½ teaspoons Parmesan cheese and 1 tablespoon croutons. Yield: 4 cups (25 calories per ½-cup serving).

PROTEIN 1.5 / FAT 1.3 / CARBOHYDRATE 1.8 / CHOLESTEROL 2 /
IRON 0.2 / SODIUM 228 / CALCIUM 40

LOBSTER BISQUE

3 (8-ounce) lobster tails, fresh or frozen, thawed
¼ cup chopped green onions
¼ cup margarine
¼ cup all-purpose flour
½ cup dry sherry
3½ cups skim milk
3 tablespoons chopped fresh parsley
¼ teaspoon salt
¼ teaspoon ground white pepper
¼ teaspoon hot sauce
¼ teaspoon paprika

Split and clean tails. Cub lobster tail meat into ½-inch pieces; set aside. Discard shells.

Sauté green onions in margarine in a small Dutch oven until tender. Add flour, stirring until smooth. Cook 1 minute, stirring constantly. Gradually add sherry; cook over low heat, stirring constantly, until thickened and bubbly. Gradually add milk; cook, stirring constantly with a wire whisk, until thickened (do not boil). Stir in parsley, salt, pepper, and hot sauce. Stir in reserved lobster meat, and cook until thoroughly heated. Ladle into individual soup bowls, and sprinkle evenly with paprika. Serve immediately. Yield: 5 cups (133 calories per ½-cup serving).

PROTEIN 12.8 / FAT 5.2 / CARBOHYDRATE 8.3 / CHOLESTEROL 49 /
IRON 0.3 / SODIUM 159 / CALCIUM 113

CREAM OF PARSNIP SOUP WITH DILLED
TOMATO SAUCE

1 pound parsnips, scraped and thinly sliced
¾ cup Chablis or other dry white wine
2 teaspoons margarine
¼ teaspoon ground white pepper
¼ teaspoon chicken-flavored bouillon granules
2¼ cups skim milk
3 tablespoons tomato sauce
1 tablespoon low-fat sour cream
¼ teaspoon dried whole dillweed

Combine parsnips, wine, margarine, pepper, and bouillon granules in a saucepan; bring to a boil. Cover; reduce heat, and cook 15 minutes or until parsnips are tender. Combine parsnip mixture and milk in container of an electric blender; top with cover, and process until smooth. Return parsnip mixture to saucepan; cook over low heat until thoroughly heated.

Combine tomato sauce, sour cream, and dillweed; stir well. Spoon soup into individual soup bowls. Drizzle 1 tablespoon tomato mixture in a circle on top of each serving. Draw a wooden pick through tomato mixture, spoke-fashion, to create a webbed effect. Serve immediately. Yield: 4 cups (151 calories per 1-cup serving).

PROTEIN 6.2 / FAT 3.0 / CARBOHYDRATE 26.2 / CHOLESTEROL 4 /
IRON 0.9 / SODIUM 228 / CALCIUM 214

The attractive presentation of Butternut-Broccoli Soup is striking yet simple to achieve.

BUTTERNUT-BROCCOLI SOUP

Vegetable cooking spray
1 teaspoon vegetable oil
1 shallot, chopped
1 (1-pound) butternut squash, peeled, seeded, and diced
⅔ cup water
1 teaspoon chopped fresh thyme
1½ teaspoons all-purpose flour
1⅔ cups water
2 teaspoons chicken-flavored bouillon granules, divided
¾ pound fresh broccoli
2 cups water
1 clove garlic, minced
½ teaspoon grated lemon rind
2 tablespoons low-fat sour cream

Coat a large Dutch oven with cooking spray; add oil. Place over medium-high heat until hot.

Add chopped shallot, and sauté 1 to 2 minutes. Add squash, ⅔ cup water, and thyme. Cover and cook over medium heat 10 to 15 minutes or until squash is tender. Stir in flour. Cook 1 minute. Stir in 1⅔ cups water and 1 teaspoon bouillon granules. Bring mixture to a boil. Reduce heat, uncover, and simmer 8 minutes. Remove from heat. Let cool slightly. Transfer mixture in batches to container of an electric blender or food processor; top with cover, and process until smooth. Set aside, and keep warm.

Trim off large leaves of broccoli; remove tough ends of lower stalks. Wash broccoli thoroughly, and chop. Combine broccoli, 2 cups water, garlic, and remaining 1 teaspoon bouillon granules in a large Dutch oven. Bring to a boil. Cover; reduce heat, and simmer 8 minutes or until broccoli is tender. Remove from heat. Transfer mixture in batches to container of an electric blender or food processor; add lemon rind. Top with cover, and process until smooth.

To serve, pour ½ cup of each mixture into individual soup bowls at the same time. Top each serving with 1 teaspoon sour cream. Serve immediately. Yield: 6 cups (64 calories per 1-cup serving).

PROTEIN 2.7 / FAT 2.1 / CARBOHYDRATE 10.9 / CHOLESTEROL 2 / IRON 1.0 / SODIUM 293 / CALCIUM 56

BRANDIED SQUASH SOUP

1 (2-pound) butternut squash
Vegetable cooking spray
1 teaspoon vegetable oil
½ cup chopped onion
1 tablespoon chicken-flavored bouillon granules
⅛ teaspoon ground cardamom
⅛ teaspoon ground cinnamon
3 cups water
2 tablespoons brandy
½ cup low-fat sour cream
½ cup skim milk

Cut squash in half lengthwise. Place cut side down in a 13- x 9- x 2-inch baking dish. Add hot water to a depth of ½ inch in dish. Cover and bake at 350° for 45 minutes or until squash is tender. Drain. Let cool to touch. Remove and discard seeds. Scoop out pulp; reserve pulp. Discard shells.

Coat a large nonstick skillet with cooking spray; add oil. Place over medium-high heat until hot. Add onion, and sauté until tender. Stir in bouillon granules, cardamom, cinnamon, water, and brandy. Bring to a boil. Cook, stirring constantly, 1 to 2 minutes. Remove from heat.

Combine half of reserved squash pulp and half of onion mixture in container of an electric blender or food processor; top with cover, and process until smooth. Transfer pureed mixture to a large saucepan. Repeat procedure with remaining squash pulp and onion mixture; add to saucepan. Stir in sour cream and milk. Cook over medium-low heat until thoroughly heated, stirring constantly with a wire whisk. Yield: 6 cups (46 calories per ¾-cup serving).

PROTEIN 1.3 / FAT 3.6 / CARBOHYDRATE 2.7 / CHOLESTEROL 6 / IRON 0.1 / SODIUM 321 / CALCIUM 38

VEGETABLE-BARLEY SOUP

4 cups water
⅓ cup uncooked pearl barley
1 tablespoon beef-flavored bouillon granules
2 cups no-salt-added vegetable juice cocktail
1 medium carrot, scraped and coarsely chopped
½ cup chopped green pepper
⅓ cup chopped onion
2 cloves garlic, minced
¼ teaspoon pepper
½ teaspoon dried whole basil
½ teaspoon dried whole oregano
3 medium tomatoes, peeled, seeded, and coarsely chopped
2 cups sliced fresh mushrooms

Combine water, barley, and bouillon granules in a large Dutch oven; bring to a boil. Uncover, reduce heat, and simmer 30 minutes. Stir in vegetable juice cocktail and next 7 ingredients. Cover and simmer 30 minutes or until barley is tender, stirring occasionally. Stir in tomatoes and mushrooms. Cover and cook an additional 15 minutes or until vegetables are tender. Yield: 8 cups (69 calories per 1-cup serving).

PROTEIN 2.4 / FAT 0.8 / CARBOHYDRATE 14.0 / CHOLESTEROL 0 / IRON 1.3 / SODIUM 373 / CALCIUM 25

 MAKE EXERCISE WORK FOR YOU

To make exercise more meaningful, incorporate several of the following activities into your daily routine.

*To overcome frustrations from a stressful day, play racquetball, tennis, or train with weights.
*To conquer early morning blahs, wake up gradually by doing easy calisthenics while still in bed.
*Take care of errands while riding a bike.
*Organize your thoughts or think through a problem while walking or running.
*For motivation and to be among others with healthy lifestyles, join an aerobic conditioning class.
*Instead of giving into a food craving, jump on a stationary bike or go for a walk and burn calories instead of storing them.
*Put some zip in your lunch hour—listen to some energizing music on your headphones while you take a brisk walk.
*Spend some quality time with your family by taking a nature hike through the woods.

RATATOUILLE SOUP

Vegetable cooking spray
1 teaspoon vegetable oil
1 medium onion, chopped
1 clove garlic, minced
1 medium-size green pepper, seeded and chopped
⅓ cup chopped celery
1 (1-pound) eggplant, peeled and cut into ½-inch cubes
1 medium zucchini, sliced
1 (16-ounce) can whole tomatoes, undrained and coarsely chopped
½ teaspoon dried whole oregano
¼ teaspoon pepper
¼ teaspoon dried whole basil
2 cups no-salt-added tomato juice
1 cup water
2 tablespoons plus 2 teaspoons grated Parmesan cheese

Coat a large Dutch oven with cooking spray; add oil. Place over medium-high heat until hot. Add onion, garlic, green pepper, and celery, and sauté 5 minutes. Add eggplant and sauté an additional 5 minutes, stirring occasionally.

Stir in zucchini and next 6 ingredients; cover, reduce heat, and cook 15 minutes or until vegetables are tender, stirring occasionally. Spoon soup into individual serving bowls. Sprinkle 1 teaspoon Parmesan cheese over each serving. Yield: 8 cups (67 calories per 1-cup serving).

PROTEIN 3.1 / FAT 1.4 / CARBOHYDRATE 12.6 / CHOLESTEROL 1 / IRON 1.0 / SODIUM 254 / CALCIUM 76

HEARTY VEGETABLE-BEEF SOUP

2 pounds lean round steak (½-inch thick)
Vegetable cooking spray
1 cup hot water
2 medium tomatoes, peeled, seeded, and chopped
1 medium onion, coarsely chopped
1 cup sliced fresh okra
1 cup fresh or frozen corn, thawed
1 medium-size green pepper, seeded and chopped
1 cup spicy hot vegetable juice cocktail
1¼ teaspoons low-sodium Worcestershire sauce
¼ teaspoon garlic powder

Trim fat from steak, and cut into 1-inch cubes. Coat a Dutch oven with cooking spray. Add steak; cook over medium heat until browned, stirring often. Add water. Cover, reduce heat, and simmer 1½ hours or until tender. Stir in tomatoes and remaining ingredients. Cover; simmer 30 minutes, stirring often. Yield: 8 cups (194 calories per 1-cup serving).

PROTEIN 24.8 / FAT 5.6 / CARBOHYDRATE 10.4 / CHOLESTEROL 61 / IRON 2.9 / SODIUM 168 / CALCIUM 25

SPAGHETTI AND MEATBALL SOUP

¾ pound ground chuck
1 egg, lightly beaten
½ teaspoon dried whole oregano
¼ teaspoon dried whole basil
¼ teaspoon garlic powder
Vegetable cooking spray
1 teaspoon beef-flavored bouillon granules
1 medium onion, chopped
1 (8-ounce) can tomato sauce
2 (16-ounce) cans no-salt-added whole tomatoes, undrained
1 quart water
2 ounces spaghetti, uncooked
1 cup sliced fresh mushrooms
3 tablespoons plus 1 teaspoon grated Parmesan cheese

Combine ground chuck, egg, oregano, basil, and garlic powder in a medium bowl; stir well. Shape into meatballs, using 1 tablespoon mixture for each meatball. Arrange meatballs on rack of a broiler pan that has been coated with cooking spray. Broil 6 inches from heat 5 minutes; turn meatballs, and broil an additional 5 minutes or until browned. Drain well on paper towels. Place meatballs in a large Dutch oven. Add bouillon granules, onion, tomato sauce, tomatoes, and water. Bring to a boil. Cover, reduce heat, and simmer 30 minutes.

Add spaghetti. Bring to a boil. Uncover, reduce heat, and simmer 15 minutes. Stir in mushrooms and simmer an additional 5 minutes. Ladle into serving bowls. Sprinkle 1 teaspoon cheese over each serving. Yield: 10 cups (135 calories per 1-cup serving).

PROTEIN 10.0 / FAT 5.6 / CARBOHYDRATE 11.9 / CHOLESTEROL 50 / IRON 1.6 / SODIUM 300 / CALCIUM 68

SPRINGTIME CHICKEN SOUP

4 (6-ounce) skinned chicken breast halves
1½ quarts water
1½ teaspoons chopped fresh dillweed
¾ teaspoon salt
¼ teaspoon pepper
¾ pound fresh asparagus, cut diagonally
  into 1-inch pieces
1 cup sliced green onions
3 medium tomatoes, peeled, seeded, and
  chopped
3 small yellow squash, cut into ½-inch
  slices
3 tablespoons lemon juice

Trim fat from chicken. Combine chicken, water, dillweed, salt, and pepper in a large Dutch oven. Bring to a boil. Cover; reduce heat, and simmer 30 minutes or until chicken is tender. Remove chicken from broth, and set broth aside. Bone chicken, and cut meat into bite-size pieces.

Combine chicken, broth, asparagus, onions, tomato, and squash in a large Dutch oven. Bring to a boil. Cover, reduce heat, and simmer 20 minutes or until vegetables are tender. Stir in lemon juice. Yield: 12 cups (70 calories per 1-cup serving).

PROTEIN 11.9 / FAT 0.7 / CARBOHYDRATE 4.4 / CHOLESTEROL 26 / IRON 1.0 / SODIUM 181 / CALCIUM 25

HAM-SWEET POTATO CHOWDER

2 cups water
2 medium-size sweet potatoes, peeled and diced
1 medium leek, chopped
½ cup chopped celery
¼ teaspoon pepper
½ pound lean cooked ham, cubed
1 tablespoon unsalted margarine
2 tablespoons all-purpose flour
1½ cups skim milk
2 tablespoons minced fresh parsley

Combine first 5 ingredients in a saucepan. Bring to a boil. Cover, reduce heat, and simmer 20 minutes or until potatoes are tender. Place ½ cup vegetable mixture in container of an electric blender; top with cover, and process until smooth. Add pureed mixture to remaining vegetable mixture; stir in ham. Set aside.

Melt margarine in a heavy saucepan over low heat; add flour, stirring until smooth. Cook 1 minute, stirring constantly. Gradually add milk; cook over medium heat until thickened and bubbly. Add white sauce mixture to ham mixture; cook until thoroughly heated (do not boil). Ladle chowder into individual bowls. Sprinkle 1½ teaspoons parsley over each serving. Yield: 4 cups (281 calories per 1-cup serving).

PROTEIN 14.0 / FAT 5.6 / CARBOHYDRATE 43.8 / CHOLESTEROL 22 / IRON 2.2 / SODIUM 534 / CALCIUM 169

CHECKUPS THAT CAN HELP PREVENT OR DETECT HEART DISEASE

Regular checkups can help prevent heart disease. In support of this, the American Heart Association (AHA) has recommended medical exam guidelines for **healthy** adults. By detecting warning signs before actual symptoms occur, the exams will aid in prevention of the disease. The AHA's recomendations are as follows.

AGE	MEDICAL HISTORY	PHYSICAL EXAM	BLOOD PRESSURE*	PLASMA LIPIDS†	BODY WEIGHT	FASTING GLUCOSE	ECG	BASELINE CHEST X-RAY
20	x	x	x	x	x	x	x	
25,30,35	x	x	x	x	x	x		
40	x	x	x	x	x	x	x	x
45,50,55	x	x	x	x	x	x		
60	x	x	x	x	x	x	x	
61-75 (every 2½ years)	x	x	x	‡	x	x		
75 and over (every year)	x	x	x	‡	x	‡		

*Blood pressure should be checked every 2½ years
†Includes fasting cholesterol and triglycerides
‡Optional—every 2½ to 5 years based on physician's recommendation

For a satisfying meal, complement Cheesy Squash Chowder with corn sticks and a tossed green salad.

CHEESY SQUASH CHOWDER

Vegetable cooking spray
1 cup chopped celery
1 cup chopped onion
1½ cups coarsely chopped yellow squash
1½ cups coarsely chopped zucchini
1 (10½-ounce) can no-salt-added chicken broth, undiluted
¼ teaspoon pepper
3 tablespoons margarine
3 tablespoons all-purpose flour
1½ cups skim milk
1 tablespoon prepared mustard
2 cups (8 ounces) shredded 40% less-fat Cheddar cheese
1 (17-ounce) can no-salt-added whole kernel corn, drained
1 (2-ounce) jar diced pimiento, drained

Coat a Dutch oven with cooking spray; place over medium-high heat until hot. Add celery and onion; sauté until crisp-tender. Stir in yellow squash and next 3 ingredients. Bring to a boil. Cover, reduce heat, and simmer 20 minutes.

Melt margarine in a heavy saucepan over low heat. Add flour, stirring until smooth. Cook 1 minute, stirring constantly. Gradually add milk. Cook over medium heat, stirring constantly, until mixture is thickened and bubbly. Add mustard and cheese, stirring until cheese melts.

Add cheese sauce, corn, and pimiento to vegetable mixture; stir well. Cook over medium heat until thoroughly heated. Yield: 8 cups (195 calories per 1-cup serving).

PROTEIN 11.2 / FAT 10.2 / CARBOHYDRATE 14.5 / CHOLESTEROL 1 / IRON 0.8 / SODIUM 308 / CALCIUM 301

VEGETABLE-LENTIL STEW

5 cups water
1 (28-ounce) can whole tomatoes, undrained and chopped
1 (9-ounce) package frozen Italian-cut green beans
2 carrots, scraped and sliced
2 cloves garlic, minced
1 small onion, chopped
⅓ cup chopped celery
1 large yellow squash, chopped
¾ cup dried lentils
½ cup chopped green pepper
¼ teaspoon dried whole basil
¼ teaspoon dried whole oregano
¼ teaspoon dried whole thyme
1 bay leaf
⅓ cup minced fresh parsley
1 tablespoon plus 1½ teaspoons Worcestershire sauce

Combine first 14 ingredients in a large Dutch oven. Bring to a boil. Cover, reduce heat, and simmer 1 hour or until lentils are tender. Stir in parsley and Worcestershire sauce. Remove and discard bay leaf before serving. Yield: 10 cups (93 calories per 1-cup serving).

PROTEIN 6.0 / FAT 0.5 / CARBOHYDRATE 18.2 / CHOLESTEROL 0 / IRON 2.5 / SODIUM 165 / CALCIUM 50

MEXICAN BEEF STEW WITH TORTILLA DUMPLINGS

1 pound ground chuck
½ teaspoon beef-flavored bouillon granules
1 teaspoon ground cumin
1 teaspoon minced fresh cilantro
½ teaspoon pepper
½ teaspoon dried whole oregano
½ teaspoon dried whole basil
2 (4-ounce) cans chopped green chiles, drained
2½ cups water
2½ cups spicy hot vegetable juice cocktail
3 (6-inch) flour tortillas, cut into 1-inch pieces

Cook ground chuck in a large Dutch oven over medium heat until browned, stirring to crumble. Drain and pat dry with paper towels. Wipe pan drippings from Dutch oven with a paper towel.

Return meat to Dutch oven; add remaining ingredients except tortillas. Bring to a boil; cover, reduce heat, and simmer 1 hour. Add tortillas; cover and cook an additional 20 minutes or until tortillas have expanded to resemble dumplings. Yield: 6 cups (240 calories per 1-cup serving).

PROTEIN 15.5 / FAT 11.7 / CARBOHYDRATE 17.2 / CHOLESTEROL 44 / IRON 2.3 / SODIUM 370 / CALCIUM 26

 ### A STEP IN THE RIGHT DIRECTION

Americans appear to have taken steps both forward and back in their eating habits. As a step in the right direction, the demand for whole milk has dropped by half over the past several years while sales of lower-fat milk have increased. But when looking at total milk consumption, there has been an alarming decrease, especially by people in their late teens and early adulthood. Since this is the very time they need to be building up calcium stores in their bones, osteoporosis could be more prevalent in the future.

BARBECUED BEEF STEW

1 (1¼-pound) lean flank steak
2 (8-ounce) cans no-salt-added tomato sauce
1 (15-ounce) can pinto beans, drained
½ cup chopped celery
1 small onion, finely chopped
2 cloves garlic, minced
1 cup flat light beer
¼ cup cider vinegar
¼ cup Worcestershire sauce
2 tablespoons brown sugar
⅛ teaspoon hot sauce

Partially freeze steak; trim fat from steak. Slice steak diagonally across grain into thin slices. Combine steak and remaining ingredients in a large Dutch oven. Bring to a boil. Cover; reduce heat, and simmer 1½ hours or until meat is tender, stirring occasionally. Yield: 6 cups (298 calories per 1-cup serving).

PROTEIN 23.4 / FAT 9.5 / CARBOHYDRATE 27.2 / CHOLESTEROL 47 / IRON 3.0 / SODIUM 342 / CALCIUM 58

VEAL MARSALA STEW

Vegetable cooking spray
1 teaspoon vegetable oil
2 pounds boneless veal, cut into 1-inch cubes
1 quart water
1 cup Marsala wine
1 large onion, chopped
2 cups sliced fresh mushrooms
2 tablespoons low-sodium Worcestershire sauce
2 cloves garlic, minced
¾ teaspoon salt
¼ teaspoon pepper
2 tablespoons all-purpose flour
2 tablespoons water

Coat a large Dutch oven with cooking spray; add oil. Place over medium-high heat until hot. Add veal and cook until brown, stirring frequently. Drain and pat dry with paper towels. Wipe pan drippings from Dutch oven with a paper towel.

Return veal to Dutch oven, add water and wine. Bring to a boil. Cover, reduce heat, and simmer 1½ hours. Stir in onion and next 5 ingredients; cover and simmer 30 minutes or until vegetables are tender.

Combine flour and water, stirring until blended. Gradually add flour mixture to meat mixture; cook over medium heat until thickened and bubbly. Yield: 8 cups (224 calories per 1-cup serving).

PROTEIN 28.5 / FAT 7.8 / CARBOHYDRATE 8.3 / CHOLESTEROL 134 / IRON 1.4 / SODIUM 310 / CALCIUM 16

NEW MEXICO GREEN CHILE STEW

¾ pound poblano chiles
1 pound boneless pork
Vegetable cooking spray
1 medium onion, chopped
1 cup peeled, cubed red potato
2 cloves garlic, minced
2 cups water
2 teaspoons chicken-flavored bouillon granules
¼ teaspoon salt
¼ cup finely chopped cilantro
1½ cups water
1 tablespoon cornstarch
Fresh cilantro sprigs (optional)

Wash and dry peppers; place on a baking sheet. Broil 3 to 4 inches from heat, turning often with tongs, until blistered on all sides. Immediately place peppers in a plastic bag; seal and let stand 10 minutes to loosen skins. Peel peppers; remove core and seeds. Chop peppers.

Trim fat from pork; cut meat into 1-inch pieces. Coat a large Dutch oven with cooking spray, place over medium-high heat until hot. Add pork and onion; cook, stirring frequently, until meat is browned on all sides. Add potatoes, garlic, 2 cups water, bouillon granules, and salt. Bring to a boil, cover, reduce heat, and simmer 45 minutes. Add reserved peppers and cilantro; simmer an additional 15 minutes.

Combine 1½ cups water and cornstarch, stirring until blended. Gradually add cornstarch mixture to meat mixture; cook over medium heat until thickened. To serve, ladle stew into individual serving bowls. Garnish with fresh cilantro sprigs, if desired. Yield: 6 cups (185 calories per 1-cup serving).

PROTEIN 18.9 / FAT 6.0 / CARBOHYDRATE 14.0 / CHOLESTEROL 48 / IRON 1.8 / SODIUM 428 / CALCIUM 31

LITE ON THE LABEL

Labels may be deceiving. Foods labeled "light" or "lite" may not be lower in calories or better food choices. The terms may mean light in color, as in the case of certain vegetable oils and chocolate, or "lite" may indicate that the product contains less sugar, fat, alcohol, or other ingredients. The product just has to contain "less of something," according to the Food and Drug Administration (FDA). The FDA monitors labeling of all food products except for meat and poultry products, which are governed by the U.S. Department of Agriculture (USDA). The USDA has approved specific guidelines for the terms, which require the product to have at least 25 percent less of an ingredient such as sodium, breading, fat, or calories.

Studies have shown that "lite" foods may still have an abundance of fat. "Lite" deep-fried fish fillets, for example, refers to the amount of breading. Also, the calorie content of "lite" products may not be reduced enough to justify the higher cost and difference in taste. When 5-ounce servings of pizza were compared, the "lite" pizza had only 15 fewer calories than a better tasting regular pizza.

CATFISH STEW WITH HUSH PUPPY CROUTONS

1 cup Chablis or other dry white wine
1 cup water
2 (14½-ounce) cans whole tomatoes, undrained and chopped
2 medium-size red potatoes, peeled and diced
1 large onion, chopped
1 medium-size green pepper, seeded and chopped
2 cloves garlic, minced
¼ teaspoon salt
⅛ teaspoon pepper
1 pound farm-raised catfish fillets, cut into 1-inch pieces
¼ cup reduced-calorie catsup
2 tablespoons lemon juice
Hush Puppy Croutons

Combine first 9 ingredients in a large Dutch oven. Bring to a boil. Cover, reduce heat, and simmer 1½ hours. Add catfish; cover and simmer an additional 30 minutes. Stir in catsup and lemon juice. Cook until thoroughly heated. To serve, ladle stew into individual serving bowls and top with Hush Puppy Croutons. Yield: 10 cups (150 calories per 1 cup stew plus ¼ cup croutons).

Hush Puppy Croutons:

½ cup cornmeal
½ cup all-purpose flour
1 teaspoon baking powder
⅛ teaspoon salt
⅛ teaspoon baking soda
½ cup nonfat buttermilk
1 egg, lightly beaten
1 tablespoon grated onion
1 teaspoon vegetable oil
Vegetable cooking spray

Combine first 4 ingredients, stirring well.
Dissolve soda in buttermilk. Combine buttermilk mixture, egg, onion, and oil; add to dry ingredients, stirring just until moistened. Spoon batter into a 9-inch square pan that has been coated with cooking spray. Bake at 400° for 10 minutes or until lightly browned. Let cool completely on a wire rack.
Cut into ½-inch cubes. Arrange cubes on an ungreased baking sheet. Bake at 250° for 20 minutes or until crisp.
To store remaining croutons, place in a plastic zip-top bag, and store in freezer. To recrisp croutons before using, place on an ungreased baking sheet and bake at 250° for 5 minutes. Yield: 4½ cups.

PROTEIN 11.4 / FAT 2.9 / CARBOHYDRATE 19.7 / CHOLESTEROL 42 / IRON 1.8 / SODIUM 277 / CALCIUM 67

LOUISIANA GUMBO

¼ cup all-purpose flour
1 cup chopped green pepper
1¾ cups chopped celery
1½ cups chopped onion
2 cups water, divided
1¾ teaspoons chicken-flavored bouillon granules
2 (16-ounce) cans no-salt-added whole tomatoes, undrained and chopped
3½ cups no-salt-added tomato juice
1 pound okra, sliced
3 cups chopped cooked turkey breast (skinned before cooking and cooked without salt)
3 tablespoons chopped fresh parsley
1 bay leaf
½ teaspoon garlic powder
½ teaspoon hot sauce
¼ teaspoon freshly ground black pepper
¼ teaspoon ground red pepper
¼ teaspoon dried whole thyme
1½ pounds medium shrimp, peeled and deveined
1 (12-ounce) container fresh Standard oysters, drained

Place flour in a shallow baking pan. Bake at 400° for 12 to 14 minutes or until browned, stirring every 4 minutes. Set aside.
Combine green pepper, celery, onion, ⅓ cup water, and bouillon granules in a large Dutch oven. Cook over medium heat 10 to 12 minutes or until vegetables are tender. Stir in reserved flour. Gradually stir in remaining 1⅔ cup water, tomato, and next 10 ingredients. Cover, reduce heat, and simmer 45 minutes.
Add shrimp and oysters; simmer 10 to 15 minutes or until shrimp are done and oysters begin to curl. Discard bay leaf. Yield: 16 cups (129 calories per 1-cup serving).

PROTEIN 16.2 / FAT 1.8 / CARBOHYDRATE 12.1 / CHOLESTEROL 72 / IRON 2.7 / SODIUM 195 / CALCIUM 80

CHICKEN BURGOO

¼ pound lean round steak (½-inch thick)
¼ pound veal cutlets, cut into 1-inch cubes
¼ pound lean boneless pork shoulder, cut into
    1-inch cubes
4 (6-ounce) skinned chicken breast halves
1½ quarts water
1 (14½-ounce) can no-salt-added whole tomatoes,
    undrained
1 (8¾-ounce) can whole kernel corn, drained
1 small onion, chopped
1 medium carrot, scraped and thinly sliced
¾ cup thinly sliced fresh okra
¾ cup shredded cabbage
½ cup peeled, cubed red potato
½ cup frozen lima beans, thawed
½ cup chopped green pepper
¼ cup chopped fresh parsley
2 hot red pepper pods
2½ teaspoons low-sodium Worcestershire sauce
¼ teaspoon salt
⅛ teaspoon ground red pepper

Trim fat from steak; cut steak into 1-inch pieces. Combine steak, veal, pork, chicken, and water in a large Dutch oven; bring mixture to a boil. Cover; reduce heat, and simmer 30 minutes or until tender. Remove meat and chicken; skim fat from broth. Bone chicken, and cut into bite-size pieces.

Combine meat, chicken, broth, tomatoes, and remaining ingredients in a large Dutch oven. Bring to a boil. Uncover, reduce heat, and simmer 2½ hours or until thickened, stirring occasionally. Discard pepper pods. Yield: 10 cups (155 calories per 1-cup serving).

PROTEIN 18.5 / FAT 3.4 / CARBOHYDRATE 12.6 / CHOLESTEROL 49 /
IRON 1.9 / SODIUM 198 / CALCIUM 41

TURKEY STOCK

1¾ pounds turkey bones
1 medium tomato, chopped
1 medium onion, sliced
1 medium stalk celery with leaves, chopped
1 medium carrot, scraped and chopped
2 sprigs fresh parsley
1 bay leaf
¼ teaspoon dried whole basil
3 black peppercorns

Combine all ingredients in a large Dutch oven; bring to a boil. Cover, reduce heat, and simmer 30 minutes. Strain turkey stock through a double layer of cheesecloth; repeat straining if necessary. Cover and chill 8 hours; remove fat from surface. Yield: 4 cups (35 calories per 1-cup serving).

PROTEIN 1.2 / FAT 0.3 / CARBOHYDRATE 7.9 / CHOLESTEROL 0 /
IRON 0.5 / SODIUM 20 / CALCIUM 25

VEGETABLE STOCK

2 quarts water
1 cup chopped carrot
1 cup chopped celery
1 cup sliced escarole
1 fennel bulb, sliced
1 medium-size sweet red pepper, seeded and
    chopped
½ cup chopped fresh parsley
1 shallot, chopped
2 fresh parsley sprigs
3 black peppercorns
1 bay leaf

Combine all ingredients in a large Dutch oven; bring to a boil. Cover, reduce heat, and simmer 2 hours. Strain vegetable stock through a double layer of cheesecloth; repeat straining if necessary. Cover and chill. Store in refrigerator or freezer. Use as a base for vegetable soups. Yield: 4 cups (17 calories per 1-cup serving).

PROTEIN 1.9 / FAT 3.9 / CARBOHYDRATE 7.7 / CHOLESTEROL 0 /
IRON 0.0 / SODIUM 19 / CALCIUM 0

Elegant Chocolate-Apricot Roulage (page 231) is flavored with amaretto and generously topped with almonds.

Desserts

HOT SHERRIED FRUIT COMPOTE

2½ cups peeled, chopped cooking
   apples
2 cups cubed fresh pineapple
1½ cups peeled, chopped fresh
   apricots
1 cup unsweetened apple juice
3 tablespoons dry sherry
¼ teaspoon ground nutmeg

Combine all ingredients except nutmeg in a nonaluminum saucepan; stir well. Cook over low heat 10 minutes or until apples are tender, stirring occasionally. Spoon fruit mixture into individual dessert dishes. Sprinkle with nutmeg. Serve warm. Yield: 10 servings (44 calories per ½-cup serving).

PROTEIN 0.5 / FAT 0.3 / CARBOHYDRATE 10.6 / CHOLESTEROL 0 /
IRON 0.4 / SODIUM 2 / CALCIUM 9

POACHED PINEAPPLE IN RASPBERRY SAUCE

2½ cups fresh raspberries
¼ cup cran-raspberry drink
1 tablespoon sugar
1½ teaspoons cornstarch
4 (¾-inch-thick) slices peeled and cored fresh
   pineapple
1 cup unsweetened pineapple juice
2 fresh mint sprigs
Fresh mint sprigs (optional)

Place raspberries in container of an electric blender or food processor; top with cover, and process until smooth. Strain raspberry puree; discard seeds. Combine puree, juice, sugar, and cornstarch in a saucepan, bring to a boil. Reduce heat and simmer 1 to 2 minutes or until thickened, stirring constantly. Cover and chill thoroughly.

Combine pineapple slices, pineapple juice, and mint in a large nonaluminum skillet; bring to a boil. Cover, reduce heat, and simmer 5 to 10 minutes or until pineapple is tender. Transfer pineapple slices and juice mixture to a shallow dish. Cover and chill thoroughly.

Pour ¼ cup raspberry sauce onto individual dessert plates. Place 1 pineapple slice in center

of each serving of sauce. Garnish with fresh mint sprigs, if desired. Yield: 4 servings (154 calories per serving).

PROTEIN 1.3 / FAT 1.0 / CARBOHYDRATE 37.9 / CHOLESTEROL 0 /
IRON 1.0 / SODIUM 3 / CALCIUM 36

FRESH PEACH FLAMBÉ

1 tablespoon cornstarch
1 tablespoon brown sugar
½ teaspoon ground ginger
½ cup unsweetened white grape juice
½ cup water
2 cups peeled, sliced fresh peaches
¼ cup brandy
3 cups vanilla ice milk

Combine first 3 ingredients in a large saucepan, stirring well. Add grape juice and water, stirring well. Bring mixture to a boil; add peaches. Reduce heat, and simmer 10 minutes or until peaches are tender.

Place brandy in a small, long-handled pan; heat just until warm (do not boil). Ignite with a long match, and pour over peach mixture. Stir gently until flames die down. Spoon ⅓ cup peach mixture over ½-cup portions of ice milk. Serve immediately. Yield: 6 servings (141 calories per serving).

PROTEIN 3.0 / FAT 2.9 / CARBOHYDRATE 26.9 / CHOLESTEROL 9 /
IRON 0.3 / SODIUM 54 / CALCIUM 95

KIWIFRUIT ICE

4 medium kiwifruit, peeled and quartered
2¼ cups unsweetened kiwifruit juice
1 tablespoon unsweetened orange juice

Combine all ingredients in container of an electric blender or food processor; top with cover, and process until smooth.

Pour kiwifruit mixture into freezer can of a hand-turned or electric freezer. Freeze according to manufacturer's instructions. Scoop into individual dessert dishes, and serve immediately. Yield: 4 cups (64 calories per ½-cup serving).

PROTEIN 0.6 / FAT 0.3 / CARBOHYDRATE 14.3 / CHOLESTEROL 0 /
IRON 0.2 / SODIUM 4 / CALCIUM 12

CANTALOUPE SORBET

¾ cup unsweetened orange juice
3 tablespoons sugar
3 cups coarsely chopped cantaloupe
1 teaspoon lime juice

Combine orange juice and sugar in a nonaluminum saucepan; bring to a boil. Boil 1 minute. Remove from heat; let cool.

Place cantaloupe in container of an electric blender or food processor. Add ¼ cup of cooled juice mixture; top with cover, and process until smooth. Combine pureed cantaloupe, remaining juice mixture, and lime juice; stir well.

Pour cantaloupe mixture into freezer can of a hand-turned or electric freezer. Freeze according to manufacturer's instructions. Scoop sorbet into individual dessert dishes, and serve immediately. Yield: 4 cups (50 calories per ½-cup serving).

PROTEIN 0.7 / FAT 0.2 / CARBOHYDRATE 12.4 / CHOLESTEROL 0 / IRON 0.2 / SODIUM 6 / CALCIUM 9

CHOCOLATE-CHOCOLATE CHIP ICE MILK

1 envelope unflavored gelatin
4 cups 1% low-fat chocolate milk, divided
3 eggs
⅓ cup sugar
¼ cup semisweet chocolate mini-morsels

Combine gelatin and 1 cup milk in a small saucepan; let stand 1 minute. Cook over medium heat, stirring constantly, about 1 minute or until gelatin is dissolved. Set aside.

Combine eggs and sugar in a large bowl; beat at high speed of an electric mixer 4 to 5 minutes or until thickened and doubled in volume. Stir in gelatin mixture, remaining 3 cups milk, and mini-morsels.

Pour mixture into freezer can of a hand-turned or electric freezer, and freeze according to manufacturer's instructions. Scoop ice milk into individual dessert dishes, and serve immediately. Yield: 7 cups (90 calories per ½-cup serving).

PROTEIN 4.1 / FAT 2.5 / CARBOHYDRATE 13.2 / CHOLESTEROL 61 / IRON 0.4 / SODIUM 59 / CALCIUM 89

PEANUT BUTTER-BANANA RIPPLE ICE MILK

½ gallon vanilla ice milk
1 large banana
1 tablespoon lemon juice
½ cup no-sugar-added peanut butter

Place ice milk in a freezerproof bowl; let soften.

Place banana and lemon juice in container of an electric blender or food processor; top with cover, and process until smooth. Gently swirl banana mixture into ice milk. Gently swirl peanut butter into ice milk. Cover; freeze until firm. Yield: 8 cups (149 calories per ½-cup serving).

PROTEIN 5.0 / FAT 7.0 / CARBOHYDRATE 18.3 / CHOLESTEROL 9 / IRON 0.3 / SODIUM 54 / CALCIUM 91

AMARETTO-COFFEE FROZEN YOGURT

1 (8-ounce) carton vanilla low-fat yogurt
2 (8-ounce) cartons coffee low-fat yogurt
⅓ cup amaretto

Combine all ingredients, stirring well. Pour into freezer can of a hand-turned or electric freezer. Freeze according to manufacturer's instructions. Scoop frozen yogurt into individual dessert dishes, and serve immediately. Yield: 3 cups (142 calories per ½-cup serving).

PROTEIN 5.5 / FAT 1.8 / CARBOHYDRATE 19.8 / CHOLESTEROL 6 / IRON 0.0 / SODIUM 108 / CALCIUM 181

NEOPOLITAN ICE MILK SANDWICHES

2⅔ cups neopolitan ice milk, softened
16 (2-inch-square) graham crackers with raisins
1 tablespoon plus 1 teaspoon wheat germ

Spread ⅓ cup ice milk onto each of 8 graham crackers. Sprinkle each with ½ teaspoon wheat germ. Top with remaining graham crackers. Place on a baking sheet; freeze until firm. Wrap sandwiches in plastic wrap, and store in freezer. Yield: 8 servings (67 calories per serving).

PROTEIN 1.5 / FAT 1.2 / CARBOHYDRATE 12.7 / CHOLESTEROL 0 / IRON 0.5 / SODIUM 75 / CALCIUM 3

Layers of ice milk and sherbet studded with pistachios and pineapple give Spumoni Loaf its distinctive flavor.

SPUMONI LOAF

2½ cups lime sherbet, softened
3 tablespoons chopped pistachios, divided
1 (8-ounce) can unsweetened crushed pineapple, drained
1½ cups vanilla ice milk, softened
2 cups raspberry sherbet, softened

Line an 8½- x 4½- x 3-inch loafpan with wax paper. Combine lime sherbet and 1 tablespoon plus 2 teaspoons pistachios, stirring well. Spread sherbet mixture in bottom of prepared pan; freeze 30 minutes.

Press pineapple between paper towels to remove excess moisture. Combine pineapple and vanilla ice milk, stirring well. Spread ice milk mixture evenly over sherbet mixture; freeze 30 minutes. Spread raspberry sherbet evenly over ice milk mixture. Cover and freeze several hours or until firm.

Invert spumoni onto a serving platter. Remove wax paper. Top with remaining 1 tablespoon plus 1 teaspoon pistachios. Let stand at room temperature 5 minutes before slicing. Yield: 8 servings (173 calories per 1-inch slice).

PROTEIN 2.7 / FAT 3.5 / CARBOHYDRATE 34.1 / CHOLESTEROL 3 / IRON 0.3 / SODIUM 95 / CALCIUM 81

CHOCOLATE-MINT TORTE

¼ cup margarine, softened
¾ cup sugar
2 egg whites
½ teaspoon vanilla extract
1¼ cups sifted cake flour
¼ cup unsweetened cocoa
¼ teaspoon baking soda
¼ teaspoon baking powder
1 (8-ounce) carton plain nonfat yogurt
Vegetable cooking spray
1 cup vanilla ice milk, softened
1 teaspoon crème de menthe
1 tablespoon powdered sugar

Cream margarine; gradually add sugar, beating well at medium speed of an electric mixer. Add egg whites (at room temperature) and vanilla; beat well. Combine flour, cocoa, soda, and baking powder; add to sugar mixture alternately with yogurt, beating well after each addition.

Pour batter into an 8-inch round cakepan that has been coated with cooking spray. Bake at 350° for 30 minutes or until a wooden pick inserted in center comes out clean. Cool in pan 10 minutes; remove from pan, and let cool completely on a wire rack.

Combine ice milk and crème de menthe, stirring well. Line one 8-inch round cakepan with wax paper, leaving an overhang around edges.

Spread ice milk mixture evenly into pan. Freeze 2 hours or until firm.

Carefully cut cake horizontally into two layers. Place bottom layer of cake on a serving plate. Invert frozen ice milk layer onto cake; remove wax paper. Top with remaining cake layer. Cover and freeze several hours or until firm. Let stand 5 minutes. Dust with powdered sugar before serving. Yield: 10 servings (192 calories per serving).

PROTEIN 4.1 / FAT 5.6 / CARBOHYDRATE 31.3 / CHOLESTEROL 2 / IRON 0.5 / SODIUM 120 / CALCIUM 80

FROZEN LIME CUPS WITH FRESH FRUIT TOPPING

1 egg, separated
¼ cup water
⅓ cup instant nonfat dry milk powder
⅓ cup sugar
¼ cup lime juice
⅛ teaspoon salt
6 chocolate wafers, crushed
2 teaspoons margarine, melted
3 medium peaches, peeled and sliced
1 cup fresh strawberries, sliced
2 teaspoons sugar

Beat egg white (at room temperature), water, and instant dry milk powder at high speed of an electric mixer until stiff peaks form; set aside.

Beat egg yolk slightly. Add ⅓ cup sugar, lime juice, and salt; beat well. Gradually add egg yolk mixture to reserved egg white mixture, beating constantly.

Combine chocolate wafer crumbs and margarine. Press crumb mixture evenly into bottoms of 6 paper-lined muffin cups. Pour egg mixture evenly into cups, filling three-fourths full. Freeze several hours or until firm. Combine peach slices, strawberries, and 2 teaspoons sugar; cover and chill thoroughly.

Remove paper linings from frozen cups. Place into 6 individual compotes. Top evenly with fruit mixture. Serve immediately. Yield: 6 servings (163 calories per serving).

PROTEIN 9.1 / FAT 12.3 / CARBOHYDRATE 30.6 / CHOLESTEROL 47 / IRON 2.5 / SODIUM 507 / CALCIUM 114

Creamy Chocolate-Raspberry Bavarian is drizzled with chocolate and topped with fresh raspberries.

CHOCOLATE-RASPBERRY BAVARIAN

2 envelopes unflavored gelatin
⅓ cup water
1⅔ cups skim milk
2 eggs, separated
3 cups part-skim ricotta cheese
½ cup plus 2 tablespoons sugar, divided
⅓ cup unsweetened cocoa
1½ teaspoons vanilla extract
Vegetable cooking spray
1½ cups fresh raspberries
1 (1-ounce) square unsweetened chocolate
2 teaspoons margarine
Fresh mint sprigs (optional)

Sprinkle gelatin over water in a medium saucepan; let stand 5 minutes. Combine milk and egg yolks, stirring well. Add to gelatin mixture. Cook over low heat, stirring constantly, until gelatin dissolves. Remove from heat.

Position knife blade in food processor bowl. Add cheese, ½ cup sugar, cocoa, vanilla, and ⅓ cup gelatin mixture; top with cover, and process until smooth. Combine remaining gelatin mixture and cheese mixture in a large bowl. Chill to consistency of unbeaten egg white.

Beat egg whites (at room temperature) at high speed of an electric mixer 1 minute. Gradually add remaining 2 tablespoons sugar, 1 tablespoon at a time, beating until stiff peaks form and sugar dissolves (2 to 4 minutes).

Gently fold egg whites into chilled chocolate mixture. Spoon mixture into a 9-inch springform pan that has been coated with cooking spray. Chill 3 hours or until firm.

Remove sides of springform pan. Place cake on a serving platter. Top with raspberries. Combine chocolate and margarine in a small saucepan; cook over low heat until chocolate and margarine melt. Drizzle chocolate mixture over cake. Garnish with fresh mint sprigs, if desired. Yield: 12 servings (191 calories per serving).

PROTEIN 11.2 / FAT 7.9 / CARBOHYDRATE 19.5 / CHOLESTEROL 65 / IRON 1.1 / SODIUM 115 / CALCIUM 222

PEACH MELBA SOUFFLÉS

½ (8-ounce) package Neufchâtel cheese, softened
1 (8-ounce) carton peach low-fat yogurt
3 tablespoons powdered sugar
¼ cup peach nectar
1 envelope unflavored gelatin
¼ cup water
½ teaspoon almond extract
2 egg whites
Raspberry Sauce
Fresh mint sprigs (optional)
Fresh raspberries (optional)

Combine first 3 ingredients in a large bowl; stir well. Add peach nectar, stirring until smooth.

Sprinkle gelatin over water in a small saucepan; let stand 5 minutes. Cook over low heat, stirring constantly, until gelatin dissolves. Add gelatin mixture to cheese mixture, beating well with a wire whisk. Stir in almond extract.

Beat egg whites (at room temperature) at high speed of an electric mixer until stiff peaks form. Gently fold egg whites into cheese mixture. Spoon into 6 individual dessert dishes; chill until set. To serve, spoon 2 tablespoons Raspberry Sauce over each soufflé. If desired, garnish with fresh mint sprigs and raspberries. Yield: 6 servings (139 calories per serving).

Raspberry Sauce:

1½ cups fresh raspberries
1 tablespoon Chambord or other raspberry-flavored liqueur
1 teaspoon cornstarch
1 tablespoon low-sugar apricot spread

Mash and strain raspberries; discard seeds. Combine strained raspberries, Chambord, and cornstarch in a small saucepan, stirring until mixture is well blended. Bring to a boil. Reduce heat and cook, stirring constantly, until smooth and thickened. Remove from heat; add apricot spread, stirring until spread melts. Cool completely. Yield: ½ cup.

PROTEIN 5.9 / FAT 5.0 / CARBOHYDRATE 18.3 / CHOLESTEROL 16 / IRON 0.3 / SODIUM 117 / CALCIUM 75

ORANGE SOUFFLÉ CUPS

4 large oranges
1 tablespoon plus 2 teaspoons all-purpose flour
1½ teaspoons sugar
½ cup skim milk
3 egg yolks
1 tablespoon unsalted margarine
¼ cup unsweetened orange juice
4 egg whites
¼ teaspoon cream of tartar
2 tablespoons sugar
1 teaspoon grated orange rind
2 teaspoons sugar, divided
1 tablespoon plus 1 teaspoon unsweetened orange juice, divided

Cut oranges in half crosswise. Clip membranes, and remove pulp. Reserve pulp for other uses. Using kitchen shears, cut edges of orange cups to resemble scallops. Set aside.

Combine flour, 1½ teaspoons sugar, and milk in a saucepan, stirring well. Bring to a boil over medium heat, stirring constantly. Boil 1 minute; remove from heat.

Beat egg yolks until thickened. Gradually stir about one-fourth of hot mixture into yolks; add to remaining hot mixture, stirring constantly. Cook for 3 minutes or until thickened, stirring constantly. Remove from heat, and stir in margarine. Let cool to room temperature. Stir in ¼ cup orange juice.

Beat egg whites (at room temperature) and cream of tartar at high speed of an electric mixer 1 minute. Gradually add 2 tablespoons sugar, 1 tablespoon at a time, beating until stiff peaks form (2 to 4 minutes). Fold in orange rind. Gently fold egg whites into cooled yolk mixture.

Spoon mixture evenly into orange cups. Sprinkle each serving with ¼ teaspoon sugar and ½ teaspoon orange juice. Arrange orange cups in a 13- x 9- x 2-inch baking dish. Bake at 400° for 10 minutes or until puffed and lightly browned. Serve immediately. Yield: 8 servings (80 calories per serving).

PROTEIN 3.5 / FAT 3.6 / CARBOHYDRATE 8.4 / CHOLESTEROL 102 / IRON 0.4 / SODIUM 43 / CALCIUM 32

CHOCOLATE-MINT SOUFFLÉ

Vegetable cooking spray
¾ cup skim milk
1 tablespoon cornstarch
¼ cup mint chocolate morsels
3 egg yolks
4 egg whites
¼ teaspoon cream of tartar
2 tablespoons sugar

Cut a piece of aluminum foil long enough to fit around a 1½-quart soufflé dish, allowing a 1-inch overlap; fold foil lengthwise into thirds. Lightly coat one side of foil and bottom of dish with cooking spray. Wrap foil around outside of dish, coated side against dish, allowing foil to extend 4 inches above rim to form a collar; secure foil with string. Set aside.

Combine milk and cornstarch in top of a double boiler. Bring water to a boil over medium heat; cook milk mixture until slightly thickened, stirring constantly. Add morsels, stirring until morsels melt.

Beat egg yolks slightly. Gradually stir about one-fourth of hot mixture into beaten egg yolks; add to remaining hot mixture, stirring constantly. Cook 5 minutes over boiling water, stirring constantly with a wire whisk, until mixture is thickened. Remove from heat, and let cool to room temperature.

Beat egg whites (at room temperature) and cream of tartar 1 minute. Gradually add sugar, 1 tablespoon at a time, beating until stiff peaks form and sugar dissolves (2 to 4 minutes). Gently fold beaten egg whites into cooled chocolate mixture.

Pour into prepared soufflé dish. Bake at 350° for 30 minutes or until puffed and set. Remove collar and serve immediately. Yield: 6 servings (110 calories per serving).

PROTEIN 5.0 / FAT 4.9 / CARBOHYDRATE 11.3 / CHOLESTEROL 137 / IRON 1.3 / SODIUM 62 / CALCIUM 53

FLAMING KAHLÚA FLAN

2 tablespoons dark brown sugar
4 eggs
¼ cup sugar
¼ cup Kahlúa or other coffee-flavored liqueur, divided
½ teaspoon vanilla extract
2 cups skim milk

Sprinkle brown sugar in bottom of a 4-cup ring mold; set aside.

Beat eggs at medium speed of an electric mixer until frothy. Add sugar, 2 tablespoons Kahlúa, and vanilla; beat just until blended. Add skim milk; beat well. Pour mixture into prepared mold. Place in a 13- x 9- x 2-inch baking dish. Pour 1 inch of hot water into baking dish. Bake at 300° for 55 minutes or until a knife inserted near edge comes out clean. Remove mold from water; let cool on a wire rack 20 minutes.

Loosen edges of flan with a knife. Invert onto a serving platter.

Place remaining 2 tablespoons Kahlúa in a small, long-handled saucepan; heat just until warm (do not boil). Remove from heat. Ignite with a long match; pour over flan. Serve when flames die down. Yield: 8 servings (94 calories per serving).

PROTEIN 5.2 / FAT 2.9 / CARBOHYDRATE 15.2 / CHOLESTEROL 138 / IRON 0.6 / SODIUM 67 / CALCIUM 91

EXERCISE WITH A PARTNER

Encourage a partner to participate in your exercise sessions. In addition to establishing a camaraderie, exercising together offers time for communication and reinforcement.

According to a study at St. Francis Medical Center, you are not as likely to quit if you exercise with your spouse. The dropout rate among men working out with their wives was only half that of those working out alone.

You and your partner should work toward similiar goals and fitness levels. Exercising with a co-worker is a great way to become better acquainted, but avoid competition because this could strain the relationship. Instead, focus on sharing time with someone who enjoys building fitness while building good health.

AMARETTO BREAD PUDDING

3 cups broken French bread slices
Vegetable cooking spray
2 cups skim milk
⅓ cup firmly packed brown sugar
¼ cup sliced natural almonds
1 tablespoon plus 1½ teaspoons amaretto
¼ teaspoon almond extract
3 eggs, beaten

Place bread pieces in a 9-inch square baking pan that has been coated with cooking spray.

Combine skim milk and remaining ingredients, stirring well with a wire whisk. Pour milk mixture over bread pieces. Bake at 350° for 50 minutes or until knife inserted in center comes out clean. Serve warm. Yield: 6 servings (198 calories per serving).

PROTEIN 8.1 / FAT 5.4 / CARBOHYDRATE 27.1 / CHOLESTEROL 139 / IRON 1.5 / SODIUM 177 / CALCIUM 142

PINEAPPLE KUGEL

3 ounces medium-size egg noodles, uncooked
1 (15¼-ounce) can unsweetened crushed pineapple, drained
½ cup low-fat cottage cheese
½ cup part-skim ricotta cheese
½ cup unsweetened pineapple juice
⅓ cup sugar
2 eggs, beaten
1 egg white
¼ teaspoon almond extract
Vegetable cooking spray
¼ cup crushed corn flakes cereal
½ teaspoon ground cinnamon

Cook noodles according to package directions, omitting salt and fat. Drain. Combine noodles, pineapple, and next 7 ingredients in a large bowl, stirring well. Spoon into a 10- x 6- x 2-inch baking dish that has been coated with cooking spray. Combine cereal and cinnamon; sprinkle evenly over noodle mixture.

Bake at 325° for 50 minutes or until set. Serve immediately. Yield: 8 servings (164 calories per serving).

PROTEIN 7.3 / FAT 3.5 / CARBOHYDRATE 26.0 / CHOLESTEROL 84 / IRON 1.0 / SODIUM 123 / CALCIUM 71

LEMON MOUSSE TORTE

3 egg whites
½ teaspoon cream of tartar
½ teaspoon almond extract
½ teaspoon vanilla extract
¼ cup superfine sugar
4 ounces Neufchâtel cheese, softened
¼ cup low-fat sour cream
¼ cup sugar
½ teaspoon almond extract
¼ teaspoon grated lemon rind
1 cup skim milk
1 egg yolk, beaten
3 tablespoons sugar
1 tablespoon cornstarch
1 teaspoon grated lemon rind
1 tablespoon lemon juice
1 lemon, peeled and thinly sliced
Fresh mint sprigs (optional)

Trace two 8-inch circles on unglazed brown paper. Place on a baking sheet. Set aside.

Beat egg whites (at room temperature) at high speed of an electric mixer 1 minute. Add cream of tarter, ½ teaspoon almond extract, and vanilla. Gradually add superfine sugar, 1 tablespoon at a time, beating until stiff peaks form and sugar dissolves (2 to 4 minutes).

Spread 2 cups meringue mixture over one circle. Fill a pastry bag fitted with star tip No. 7 with remaining meringue mixture. Pipe a ring ½ inch from outer edge on remaining paper circle. Bake at 225° for 2 hours. Turn off oven, and let meringue cool for 2 hours before opening oven door. Carefully remove baked meringue from brown paper. Use immediately or store in zip-top plastic bags.

Combine cheese and next 4 ingredients in a small bowl, stirring until well blended. Cover and chill thoroughly.

Combine milk and egg yolk; set aside. Combine sugar and cornstarch in a medium saucepan. Gradually stir milk mixture into sugar mixture. Cook over medium heat, stirring constantly, until mixture comes to a boil. Boil 1 minute. Remove mixture from heat, and cool slightly. Stir in lemon rind and juice. Cover and chill thoroughly.

Place solid meringue circle on a serving platter. Spread sour cream mixture over top. Place meringue ring on top of sour cream mixture. Fill center ring with chilled custard. Arrange lemon slices over custard. Garnish with fresh mint sprigs, if desired. Serve immediately. Yield: 8 servings (146 calories per serving).

PROTEIN 4.4 / FAT 5.0 / CARBOHYDRATE 21.4 / CHOLESTEROL 48 / IRON 0.2 / SODIUM 108 / CALCIUM 63

BOSTON CREAM PIE

2 egg yolks
¼ cup sugar
4 egg whites
½ teaspoon cream of tartar
¼ cup sugar
⅔ cup all-purpose flour
2 tablespoons margarine, melted
Vegetable cooking spray
Filling (recipe follows)
Glaze (recipe follows)

Combine egg yolks and ¼ cup sugar in a large bowl. Beat at medium speed of an electric mixer until thick and lemon colored.

Beat egg whites (at room temperature) and cream of tartar at high speed of an electric mixer 1 minute. Gradually add ¼ cup sugar, 1 tablespoon at a time, beating until stiff peaks form and sugar dissolves (2 to 4 minutes). Gently fold egg white mixture into yolk mixture.

Sift flour; gently fold flour and margarine alternately into egg mixture. Spoon batter into a wax paper-lined 9-inch round cakepan that has been coated with cooking spray. Bake at 325° for 30 minutes or until a wooden pick inserted in center comes out clean. Cool in pan 10 minutes; remove from pan and peel off wax paper. Let cool completely on a wire rack.

Split cake horizontally into 2 layers. Spread filling between layers. Spread glaze over top of cake. Refrigerate until ready to serve. Yield: 8 servings (182 calories per serving).

Filling:

3 tablespoons sugar
1 tablespoon cornstarch
1 cup skim milk
1 egg yolk, beaten
1 teaspoon vanilla extract

Combine sugar and cornstarch in a medium saucepan. Gradually stir in milk and egg yolk. Cook over medium heat, stirring constantly, until mixture comes to a boil. Boil 1 minute or until thickened. Remove from heat, and stir in vanilla. Cover with plastic wrap, gently pressing directly on pudding. Chill thoroughly. Yield: 1 cup plus 2 tablespoons.

Glaze:

½ cup sifted powdered sugar
3 tablespoons unsweetened cocoa
2 tablespoons 1% low-fat chocolate milk
1 teaspoon margarine, melted
½ teaspoon vanilla extract

Combine sugar and cocoa; stir until well blended. Add remaining ingredients; stir until smooth. Yield: ¼ cup plus 2 tablespoons.

PROTEIN 4.6 / FAT 4.8 / CARBOHYDRATE 30.1 / CHOLESTEROL 82 / IRON 0.9 / SODIUM 79 / CALCIUM 48

FRUIT DESSERT PIZZA

1 (16-ounce) carton vanilla low-fat yogurt
1 teaspoon grated lemon rind
1¼ cups plus 2 tablespoons all-purpose flour
¾ teaspoon baking powder
⅓ cup unsalted margarine
2 tablespoons sugar
¼ cup firmly packed brown sugar
1 egg
1 teaspoon vanilla extract
Vegetable cooking spray
1 (8-ounce) can unsweetened pineapple tidbits, drained
⅔ cup sliced fresh strawberries
⅓ cup fresh blueberries
1 kiwifruit, peeled and sliced

Line a colander or sieve with a double layer of cheesecloth that has been rinsed out and squeezed dry. Allow cheesecloth to extend over outside edges of colander. Combine yogurt and lemon rind, stirring well. Pour into colander and fold edges of cheesecloth over to cover yogurt. Place colander in a large bowl to drain; refrigerate overnight. Remove yogurt from colander and discard liquid in bowl. Remove cheesecloth from yogurt. Set yogurt mixture aside.

Combine flour and baking powder. Cut in margarine with a pastry blender until mixture resembles coarse meal. Combine sugars, egg, and vanilla; stir well. Add to flour mixture; stir with a fork until dry ingredients are moistened. Shape into a ball; cover and chill.

Pat dough onto a 12-inch pizza pan that has been coated with cooking spray. Bake at 375° for 12 minutes or until golden brown. Let cool completely on a wire rack.

Spread yogurt mixture over cooled crust. Press pineapple between paper towels to remove excess moisture. Arrange pineapple, strawberries, blueberries, and kiwifruit on top of yogurt. Cut into wedges to serve. Yield: 12 servings (183 calories per serving).

PROTEIN 4.3 / FAT 6.3 / CARBOHYDRATE 27.4 / CHOLESTEROL 25 / IRON 0.8 / SODIUM 52 / CALCIUM 91

APPLE-RUM RAISIN CHEESECAKE

3 tablespoons raisins, coarsely chopped
2 tablespoons rum
Vegetable cooking spray
1 tablespoon graham cracker crumbs
3 (8-ounce) packages Neufchâtel cheese, softened
¾ cup sugar
⅓ cup unsweetened apple juice
4 eggs

Combine raisins and rum in a small bowl. Cover and let stand several hours.

Coat bottom of a 9-inch springform pan with cooking spray. Dust with cracker crumbs.

Combine cheese, sugar, and apple juice in a large bowl; beat at medium speed of an electric mixer until smooth. Add eggs, 1 at a time, beating well after each addition.

Pour batter into prepared pan. Sprinkle raisin mixture over batter. Swirl gently with a knife. Place pan in a large shallow baking dish. Fill baking dish with hot water to a depth of 1 inch. Bake at 350° for 1 hour. Remove cheesecake from water bath, and let cool on a wire rack. Cover and chill thoroughly. Remove sides of pan before serving. Yield: 16 servings (176 calories per serving).

PROTEIN 5.9 / FAT 11.4 / CARBOHYDRATE 13.0 / CHOLESTEROL 101 / IRON 0.5 / SODIUM 190 / CALCIUM 40

MOCHA CHIP CHEESECAKE

2 cups low-fat cottage cheese
3 eggs
½ cup sugar
1 tablespoon cornstarch
1 (8-ounce) carton low-fat sour cream
1 tablespoon instant coffee granules
1 tablespoon hot water
Vegetable cooking spray
⅓ cup semisweet chocolate mini-morsels

Combine cottage cheese and eggs in container of an electric blender or food processor, top with cover, and process until smooth. Combine sugar and cornstarch, stirring well. Add cornstarch mixture and sour cream to cheese mixture. Dissolve coffee in water. Add to cheese mixture; process until smooth. Pour into a 9-inch pieplate that has been coated with cooking spray. Sprinkle with chocolate morsels. Bake at 325° for 45 to 50 minutes. Let cool on a wire rack. Cover and chill thoroughly. Yield: 10 servings (169 calories per serving).

PROTEIN 9.1 / FAT 7.4 / CARBOHYDRATE 17.3 / CHOLESTEROL 94 / IRON 0.6 / SODIUM 214 / CALCIUM 66

STRAWBERRY JELLY ROLL

Vegetable cooking spray
5 eggs, separated
½ cup sugar
1 cup sifted cake flour
¼ teaspoon salt
1 tablespoon grated lemon rind
2 tablespoons lemon juice
½ teaspoon ground cinnamon
3 tablespoons powdered sugar, divided
Strawberry Filling
Lemon twists (optional)

Coat a 15- x 10- x 1-inch jellyroll pan with cooking spray, and line with wax paper. Coat wax paper with cooking spray; set aside.

Beat egg yolks at high speed of an electric mixer until thick and lemon colored. Gradually add ½ cup sugar, beating well. Sift together flour and salt. Fold into yolk mixture.

Beat egg whites (at room temperature) at high speed of an electric mixer until stiff but not dry. Fold in lemon rind, juice, and cinnamon. Fold one-third of egg whites into egg yolk mixture. Gently fold egg yolk mixture into remaining egg whites. Spread batter evenly in prepared pan. Bake at 350° for 15 minutes or until cake springs back when lightly touched.

Sift 2 tablespoons powdered sugar in a 15- x 10-inch rectangle on a linen towel. When cake is done, loosen from sides of pan, and turn out onto powdered sugar; peel off wax paper. Starting at narrow end, roll up cake and towel together; let cool on a wire rack, seam side down.

Unroll cake. Spread Strawberry Filling evenly over cake, and carefully reroll cake, without towel. Place on a serving plate, seam side down. Sift remaining 1 tablespoon powdered sugar over cake. Garnish with lemon twists, if desired. To serve, cut into 1-inch slices. Yield: 10 servings (146 calories per serving).

Strawberry Filling:

1 cup low-sugar strawberry spread
1 tablespoon cornstarch
1 tablespoon water
1 tablespoon strawberry schnapps

Place spread in a saucepan; bring to a boil over medium heat. Combine cornstarch, water, and schnapps, stirring until blended. Add to spread; cook, stirring constantly, until mixture returns to a boil and thickens. Remove from heat and let cool completely. Yield: ¾ cup.

PROTEIN 3.8 / FAT 3.0 / CARBOHYDRATE 26.2 / CHOLESTEROL 137 / IRON 0.6 / SODIUM 94 / CALCIUM 19

STRESS RELIEVERS FOR THE OFFICE

Feeling tense or strained at work? Treat yourself to a few moments of stress-relieving relaxation. Push your chair back and let your mind relax while trying the following:
*Sit tall—imagine a balloon pulling you up.
*Do shoulder shrugs and rotate the shoulders in a circular motion.
*Lower your chin toward your chest and gently turn your head from side to side.
*Massage your shoulders using your right hand to rub your left shoulder. Repeat on the opposite side.
*Take a deep breath and relax.

CHOCOLATE-APRICOT ROULAGE

Vegetable cooking spray
3 egg yolks
¼ cup sugar
2 tablespoons amaretto
½ cup sifted cake flour
3 tablespoons unsweetened
  cocoa
¾ teaspoon baking powder
4 egg whites
⅛ teaspoon salt
3 tablespoons sugar
1 tablespoon unsweetened cocoa
Apricot Filling
2 tablespoons chopped blanched
  almonds

Coat a 15- x 10- x 1-inch jellyroll pan with cooking spray. Line pan with wax paper, and coat wax paper with cooking spray. Set jellyroll pan aside.

Beat egg yolks at high speed of an electric mixer until thick and lemon colored. Gradually beat in ¼ cup sugar, 1 tablespoon at a time; stir in amaretto. Sift together flour, 3 tablespoons cocoa, and baking powder. Gently fold flour mixture into egg yolk mixture.

Beat egg whites (at room temperature) and salt at high speed of an electric mixer 1 minute. Gradually add 3 tablespoons sugar, 1 tablespoon at a time, beating until stiff peaks form and sugar dissolves (2 to 4 minutes). Gently fold whites into cocoa mixture. Spread batter evenly in prepared pan. Bake at 375° for 10 to 12 minutes.

Sift 1 tablespoon cocoa in a 15- x 10-inch rectangle on a linen towel. When cake is done, immediately loosen from sides of pan, and turn out onto cocoa; peel off wax paper. Starting at narrow end, roll up cake and towel together, and let cake cool completely on a wire rack, seam side down.

Unroll cake. Spread filling evenly over cake, and carefully reroll cake, without towel. Place on a baking sheet, seam side down; freeze until filling is firm.

To serve, sprinkle almonds evenly over top of cake; let stand at room temperature 10 minutes before cutting into 1-inch slices. Yield: 10 servings (189 calories per serving).

Apricot Filling:

1 (8-ounce) package Neufchâtel cheese, softened
½ cup low-sugar apricot spread
1 tablespoon sifted powdered sugar

Combine all ingredients; stir until well blended. Cover and freeze 30 to 45 minutes or until firm but still spreadable, stirring after 20 minutes. Yield: 1¼ cups.

PROTEIN 5.7 / FAT 8.1 / CARBOHYDRATE 22.3 / CHOLESTEROL 99 / IRON 0.8 / SODIUM 178 / CALCIUM 49

QUICK CARROT CAKE

⅔ cup whole wheat flour
½ cup all-purpose flour
1 teaspoon baking powder
1 teaspoon ground cinnamon
¼ teaspoon ground allspice
1 egg
¼ cup plus 2 tablespoons firmly packed brown sugar
½ cup skim milk
¼ cup reduced-calorie mayonnaise
1 teaspoon vanilla extract
1 cup shredded carrot
¼ cup unsweetened grated coconut
Vegetable cooking spray
3 ounces Neufchâtel cheese, softened
2 tablespoons plus 1 teaspoon powdered
  sugar
½ teaspoon skim milk

Combine first 5 ingredients, set aside. Combine egg and next 4 ingredients in a large bowl; beat at medium speed of an electric mixer until well blended. Add dry ingredients, stirring just until dry ingredients are moistened. Stir in carrot and coconut.

Spoon batter into an 8-inch square baking dish that has been coated with cooking spray. (Batter will be thin in pan.) Bake at 350° for 20 to 25 minutes or until a wooden pick inserted in center comes out clean. Let cool completely in pan on a wire rack.

Combine cheese, sugar, and ½ teaspoon milk; stir until well blended. Spread mixture over top of cake. Cut cake into squares to serve. Yield: 9 servings (178 calories per serving).

PROTEIN 4.4 / FAT 6.4 / CARBOHYDRATE 26.6 / CHOLESTEROL 40 / IRON 1.2 / SODIUM 144 / CALCIUM 68

GINGERBREAD WITH ORANGE-RUM SAUCE

1¼ cups whole wheat flour
½ cup all-purpose flour
1 teaspoon baking powder
1 teaspoon baking soda
¼ teaspoon salt
2 teaspoons ground ginger
¼ teaspoon ground cinnamon
¼ teaspoon ground nutmeg
¼ teaspoon ground mace
¼ cup plus 2 tablespoons unsalted margarine
¼ cup firmly packed brown sugar
2 eggs, lightly beaten
2 tablespoons molasses
1 tablespoon grated orange rind
¾ cup nonfat buttermilk
Vegetable cooking spray
Orange-Rum Sauce

Combine first 9 ingredients; set aside. Cream margarine; gradually add sugar, beating well at medium speed of an electric mixer until light and fluffy. Add eggs, molasses, and orange rind, beating well. Add flour mixture to creamed mixture alternately with buttermilk, beginning and ending with flour mixture. Mix well after each addition.

Pour into an 8½- x 4½- x 3-inch loafpan that has been coated with cooking spray. Bake at 350° for 50 minutes or until a wooden pick inserted in center comes out clean. Cool in pan 10 minutes. Remove from pan, and cool completely on a wire rack. Spoon 1 tablespoon Orange-Rum Sauce over each serving. Yield: 16 servings (136 calories per serving).

Orange-Rum Sauce:

¾ cup plus 3 tablespoons unsweetened orange juice
1 tablespoon cornstarch
2 tablespoons honey
½ teaspoon grated orange rind

Combine orange juice and cornstarch in a nonaluminum saucepan, stirring well. Cook over medium heat, stirring constantly, until mixture thickens. Add honey and orange rind, stirring well. Serve warm. Yield: 1 cup.

PROTEIN 3.1 / FAT 5.3 / CARBOHYDRATE 20.2 / CHOLESTEROL 34 / IRON 0.9 / SODIUM 130 / CALCIUM 42

MAPLE-SPICE CHIFFON CAKE

1 cup sifted cake flour
1½ teaspoons baking powder
¼ teaspoon salt
½ cup firmly packed brown sugar
¼ cup vegetable oil
4 eggs, separated
¼ cup water
1 teaspoon maple flavoring
½ teaspoon cream of tartar
½ cup sugar
1½ teaspoons ground cinnamon
½ teaspoon ground nutmeg
½ teaspoon ground cloves
½ teaspoon ground allspice

Sift flour, baking powder, and salt; stir in brown sugar. Make a well in center; add oil, egg yolks, water, and flavoring. Beat at high speed of an electric mixer 5 minutes or until smooth.

Beat egg whites (at room temperature) and cream of tartar in a mixing bowl at high speed of electric mixer 1 minute. Gradually add sugar, 1 tablespoon at a time, beating until stiff peaks form and sugar dissolves (2 to 4 minutes).

Pour egg yolk mixture in a thin, steady stream over entire surface of egg whites; gently fold whites into yolk mixture.

Combine spices; set aside.

Pour one-third of batter into an ungreased 10-inch tube pan; spread evenly. Sprinkle half of cinnamon mixture over batter. Repeat layers, ending with batter. Bake at 325° for 1 hour or until cake springs back when lightly touched. Invert pan; cool 40 minutes. Loosen cake from sides of pan; remove from pan. Yield: 16 servings (124 calories per serving).

PROTEIN 2.0 / FAT 4.9 / CARBOHYDRATE 18.1 / CHOLESTEROL 69 / IRON 0.6 / SODIUM 91 / CALCIUM 35

THE RIGHT WAY IS BEST

According to exercise physiologists, exercising incorrectly can be just as bad as not exercising at all. If the correct body position is not maintained throughout the exercise, you may not work the muscles intended. Worse, you can cause injury by placing a strain where it does not belong.

GLAZED CITRUS CAKES

3 eggs, separated
½ cup sugar, divided
1 tablespoon plus 1½ teaspoons lemon juice
1 tablespoon plus 1½ teaspoons unsweetened orange juice
1 teaspoon grated lemon rind
1 teaspoon grated orange rind
¼ teaspoon vanilla extract
1 cup sifted cake flour
¼ teaspoon cream of tartar
¼ teaspoon salt
Vegetable cooking spray
Glaze (recipe follows)
1 tablespoon plus 1 teaspoon powdered sugar
4 medium navel oranges, peeled, seeded, and sectioned

Beat egg yolks at medium speed of an electric mixer 5 minutes or until thick and lemon colored. Add ¼ cup sugar, 1 tablespoon at a time; beat well after each addition. Add lemon juice and next 4 ingredients; mix well. Gradually add flour, mixing just until blended.

Beat egg whites (at room temperature), cream of tartar, and salt at high speed of an electric mixer 1 minute. Gradually add remaining ¼ cup sugar, 1 tablespoon at a time, beating until stiff peaks form and sugar dissolves (2 to 4 minutes).

Gently fold egg white mixture into yolk mixture. Spoon batter evenly into 8 sponge cake cups that have been coated with cooking spray. Bake at 350° for 15 to 20 minutes or until cakes spring back when lightly touched. Carefully remove from pans; cool completely on wire racks. To serve, place cakes on individual plates. Spoon 1 tablespoon glaze over each cake. Sift ½ teaspoon powdered sugar over each. Place orange sections alongside cakes. Yield: 8 servings (166 calories per serving).

Glaze:

2 teaspoons sugar
1½ teaspoons cornstarch
⅓ cup plus 1 tablespoon unsweetened orange juice
2 tablespoons lemon juice

Combine sugar and cornstarch in a nonaluminum saucepan; stir in juices. Cook over medium heat, stirring constantly, until thickened. Remove from heat; let cool. Yield: ½ cup.

PROTEIN 3.9 / FAT 2.5 / CARBOHYDRATE 33.1 / CHOLESTEROL 103 / IRON 0.5 / SODIUM 107 / CALCIUM 35

PEANUTTY SURPRISE CUPCAKES

2 ounces Neufchâtel cheese, softened
3 tablespoons no-sugar-added creamy peanut butter
1 tablespoon honey
½ cup regular oats, uncooked
¾ cup boiling water
⅓ cup shortening
½ cup firmly packed brown sugar
1 egg
½ teaspoon vanilla extract
¾ cup all-purpose flour
½ teaspoon baking soda
1 teaspoon ground cinnamon
½ teaspoon ground cloves
¼ teaspoon ground nutmeg
⅛ teaspoon salt

Combine first 3 ingredients in a small bowl, stirring well; set aside.

Combine oats and boiling water in a small bowl, stirring well. Set aside, and let cool.

Cream shortening; gradually add sugar, beating well at medium speed of an electric mixer. Add egg and vanilla, beating well. Combine flour, soda, cinnamon, cloves, nutmeg, and salt; add to creamed mixture alternately with oatmeal mixture, beginning and ending with flour mixture. Mix well after each addition.

Spoon 1 tablespoon batter into each of 12 paper-lined muffin cups. Spoon 2 teaspoons peanut butter mixture into each muffin cup. Fill each cup two-thirds full with remaining batter. Bake at 375° for 20 minutes. Remove cupcakes from pans, and let cool on wire racks. Yield: 1 dozen (170 calories each).

PROTEIN 3.6 / FAT 8.7 / CARBOHYDRATE 20.2 / CHOLESTEROL 26 / IRON 1.0 / SODIUM 87 / CALCIUM 29

CHOCOLATE-ZUCCHINI CUPCAKES

¼ cup plus 2 tablespoons margarine
1 cup sugar
2 eggs
1¼ cups all-purpose flour
¼ cup unsweetened cocoa
1¼ teaspoons baking powder
¾ teaspoon baking soda
½ teaspoon ground cloves
¼ teaspoon salt
¼ cup skim milk
1½ cups finely shredded zucchini
1 teaspoon vanilla extract
1 tablespoon powdered sugar

Cream margarine in a medium bowl; gradually add sugar, beating well at medium speed of an electric mixer. Add eggs, one at a time, beating well after each addition. Combine flour, cocoa, baking powder, soda, cloves, and salt in a small bowl; add to creamed mixture alternately with milk, beginning and ending with flour mixture. Mix well after each addition. Stir in zucchini and vanilla.

Spoon batter into paper-lined muffin cups, filling two-thirds full. Bake at 350° for 20 minutes or until a wooden pick inserted in center comes out clean. Cool in pans 10 minutes; remove to wire racks to cool completely. Sift powdered sugar over cupcakes. Yield: 22 cupcakes (108 calories each).

PROTEIN 1.9 / FAT 3.9 / CARBOHYDRATE 16.5 / CHOLESTEROL 25 / IRON 0.6 / SODIUM 117 / CALCIUM 29

CHOCOLATE CREAM PUFFS

1 cup water
¼ cup plus 2 tablespoons margarine
1 cup all-purpose flour
¼ teaspoon salt
4 eggs
Chocolate Filling
1 tablespoon powdered sugar

Combine water and margarine in a medium saucepan; bring to a boil. Add flour and salt all at once, stirring vigorously over medium heat about 1 minute or until mixture leaves sides of pan and forms a smooth ball. Remove from heat, and cool slightly.

Add eggs to flour mixture, one at a time, beating with a wooden spoon after each addition; beat until batter is smooth. Drop batter into 12 mounds, 2 inches apart, on ungreased baking sheets.

Bake at 400° for 30 minutes or until golden and puffed. Cool away from drafts. Cut tops off cream puffs; pull out and discard soft dough inside. Fill cream puffs evenly with Chocolate Filling. Replace tops. Sift powdered sugar over cream puffs. Yield: 1 dozen (186 calories each).

Chocolate Filling:

⅓ cup sugar
3 tablespoons cornstarch
2 tablespoons unsweetened cocoa
⅛ teaspoon salt
2 cups 1% low-fat chocolate milk
1 egg yolk
½ teaspoon vanilla extract

Combine sugar, cornstarch, cocoa, and salt in a saucepan. Gradually stir in milk. Cook over medium heat, stirring constantly, until thickened. Beat egg yolk until thick and lemon colored. Gradually stir about one-fourth hot mixture into yolk; add to remaining hot mixture. Cook until thickened, stirring constantly. Remove from heat; stir in vanilla. Cover and chill thoroughly. Yield: 2 cups.

PROTEIN 5.2 / FAT 8.7 / CARBOHYDRATE 21.7 / CHOLESTEROL 115 / IRON 1.0 / SODIUM 190 / CALCIUM 65

PEACH-GINGER CRUMBLE

4 cups peeled, sliced fresh peaches
2 tablespoons sugar
1 tablespoon all-purpose flour
Vegetable cooking spray
10 gingersnaps, crumbled
¼ teaspoon ground nutmeg
2 teaspoons margarine, softened

Combine peaches, sugar, and flour in a large bowl; toss gently. Coat a shallow 1-quart baking dish with cooking spray. Spoon peach mixture into dish; let stand for 15 minutes.

Combine gingersnaps, nutmeg, and margarine; blend well. Sprinkle evenly over peach mixture. Bake at 375° for 30 minutes or until peaches are tender. Serve warm. Yield: 6 servings (148 calories per ½-cup serving).

PROTEIN 1.9 / FAT 3.7 / CARBOHYDRATE 28.5 / CHOLESTEROL 5 / IRON 0.9 / SODIUM 33 / CALCIUM 31

FRESH APPLE-PEAR COBBLER

3 tablespoons brown sugar
1 tablespoon cornstarch
¼ teaspoon ground cinnamon
¼ teaspoon ground nutmeg
1 cup water
3 medium-size fresh pears, peeled, cored, and chopped
2 large cooking apples, peeled, cored, and sliced
¼ cup raisins
Vegetable cooking spray
½ cup plus 1 tablespoon all-purpose flour
1 tablespoon sugar
1 teaspoon baking powder
¼ cup skim milk
1 tablespoon chopped blanched almonds
2 teaspoons sugar
⅛ teaspoon ground cinnamon

Combine first 4 ingredients in a medium saucepan, stirring well. Add water, stirring well. Bring to a boil over medium heat. Cook 1 minute, stirring constantly. Remove from heat. Gently stir in pears, apples, and raisins. Spoon mixture into an 8-inch square baking dish that has been coated with cooking spray.

Combine flour, 1 tablespoon sugar, and baking powder in a medium bowl. Add skim milk, stirring just until dry ingredients are moistened. Drop dumpling mixture by level tablespoons over apple-pear mixture. Combine almonds, 2 teaspoons sugar, and cinnamon; stir well. Sprinkle cinnamon mixture over dumplings. Bake at 400° for 25 to 30 minutes or until dumplings are lightly browned. Yield: 8 servings (133 calories per serving).

PROTEIN 1.9 / FAT 1.3 / CARBOHYDRATE 30.1 / CHOLESTEROL 0 / IRON 0.7 / SODIUM 44 / CALCIUM 51

MINTY MANGO COBBLER

2 cups peeled, sliced fresh peaches
1 cup peeled, cubed mango
¾ cup fresh blueberries
2 tablespoons lemon juice
3 tablespoons cornstarch
¼ cup sugar
1½ teaspoons minced fresh mint
Vegetable cooking spray
½ cup all-purpose flour
⅛ teaspoon salt
2 tablespoons plus 1½ teaspoons margarine
1 tablespoon plus 1 teaspoon cold water

Combine first 7 ingredients in a large bowl; toss well. Let stand 15 minutes. Spoon fruit mixture into a 10- x 6- x 2-inch baking dish that has been coated with cooking spray. Set aside.

Combine flour and salt in a medium bowl; cut in margarine with a pastry blender until mixture resembles coarse meal. Sprinkle cold water evenly over surface; stir with a fork until dry ingredients are moistened. Shape into a ball; chill. Roll pastry to ⅛-inch thickness on a lightly floured surface; cut into decorative shapes.

Place pastry cutouts on top of fruit mixture; bake at 425° for 10 minutes. Reduce heat to 350° and bake for 25 minutes or until fruit is tender and pastry is lightly browned. Yield: 8 servings (141 calories per serving).

PROTEIN 1.5 / FAT 3.9 / CARBOHYDRATE 26.5 / CHOLESTEROL 0 / IRON 0.4 / SODIUM 80 / CALCIUM 9

MOTIVATION IS THE KEY

When starting a fitness program, take a positive attitude into the session; this can be vital to your success. Focus on yourself and your own capabilities. Establishing and maintaining your own pace will keep you in the action longer and make exercise more fun. Participating regularly in a fitness program will help you feel and look better.

Base your participation on personal reasons—the personal rewards that you want to achieve. Since everyone has different abilities and body types, avoid comparing yourself to others. Concentrating on proper form during your exercise session and working at a comfortable pace will keep your momentum and motivation at their peak.

FRESH RHUBARB PIE

1 cup all-purpose flour
¼ teaspoon salt
¼ cup margarine
3 tablespoons cold water
3 cups chopped fresh rhubarb
¼ cup unsweetened orange juice
⅓ cup sugar
2 tablespoons cornstarch
2 tablespoons water
3 egg whites
¼ teaspoon cream of tartar
2 tablespoons sugar

Combine flour and salt; cut in margarine with a pastry blender until mixture resembles coarse meal. Sprinkle cold water evenly over surface of flour mixture; stir with a fork until dry ingredients are moistened. Shape dough into a ball, and chill. Roll dough to ⅛-inch thickness. Place in a 9-inch pieplate; fold edges under. Prick bottom and sides with a fork. Bake at 425° for 12 to 15 minutes. Cool.

Combine chopped rhubarb, orange juice, and sugar in a medium saucepan. Place over medium heat and cook until mixture is thickened. Dissolve cornstarch in water; stir cornstarch mixture into rhubarb mixture. Pour into baked pie shell. Set aside.

Beat egg whites (at room temperature) and cream of tartar at high speed of an electric mixer 1 minute. Gradually add sugar, 1 tablespoon at a time, beating until stiff peaks form and sugar dissolves (2 to 4 minutes). Spread meringue over hot filling, sealing to edge of pastry. Bake at 425° for 5 minutes or until meringue is golden brown. Yield: 8 servings (184 calories per serving).

PROTEIN 3.5 / FAT 6.0 / CARBOHYDRATE 29.3 / CHOLESTEROL 0 / IRON 0.6 / SODIUM 168 / CALCIUM 47

PEAR-ALMOND TART

1 cup all-purpose flour
3 tablespoons shortening
¼ cup cold water
¼ cup chopped blanched almonds
2 tablespoons sugar
1 egg, lightly beaten
2 cups water
2 tablespoons lemon juice
3 medium-size fresh pears
2½ teaspoons sugar
2 tablespoons slivered blanched
    almonds
1 tablespoon margarine, melted
⅓ cup low-sugar apricot spread

Place flour in a large bowl; cut in shortening with a pastry blender until mixture resembles coarse meal. Sprinkle cold water, 1 tablespoon at a time, evenly over surface of mixture; stir with a fork until dry ingredients are moistened. Shape into a ball; chill. Roll dough into a 12-inch circle on a lightly floured surface. Fit pastry into a 9-inch tart pan; trim excess pastry along edges. Set pastry aside.

Combine ¼ cup almonds, sugar, and egg in a small bowl, stirring well. Spread almond mixture over pastry.

Combine water and lemon juice in a medium bowl, stirring well. Peel and core pears. Dip pears in lemon juice mixture, and drain well. Cut pears in half vertically, and then cut into ⅛-inch-thick lengthwise slices, keeping slices in order as they are cut. Arrange slices over almond mixture in the shape of 6 pear halves, letting slices fan out slightly. Sprinkle with sugar and top with 2 tablespoons slivered almonds. Drizzle with melted margarine. Bake at 400° for 40 minutes or until golden brown.

Melt apricot spread over low heat, stirring constantly. Strain spread; discard preserves. Carefully brush spread over tart. Remove tart from pan before serving. Yield: 8 servings (200 calories per serving).

PROTEIN 3.5 / FAT 8.3 / CARBOHYDRATE 29.6 / CHOLESTEROL 34 / IRON 0.9 / SODIUM 26 / CALCIUM 27

Pear-Almond Tart and Lemon Mousse Torte (page 228) let the fresh flavors of fruit shine through.

Clockwise from top: Chocolate-Mint Meringue Kisses (page 240), Pistachio Cookie Curls, Two-Tone Spirals (page 240), lower right: Café Vienna Cookies, Iced Spiced Cookies (page 240).

CAFÉ VIENNA COOKIES

⅓ cup margarine, softened
½ cup sugar
1 egg
2 tablespoons skim milk
½ teaspoon almond extract
2 cups all-purpose flour
2 tablespoons instant coffee
  granules
1 teaspoon ground cinnamon

Cream margarine; gradually add sugar, beating at medium speed of an electric mixer until light and fluffy. Add egg, milk, and extract, beating well.

Combine flour, coffee granules, and cinnamon; add to creamed mixture, mixing well.

Press dough from a cookie press onto ungreased cookie sheets, making 2-inch ribbon-like strips. Bake at 400° for 6 minutes or until edges are lightly browned. Remove from cookie sheets, and let cool completely on wire racks. Yield: 5 dozen (34 calories each).

PROTEIN 0.6 / FAT 1.2 / CARBOHYDRATE 5.2 / CHOLESTEROL 5 / IRON 0.2 / SODIUM 13 / CALCIUM 3

PISTACHIO COOKIE CURLS

¼ cup finely chopped pistachios
¼ cup sugar
1 egg white
1 tablespoon margarine, melted
1 tablespoon all-purpose flour
¼ teaspoon ground nutmeg
Vegetable cooking spray

Combine first 6 ingredients in a small bowl, stirring well.

Coat a cookie sheet heavily with cooking spray, and divide it into four sections. Spoon 1½ teaspoons of batter in the center of each section. Spread each portion of batter evenly with a spatula to make a 4- x 3-inch oval. Bake at 425° for 3 minutes or until edges are golden brown.

Let cool 20 seconds. Loosen cookies with a metal spatula, but leave on cookie sheet. Place one cookie upside down on counter, and quickly roll it lengthwise around the handle of a wooden spoon. Remove cookie, and let cool on a wire rack. Repeat procedure with remaining cookies as quickly as possible. (If cookies become too stiff before rolling, return cookie sheet to oven briefly to soften them.) Continue procedure with remaining cookie batter. Yield: 1 dozen (46 calories each).

PROTEIN 0.9 / FAT 2.5 / CARBOHYDRATE 5.4 / CHOLESTEROL 0 / IRON 0.2 / SODIUM 16 / CALCIUM 4

CHOCOLATE PINWHEEL COOKIES

¼ cup margarine, softened
¼ cup sugar
⅓ cup vanilla low-fat yogurt
1 egg
2 teaspoons vanilla extract
2 cups plus 2 tablespoons all-purpose flour
½ (8-ounce) package Neufchâtel cheese,
  softened
1 (1-ounce) square semisweet chocolate,
  melted
2 tablespoons plus 1 teaspoon powdered
  sugar

Cream margarine; gradually add sugar, beating at medium speed of an electric mixer until light and fluffy. Add yogurt, egg, and vanilla; beat well. Stir in flour. Shape dough into a flat disc, and chill thoroughly.

Roll dough to ⅛-inch thickness on a lightly floured surface. Cut into 1-inch squares. Cut each square diagonally from the corners to the center, leaving a ½-inch portion of dough in center uncut.

Combine cheese, chocolate, and powdered sugar in a small bowl, beating at low speed of an electric mixer until well blended. Spoon a heaping ¼ teaspoon chocolate mixture onto center of each square. Fold every other point of cut corners to the center to form a pinwheel. Press firmly to seal seam of points. Place pinwheels on ungreased cookie sheets. Bake at 375° for 10 to 12 minutes or until lightly browned. Cool on wire racks. Yield: 4½ dozen (43 calories each).

PROTEIN 1.0 / FAT 1.7 / CARBOHYDRATE 6.0 / CHOLESTEROL 7 / IRON 0.2 / SODIUM 21 / CALCIUM 6

TWO-TONE SPIRALS

¼ cup margarine, softened
¼ cup no-sugar-added creamy peanut butter
⅔ cup firmly packed brown sugar
1 egg, beaten
1 teaspoon vanilla extract
1¾ cups all-purpose flour
½ teaspoon baking soda
¼ teaspoon salt
1 tablespoon plus 2 teaspoons unsweetened cocoa

Cream margarine and peanut butter; gradually add sugar, beating at medium speed of an electric mixer. Add egg and vanilla, beating well. Combine flour, soda, and salt; add to peanut butter mixture, beating well. Divide dough in half. Add cocoa into one half of dough, stirring until well blended. Roll each portion of dough into a 14- x 8-inch rectangle on wax paper. Gently place chocolate rectangle directly on top of peanut butter rectangle. Press chocolate dough firmly to peanut butter dough with a rolling pin; roll up, jellyroll fashion, starting with long side. Wrap dough in wax paper, and refrigerate or freeze until firm.

Unwrap roll, and cut dough into ¼-inch slices. Place 1 inch apart on ungreased cookie sheets. Bake at 350° for 10 to 12 minutes. Cool on wire racks. Yield: 5½ dozen (42 calories each).

PROTEIN 0.9 / FAT 1.6 / CARBOHYDRATE 6.1 / CHOLESTEROL 5 / IRON 0.3 / SODIUM 30 / CALCIUM 6

SOUR CREAM-PECAN BALLS

¼ cup margarine
¼ cup plus 2 tablespoons sifted powdered sugar
¼ cup low-fat sour cream
1 teaspoon vanilla extract
1¼ cups all-purpose flour
⅓ cup ground pecans
Vegetable cooking spray
2 teaspoons powdered sugar

Cream margarine; gradually add ¼ cup plus 2 tablespoons sugar, beating at medium speed of an electric mixer until light and fluffy. Add sour cream and vanilla; beat well. Stir in flour and pecans. Shape into a ball; chill thoroughly.
Shape dough into 1-inch balls. Place on a

cookie sheet that has been coated with cooking spray. Bake at 350° for 14 minutes or until lightly browned. Cool on wire racks. Sift remaining 2 teaspoons powdered sugar over cookies. Yield: 3 dozen (45 calories each).

PROTEIN 0.7 / FAT 2.3 / CARBOHYDRATE 5.3 / CHOLESTEROL 1 / IRON 0.2 / SODIUM 16 / CALCIUM 3

CHOCOLATE-MINT MERINGUE KISSES

2 egg whites
⅓ cup sugar
½ cup semisweet chocolate mini-morsels
½ teaspoon peppermint extract

Beat egg whites (at room temperature) in a large bowl at high speed of an electric mixer 1 minute. Gradually add sugar, 1 tablespoon at a time, beating until stiff peaks form and sugar dissolves (2 to 4 minutes). Gently fold in chocolate morsels and peppermint extract.

Drop by heaping teaspoonfuls onto cookie sheets lined with wax paper. Bake at 300° for 35 minutes. Cool slightly on cookie sheets; gently remove from wax paper, and cool completely on wire racks. Yield: 3½ dozen (17 calories each).

PROTEIN 0.2 / FAT 0.7 / CARBOHYDRATE 2.8 / CHOLESTEROL 0 / IRON 0.1 / SODIUM 2 / CALCIUM 1

ICED SPICED COOKIES

⅓ cup margarine, softened
⅔ cup sugar
1 egg, beaten
1½ cups all-purpose flour
1½ teaspoons baking powder
1 teaspoon ground cinnamon
½ teaspoon ground allspice
¼ teaspoon salt
¼ teaspoon ground cloves
¼ cup skim milk
1 tablespoon vanilla extract
Vegetable cooking spray
Glaze (recipe follows)

Cream margarine; gradually add sugar, beating well at medium speed of an electric mixer.

Add egg, beating well. Combine flour, baking powder, cinnamon, allspice, salt, and cloves; add to creamed mixture alternately with milk, beginning and ending with flour mixture. Mix after each addition. Stir in vanilla.

Drop dough by rounded teaspoonfuls 2 inches apart onto cookie sheets that have been coated with cooking spray. Bake at 325° for 15 to 20 minutes. Cool slightly on cookie sheets. Remove cookies to wire racks to cool completely. Drizzle ¼ teaspoon glaze over each cookie. Yield: 4 dozen (48 calories each).

Glaze:

⅔ cup sifted powdered sugar
1 tablespoon skim milk

Combine sugar and milk, stirring until smooth. Yield: ¼ cup.

PROTEIN 0.6 / FAT 1.5 / CARBOHYDRATE 8.0 / CHOLESTEROL 6 / IRON 0.2 / SODIUM 39 / CALCIUM 11

ADDING FLAVOR, NOT CALORIES

For flavor without the calories, alcohol and liqueurs can be added to baked products such as in Bourbon-Walnut Brownies. The alcohol evaporates during the baking, leaving only its flavor to enhance the product.

LINZER BARS

½ cup margarine, softened
½ cup sugar
¼ cup unsweetened apricot nectar
1 egg
1 teaspoon grated lemon rind
1 teaspoon vanilla extract
2½ cups all-purpose flour
3 tablespoons ground hazelnuts
1 tablespoon unsweetened cocoa
1 teaspoon ground cinnamon
¼ teaspoon salt
⅛ teaspoon ground cloves
Vegetable cooking spray
1 cup low-sugar apricot spread

Cream margarine; gradually add sugar, beating well at medium speed of an electric mixer.

Add nectar, egg, lemon rind, and vanilla; beat well. Combine flour and next 5 ingredients; add to creamed mixture, ½ cup at a time, beating well after each addition. (Dough will be sticky.)

Place 1 cup of dough between 2 sheets of wax paper, and roll into an 8-inch square. Freeze dough square 10 minutes. Press remaining dough into an 8-inch square pan that has been coated with cooking spray.

Place apricot spread in a small bowl; stir well. Spread evenly over dough in pan. Cut frozen dough into sixteen 8- x ½-inch strips. Freeze strips 5 minutes. Carefully arrange strips in a lattice fashion over apricot spread. Bake at 375° for 30 to 35 minutes. Cool on a wire rack. Cut into 2- x 1½-inch bars. Yield: 2½ dozen (107 calories each).

PROTEIN 1.7 / FAT 3.9 / CARBOHYDRATE 16.6 / CHOLESTEROL 9 / IRON 0.5 / SODIUM 66 / CALCIUM 7

BOURBON-WALNUT BROWNIES

⅔ cup margarine
⅔ cup sugar
2 eggs
3 tablespoons bourbon
1 teaspoon vanilla extract
½ cup all-purpose flour
¼ cup plus 2 tablespoons unsweetened cocoa
½ teaspoon baking powder
¼ teaspoon salt
3 tablespoons finely chopped walnuts
Vegetable cooking spray

Cream margarine; gradually add ⅔ cup sugar, beating well at medium speed of an electric mixer. Add eggs, bourbon, and vanilla extract, beating well.

Combine flour, cocoa, baking powder, and salt; add to creamed mixture, beating until well blended. Stir in walnuts.

Spoon batter into an 8-inch square baking pan that has been coated with cooking spray. Bake at 350° for 25 minutes or until a wooden pick inserted in center comes out clean. Cool in pan on a wire rack. Cut into 2- x 1-inch bars. Yield: 32 brownies (72 calories each).

PROTEIN 1.1 / FAT 4.7 / CARBOHYDRATE 6.5 / CHOLESTEROL 17 / IRON 0.3 / SODIUM 72 / CALCIUM 9

Cooking Light Menu Plans

This plan for seven days of calorie-controlled meals provides a healthful approach to weight loss. Follow the plan precisely, or use it as a model for planning your own balanced meals by substituting foods of comparable calories and nutrients. Refer to the Calorie/Nutrient Chart on pages 244-254 for these values. The items with an asterisk represent recipes which can be located in the menu and recipe sections. Of the total calories provided, over 50 percent are from carbohydrate, less than 30 percent are from fat, and less than 20 percent are from protein.

Most women can safely lose weight while eating 1,200 calories per day and most men, while eating 1,600. Once weight is lost, modify the menu plan according to the calories needed to maintain your ideal weight. If you feel you are losing weight too slowly, keep in mind that eating fewer calories to speed up weight loss may rob you of the nutrients your body needs to stay healthy. Also, your metabolism may slow down to accommodate a very limited food supply. Exercising is the key to speeding up weight loss.

1200 calories		DAY 1	1600 calories	
		Breakfast		
1 pancake	85	*Golden Orange Pancakes	2 pancakes	170
1 tablespoon	6	Reduced-Calorie Maple Syrup	2 tablespoons	12
½ cup	94	*Warm Spiced Plums	½ cup	94
1 cup	86	Skim Milk	1 cup	86
	271			362
		Lunch		
1 cup	70	*Springtime Chicken Soup	1 cup	70
—	—	*Fresh Apple-Spinach Salad	1 cup	70
1 serving	141	*Cracked Wheat-Zucchini Bread	1 serving	141
1 tablespoon	40	*Garlic Spread	1 tablespoon	40
1 serving	80	*Orange Soufflé Cups	1 serving	80
—	—	*Cafe Vienna Cookies	3 cookies	102
1 cup	12	*Mint Tea Juleps	1 cup	12
	343			515
		Dinner		
1 serving	167	*Hawaiian Lamb Kabobs	1 serving	167
½ cup	103	Hot Cooked Rice	½ cup	103
1 cup	68	*Spicy Zucchini Toss	1 cup	68
½ cup	142	*Amaretto-Coffee Frozen Yogurt	½ cup	142
—	—	*Blushing Bulls	1 cup	51
	480			531
		Snack		
1 tablespoon	23	*Garden Cheese Ball	2 tablespoons	46
7 crackers	77	Melba Rounds	12 crackers	132
	100			178
Total	1194		Total	1586

1200 calories		DAY 2	1600 calories	
		Breakfast		
1 waffle	107	*Apple-Buckwheat Waffles	1 waffle	107
2 tablespoons	12	Reduced-Calorie Syrup	2 tablespoons	12
—	—	Whole Grain Wheat Cereal	1 serving	79
—	—	Banana	1 serving	109
1 cup	86	Skim Milk	1 cup	86
	205			393
		Lunch		
1 serving	154	*Vegetarian Pita Sandwiches	1 serving	154
—	—	*Vegetable-Lentil Stew	1 cup	93
½ cup	53	*Brussels Sprouts Stir-Fry	½ cup	53
1 cupcake	108	*Chocolate-Zucchini Cupcakes	1 cupcake	108
	315			408
		Dinner		
1 serving	233	*Grilled Garlic Steak	1 serving	223
½ cup	105	*Springtime Rice	½ cup	105
1 serving	54	*Grilled Squash and Peppers	1 serving	54
—	—	*Angel Biscuits	1 biscuit	139
½ cup	65	*Three Berry Dessert Soup	½ cup	65
1 cup	55	*Faux Pink Champagne	1 cup	55
	502			641
		Snack		
1 serving	163	*Frozen Lime Cups with Fresh Fruit Topping	1 serving	163
Total	1185		Total	1605

1200 calories		DAY 3	1600 calories	
		Breakfast		
½ grapefruit	33	Grapefruit	½ grapefruit	33
1 serving	114	*Fig Coffee Cake	1 serving	114
—	—	Lean Cooked Ham	1 ounce	41
1 cup	86	Skim Milk	1 cup	86
	233			274
		Lunch		
1 serving	288	*Hearty Hero Sandwiches	1 serving	288
—	—	*Peppery Pasta Salad	1 serving	78
2 cookies	90	*Sour Cream-Pecan Balls	2 cookies	90
—	—	Skim Milk	1 cup	86
	378			542
		Dinner		
1 serving	254	*Oven-Fried Perch with Cucumber Sauce	1 serving	254
½ cup	84	*Wild Spanish Rice	½ cup	84
½ cup	15	*Cumin-Spiked Cabbage	½ cup	15
—	—	Whole Wheat Bread	1 slice	61
1 serving	173	*Spumoni Loaf	1 serving	173
	526			587
		Snack		
1 medium	54	Fresh Peach	1 medium	54
—	—	Plain Nonfat Yogurt	1 cup	127
	54			181
Total	1191		Total	1584

DAY 4

	1200 calories		1600 calories	
Breakfast				
1 muffin	150	*Blueberry English Muffin	1 muffin	150
1 teaspoon	34	Margarine	1 teaspoon	34
—	—	Oatmeal	½ cup	73
1 cup	86	Skim Milk	1 cup	86
	270			343
Lunch				
1 serving	247	*Baked Chicken Salad in Artichokes	1 serving	247
1 roll	123	Whole Wheat Rolls	1 roll	123
1 cup	74	*Refreshing Fruit Spritzer	1 cup	74
—	—	*Lemon Mousse Torte	1 serving	146
	444			590
Dinner				
1 serving	336	*Vegetable-Enchilada Casserole	1 serving	336
—	—	*Creole Cauliflower	1 serving	51
1 serving	7	Lettuce Wedge	1 serving	7
1 tablespoon	8	*Cucumber-Buttermilk Dressing	1 tablespoon	10
½ cup	90	*Chocolate-Chocolate Chip Ice Milk	½ cup	90
	443			494
Snack				
½ cup	45	*Strawberry-Melon Cooler	½ cup	45
—	—	*Two-Tone Spirals	3 cookies	126
	45			171
Total	1202		Total	1598

DAY 5

	1200 calories		1600 calories	
Breakfast				
1 serving	41	Lean Cooked Ham	1 serving	41
½ cup	61	*Wake-Me-Up Grits	½ cup	61
1 slice	61	Whole Wheat Toast	1 slice	61
—	—	Margarine	1 teaspoon	34
1 cup	86	Skim Milk	1 cup	86
	249			283
Lunch				
1 serving	323	*Spicy Red Beans and Chunky Rice	1 serving	323
—	—	*Garden Batter Bread	1 serving	149
1 serving	55	*California Green Salad	1 serving	55
1 kabob	33	*Frozen Fruit Kabobs	1 kabob	33
	411			560
Dinner				
1 serving	221	*One-Dish Seafood Supper	1 serving	221
1 serving	57	*Garlicky Green Salad	1 serving	57
2 twists	64	*Poppy Seed-Onion Twists	3 twists	96
1 serving	53	*Burgundy Poached Pears	1 serving	53
	395			427
Snack				
2 crackers	128	*Fruit Bits Graham Crackers	2 crackers	128
—	—	Peanut Butter	1 tablespoon	95
—	—	Skim Milk	1 cup	86
	128			309
Total	1183		Total	1579

DAY 6

	1200 calories		1600 calories	
Breakfast				
½ cup	88	*Honeyed Citrus Medley	½ cup	88
—	—	Poached Egg	1 egg	79
—	—	Oatmeal	½ cup	73
1 muffin	148	*Hearty Breakfast Muffin	1 muffin	148
1 cup	86	Skim Milk	1 cup	86
	322			474
Lunch				
1 cup	155	*Chicken Burgoo	1 cup	155
½ cup	81	*Tangy Broccoli Potato Salad	½ cup	81
—	—	*Wild Pecan Rice Muffins	1 muffin	148
½ cup	64	*Kiwifruit Ice	½ cup	64
	300			448
Dinner				
1 serving	248	*Teriyaki Steak Rolls	1 serving	248
½ cup	85	Hot Cooked Wild Rice	½ cup	85
½ cup	68	*Minted Carrots and Pineapple	½ cup	68
4 cookies	68	*Chocolate-Mint Meringue Kisses	4 cookies	68
½ cup	52	*Bellini Freeze	½ cup	52
	521			521
Snack				
½ cup	50	*Cantaloupe Sorbet	½ cup	50
—	—	*Linzer Bars	1 bar	107
	50			157
Total	1193		Total	1600

DAY 7

	1200 calories		1600 calories	
Breakfast				
½ cup	64	Bran Flakes Cereal	½ cup	64
1 tablespoon	27	Raisins	1 tablespoon	27
—	—	Whole Wheat Toast	1 slice	61
1 cup	54	*Hot Spiced Mint Tea	1 cup	54
1 cup	86	Skim Milk	1 cup	86
	231			292
Lunch				
1 cup	150	*Catfish Stew with Hush Puppy Croutons	1 cup	150
1 serving	62	*Lemon Baked Okra	1 serving	62
—	—	*Sourdough Tomato Bread	1 serving	128
1 slice	166	Angel Food Cake	1 slice	166
2 tablespoons	26	*Fresh Peach Sauce	2 tablespoons	26
	404			532
Dinner				
1 serving	249	*Veal Stroganoff	1 serving	249
1 serving	34	*Zucchini Boats with Vegetable Medley	1 serving	34
—	—	Baked Potato	1 medium	181
—	—	Margarine	1 teaspoon	34
1 serving	36	*Peppery Garlic Baguette	1 serving	36
1 serving	141	*Minty Mango Cobbler	1 serving	141
	460			675
Snack				
1 cup	110	*Carrot Delight	1 cup	110
Total	1205		Total	1609

Calorie/Nutrient Chart

FOOD	APPROXIMATE MEASURE	FOOD ENERGY (CALORIES)	PROTEIN (GRAMS)	FAT (GRAMS)	CARBOHYDRATES (GRAMS)	CHOLESTEROL (MILLIGRAMS)	IRON (MILLIGRAMS)	SODIUM (MILLIGRAMS)	CALCIUM (MILLIGRAMS)
Apple									
Fresh, with skin	1 medium	81	0.2	0.5	21.0	0	0.2	0	10
Juice, unsweetened	½ cup	58	0.1	0.1	14.5	0	0.5	4	9
Applesauce, unsweetened	½ cup	52	0.2	0.1	13.8	0	0.1	2	4
Apricot									
Canned, in light syrup	½ cup	75	0.7	0.1	19.0	—	0.3	1	12
Dried, uncooked	1 each	17	0.3	0.0	4.3	0	0.3	1	3
Fresh	1 each	18	0.4	0.1	4.1	0	0.2	0	5
Nectar	½ cup	70	0.5	0.1	18.0	0	0.5	4	9
Artichoke, fresh, cooked	1 each	53	2.6	0.2	12.4	0	1.6	79	47
Asparagus, fresh, cooked	½ cup	23	2.3	0.3	4.0	0	0.6	4	22
Arugula	3 ounces	20	2.2	0.3	3.3	0	1.0	—	263
Avocado	1 medium	322	3.9	30.6	14.8	0	2.0	20	22
Bacon									
Canadian-style	1 ounce	52	6.9	2.4	0.3	16	0.2	438	3
Cured, broiled	1 slice	29	1.4	2.6	0.1	4	0.1	95	0
Bamboo shoots, cooked	½ cup	7	0.9	0.1	1.1	0	0.1	2	7
Banana									
Mashed	½ cup	101	1.1	0.5	25.8	0	0.3	1	7
Whole	1 medium	109	1.2	0.5	27.6	0	0.4	1	7
Barley, dry	½ cup	349	8.1	1.0	78.8	0	2.0	3	16
Bean sprouts, raw	½ cup	16	1.6	0.1	3.1	0	0.5	3	7
Beans									
Black, cooked	½ cup	114	7.6	0.5	20.4	0	1.8	1	23
Garbanzo, cooked	½ cup	134	7.3	2.1	22.5	0	2.4	6	40
Great Northern, cooked	½ cup	132	9.3	0.5	23.7	0	2.4	2	76
Green, canned, regular pack	½ cup	18	1.0	0.1	4.2	0	1.0	442	29
Green, fresh, cooked	½ cup	22	1.2	0.2	4.9	0	0.8	2	29
Kidney, cooked	½ cup	112	7.7	0.4	20.2	0	2.6	2	25
Lima, frozen, baby	½ cup	94	6	0.3	17.5	0	1.8	26	25
Pinto, cooked	½ cup	117	7.0	0.4	21.9	0	2.2	2	41
Red, cooked	½ cup	112	7.7	0.4	20.2	0	2.6	2	25
Yellow or wax, canned, regular pack	½ cup	17	0.9	0.2	3.6	—	1.1	208	32
Beef, trimmed of fat									
Flank steak, broiled	3 ounces	207	21.6	12.7	0.0	60	2.2	71	5
Ground, extra-lean	3 ounces	213	22.5	13.7	0.0	70	1.9	42	6
Liver, braised	3 ounces	137	20.7	4.2	2.9	331	5.7	60	6
Roast	3 ounces	204	23.1	11.7	0.0	69	2.2	63	9
Round, bottom, braised	3 ounces	189	26.9	8.2	0.0	82	2.9	43	4
Round, eye of, cooked	3 ounces	156	24.7	5.5	0.0	59	1.7	53	4
Round, eye, cooked	3 ounces	156	24.7	5.5	0.0	59	1.7	53	4
Sirloin, broiled	3 ounces	177	25.8	7.4	0.0	76	2.9	56	9
Beverages									
Beer	12 fluid ounces	146	1.1	0.0	13.1	0	0.1	18	18
Beer, light	12 fluid ounces	99	0.7	0.0	4.6	0	0.1	11	18
Champagne	6 fluid ounces	134	0.5	0.0	2.1	0	0.9	7	5
Coffee, black	1 cup	5	0.2	0.0	0.9	0	1.0	5	5
Coffee liqueur	1 fluid ounce	99	0.0	0.1	13.9	0	0.0	2	0
Cognac brandy	1 fluid ounce	72	—	—	—	0	—	—	—

Tr = Trace amount of nutrient   Dash (-) indicates insufficient data available

FOOD	APPROXIMATE MEASURE	FOOD ENERGY (CALORIES)	PROTEIN (GRAMS)	FAT (GRAMS)	CARBOHYDRATES (GRAMS)	CHOLESTEROL (MILLIGRAMS)	IRON (MILLIGRAMS)	SODIUM (MILLIGRAMS)	CALCIUM (MILLIGRAMS)
Beverages *(continued)*									
Crème de menthe liqueur	1 tablespoon	62	0.0	0.1	7.0	0	0.0	1	0
Gin, rum, vodka, or whiskey, 80 proof	1 fluid ounce	68	0.0	0.0	0.0	0	0.0	0.0	0
Sherry, sweet	1 fluid ounce	39	0.1	0.0	2.0	0	0.1	4	2
Vermouth, dry	1 fluid ounce	33	0.0	0.0	1.6	0	0.1	5	2
Vermouth, sweet	1 fluid ounce	43	0.0	0.0	4.5	0	0.1	8	2
Wine, red	6 fluid ounces	116	0.3	0.0	0.4	0	1.4	16	12
Wine, white, dry	6 fluid ounces	113	0.2	0.0	1.1	0	0.9	7.5	15
Beets									
Canned, regular pack	½ cup	30	0.8	0.1	7.2	—	0.5	209	15
Fresh, diced, cooked	½ cup	26	0.9	0.4	5.7	0	0.5	42	9
Blackberries, fresh	½ cup	37	0.5	0.3	9.2	0	0.4	0	23
Blueberries, fresh	½ cup	41	0.5	0.3	10.2	0	0.1	4	4
Bouillon, dry									
Beef-flavored cubes	1 cube	3	0.1	0.0	0.2	—	—	400	—
Beef-flavored granules	1 teaspoon	5	0.0	0.5	0.0	—	—	461	—
Chicken-flavored cubes	1 cube	7	0.2	0.1	0.5	—	—	800	—
Chicken-flavored granules	1 teaspoon	5	0.2	0.5	0.2	—	0.0	381	—
Bran									
Oat	½ cup	168	8.4	4.2	23.8	0	2.0	4	28
Wheat, raw	½ cup	59	4.0	1.3	7.5	0	4.4	3	36
Bread									
Bagel, plain	1 each	161	5.9	1.5	30.5	—	1.4	196	23
Bun, hamburger or hot dog	1 each	136	3.2	3.4	22.4	13	0.8	112	19
English muffin	1 each	174	5.3	1.4	34.6	0	1.9	334	107
French/vienna	1 slice	73	2.3	0.5	13.9	1	0.6	145	11
Pita, whole wheat	1 medium	122	2.4	0.9	23.5	0	1.4	—	39
Pumpernickel	1 slice	76	2.8	0.4	16.4	0	0.7	176	26
Raisin	1 slice	66	1.6	0.7	13.4	1	0.3	91	18
Rye	1 slice	61	2.3	0.3	13.0	0	0.4	139	19
White	1 slice	67	2.2	0.8	12.6	1	0.6	127	18
Whole wheat	1 slice	61	2.6	0.8	11.9	1	0.6	132	25
Breadcrumbs, fine, dry	½ cup	196	6.3	2.2	36.7	2	1.7	368	61
Broccoli, fresh, chopped, cooked	½ cup	26	2.8	0.1	4.9	0	0.6	22	47
Broth, beef, homemade	1 cup	22	0.5	0.0	1.9	0	0.0	7	0
Brussel sprouts, fresh, cooked	½ cup	30	2.0	0.4	6.8	0	0.9	16	28
Bulgur, uncooked	½ cup	301	9.5	1.3	64.3	0	3.1	3	25
Butter									
Regular	1 tablespoon	102	0.1	11.5	0.0	31	0.0	117	3
Unsalted	1 tablespoon	102	0.1	11.5	0.0	31	0.0	2	3
Whipped	1 tablespoon	68	0.1	7.7	0.0	21	0.0	78	2
Cabbage									
Bok choy	1 cup	9	1.0	0.1	1.5	0	0.6	45	73
Common varieties, raw, shredded	½ cup	8	0.4	0.1	1.9	0	0.2	6	16
Cake, without frosting									
Angel food	1 (2-ounce) slice	166	3.3	0.1	38.1	—	0.1	56	4
Pound	1 (1-ounce) slice	305	3.6	17.5	33.7	134	0.5	245	27
Sponge, cut into 12 slices	1 piece	183	3.6	5.0	30.8	221	0.8	99	44
Yellow, cut into 12 slices	1 piece	227	3.6	9.0	33.0	80	0.5	404	30
Candy									
Fudge, chocolate	1 ounce	113	0.8	3.4	21.3	0	0.3	54	22
Gumdrops	1 ounce	98	0.0	0.2	24.8	0	0.1	10	2
Hard	1 each	27	0.0	0.0	6.8	0	0.1	2	1
Jelly beans	1 ounce	104	0.0	0.1	26.4	0	0.3	3	3
Marshmallows, large	1 each	26	0.2	0.0	6.4	0	0.1	3	1
Milk chocolate	1 ounce	149	2.0	7.9	16.9	6	—	23	60

FOOD	APPROXIMATE MEASURE	FOOD ENERGY (CALORIES)	PROTEIN (GRAMS)	FAT (GRAMS)	CARBOHYDRATES (GRAMS)	CHOLESTEROL (MILLIGRAMS)	IRON (MILLIGRAMS)	SODIUM (MILLIGRAMS)	CALCIUM (MILLIGRAMS)
Cantaloupe, raw, diced	½ cup	28	0.7	0.2	6.7	0	0.2	7	9
Capers	1 tablespoon	4	0.4	0.0	0.6	0	—	670	—
Carrot									
Raw	1 medium	30	0.7	0.1	7.1	0	0.3	25	19
Cooked, sliced	½ cup	35	0.8	0.1	8.1	0	0.5	51	24
Catsup									
Regular	1 tablespoon	18	0.3	0.1	4.3	0	0.1	178	4
No-salt-added	1 tablespoon	15	0.0	0.0	4.0	—	—	6	—
Cauliflower									
Raw, flowerets	½ cup	10	0.8	0.1	2.1	0	0.2	6	12
Cooked, flowerets	½ cup	15	1.2	0.1	2.8	0	0.2	4	17
Caviar	1 tablespoon	54	5.8	2.8	0.8	65	2.0	374	47
Celery									
Raw, diced	½ cup	10	0.4	0.1	2.2	0	0.3	53	23
Cooked	½ cup	11	0.4	0.1	2.6	0	0.1	48	27
Cereal									
Bran, whole	½ cup	106	6.1	0.7	31.6	0	6.7	480	34
Bran flakes	½ cup	64	2.5	0.4	15.3	0	5.6	182	10
Corn flakes	½ cup	44	0.9	0.0	9.8	0	0.7	140	0
Granola	½ cup	251	5.7	9.8	37.7	0	1.9	116	36
Crispy rice	½ cup	55	0.9	0.1	12.4	0	0.3	103	3
Whole grain wheat flakes	½ cup	79	1.9	0.2	18.6	0	0.6	150	6
Puffed wheat	½ cup	28	1.6	0.1	5.5	—	0.1	2	32
Raisin bran	½ cup	77	2.7	0.5	18.6	0	3.0	179	9
Shredded wheat miniatures	½ cup	76	2.3	0.5	17.0	0	0.9	2	8
Toasted oat cereal	½ cup	44	1.7	0.7	7.8	0	1.8	123	19
Cheese									
American, processed, skim	1 ounce	69	6.0	5.0	1.0	10	—	—	149
American, processed	1 ounce	106	6.3	8.9	0.5	27	0.1	405	175
Blue	1 ounce	100	6.0	8.1	0.7	21	0.1	395	150
Brie	1 ounce	95	5.9	7.8	0.1	28	0.1	178	52
Cheddar	1 ounce	114	7.0	9.4	0.3	30	0.2	176	204
Cheddar, 40% less fat	1 ounce	71	5.0	4.1	6.0	—	0.1	—	192
Cottage, dry curd, no-salt-added	½ cup	62	12.5	0.3	1.3	5	0.2	9	23
Cottage, lowfat, (1% milk-fat)	½ cup	81	14.0	1.1	3.1	5	0.2	459	69
Cottage, lowfat, (2% milk-fat)	½ cup	102	15.5	2.2	4.1	9	0.2	459	77
Cottage, (4% milk-fat)	½ cup	108	13.1	4.7	2.8	16	0.1	425	63
Cream, light	1 ounce	60	3.0	5.0	2.0	—	—	159	40
Farmers	1 ounce	40	4.0	3.0	1.0	—	—	—	30
Feta	1 ounce	75	4.0	6.0	1.2	25	0.2	316	139
Fontina	1 ounce	110	7.3	8.8	0.4	33	0.1	—	156
Gruyère	1 ounce	117	8.4	9.2	0.1	31	—	95	287
Monterey Jack	1 ounce	64	9.9	3.0	1.0	9	—	64	298
Mozzarella, part-skim	1 ounce	72	6.9	4.5	0.8	16	0.1	132	183
Mozzarella, whole milk	1 ounce	80	5.5	6.1	0.6	22	0.0	106	147
Muenster	1 ounce	104	6.6	8.5	0.3	27	0.1	178	203
Neufchâtel	1 ounce	74	2.8	6.6	0.8	22	0.1	113	21
Parmesan, grated	1 ounce	111	10.1	7.3	0.9	19	0.2	454	336
Provolone	1 ounce	100	7.2	7.5	0.6	20	0.1	248	214
Ricotta, part-skim	1 ounce	39	3.2	2.2	1.5	9	0.1	35	77
Romano, grated	1 ounce	110	9.0	7.6	1.0	29	—	340	302
Swiss	1 ounce	107	8.1	7.8	1.0	26	0.0	74	272
Cherries									
Fresh, sweet	½ cup	52	0.9	0.7	12.0	0	0.3	0	11
Sour, sweetened	½ cup	127	1.0	1.1	33.1	0	1.7	10	14
Sour, unsweetened	½ cup	36	0.7	0.3	8.5	0	0.4	1	10
Chicken, skinned, boned and roasted									
White meat	3 ounces	140	26.4	3.0	0.0	72	0.9	63	13

Tr = Trace amount of nutrient   Dash (-) indicates insufficient data available

FOOD	APPROXIMATE MEASURE	FOOD ENERGY (CALORIES)	PROTEIN (GRAMS)	FAT (GRAMS)	CARBOHYDRATES (GRAMS)	CHOLESTEROL (MILLIGRAMS)	IRON (MILLIGRAMS)	SODIUM (MILLIGRAMS)	CALCIUM (MILLIGRAMS)
Chicken, *(continued)*									
Dark meat	3 ounces	174	23.3	8.3	0.0	79	1.1	79	13
Liver	3 ounces	134	20.7	4.6	0.7	537	7.2	43	12
Chives, raw, chopped	1 tablespoon	1	0.1	0.0	0.1	0	0.0	0	2
Chocolate									
Semisweet	1 ounce	144	1.2	10.1	16.2	0	0.7	1	9
Sweet	1 ounce	150	1.2	9.9	16.4	0	0.4	9	27
Syrup, fudge	1 tablespoon	65	0.9	2.5	9.6	—	0.2	22	19
Unsweetened, baking	1 ounce	141	3.1	14.7	8.5	0	2.0	1	23
Chutney	1 tablespoon	41	0.2	0.0	10.5	—	0.2	34	5
Cilantro, fresh, minced	1 tablespoon	1	0.1	0.0	0.3	0	0.2	1	5
Clams									
Canned, drained	½ cup	118	20.4	1.6	4.1	54	22.4	90	74
Raw	½ cup	92	15.8	1.2	3.2	42	17.3	69	57
Cocoa powder, unsweetened	1 tablespoon	24	1.6	0.7	2.6	—	0.9	0	8
Coconut									
Fresh, grated	1 cup	526	5.5	51.4	18.8	0	2.6	30	21
Dried, unsweetened, shredded	1 cup	526	5.5	51.4	18.8	0	2.6	30	21
Dried, sweetened, shredded	1 cup	463	2.7	32.8	44.0	0	1.8	242	14
Cookies									
Chocolate	1 each	72	1.0	3.4	9.4	13	0.4	61	18
Chocolate chip, homemade	1 each	69	0.9	4.6	6.8	7	0.3	30	7
Oatmeal, plain	1 each	57	0.9	2.7	7.2	9	0.3	46	13
Sandwich, with creme	1 each	40	0.3	1.7	6.0	—	0.2	41	2
Vanilla wafers	1 each	19	0.2	0.9	2.5	—	0.1	16	2
Corn									
Cream-style, regular pack	½ cup	92	2.2	0.5	23.2	0	0.5	365	4
Fresh, kernels, cooked	½ cup	89	2.6	1.0	20.6	0	0.5	14	2
Cornmeal									
Enriched, dry	1 cup	453	10.9	1.7	95.2	0	4.0	1	8
Self rising	1 cup	465	11.4	4.3	95.8	0	2.3	1849	402
Cornstarch	1 tablespoon	29	0.0	0.0	7.0	0	0.0	0	0
Couscous, cooked	½ cup	98	3.5	0.0	20.0		0.5	—	10
Crab									
Blue, cooked	3 ounces	87	17.2	1.5	0.0	85	0.8	237	88
Imitation	3 ounces	75	10.2	0.0	8.4	—	0.6	—	255
Crackers									
Animal	1 each	14	0.2	0.4	2.3	—	—	11	—
Butter	1 each	17	0.0	1.0	2.0	—	0.1	32	4
Graham, plain	1 each	54	1.1	1.3	10.3	0	0.2	94	6
Melba rounds, plain	1 each	11	0.4	0.2	2.0	—	0.1	26	—
Saltine	1 each	13	0.3	0.3	2.0	—	0.1	43	5
Whole wheat	1 each	27	0.5	1.0	3.5	—	0.1	50	0
Cranberry									
Fresh, whole	½ cup	23	0.2	0.1	6.0	0	0.1	0	3
Juice cocktail, reduced-calorie	½ cup	24	0.0	0.0	5.9	—	2.8	4	7
Juice cocktail, regular	½ cup	75	0.0	0.1	19.2	0	0.2	5	4
Sauce, sweetened	¼ cup	105	0.1	0.1	26.9	0	0.1	20	3
Cream									
Half-and-half	1 tablespoon	20	0.5	1.7	0.7	6	0.0	6	16
Sour	1 tablespoon	31	0.5	0.3	0.6	6	0.0	8	17
Sour, reduced-calorie	1 tablespoon	20	0.4	1.8	0.6	6	0.0	6	16
Creamer, non-dairy	1 teaspoon	11	0.1	0.7	1.1	0	0.0	4	16
Croutons, seasoned	1 ounce	139	3.0	5.0	18.9	—	0.3	—	20
Cucumbers, raw, whole	1 medium	32	1.3	0.3	7.1	0	0.7	5	34
Currants	1 tablespoon	25	0.3	0.2	6.1	—	0.3	3	8
Dates, pitted, unsweetened	5 each	114	0.8	0.2	30.5	0	0.5	1	13

FOOD	APPROXIMATE MEASURE	FOOD ENERGY (CALORIES)	PROTEIN (GRAMS)	FAT (GRAMS)	CARBOHYDRATES (GRAMS)	CHOLESTEROL (MILLIGRAMS)	IRON (MILLIGRAMS)	SODIUM (MILLIGRAMS)	CALCIUM (MILLIGRAMS)
Doughnut									
Cake type	1 each	156	1.8	7.4	20.6	24	0.5	200	16
Plain, yeast	1 each	166	2.5	10.7	15.1	10	0.6	94	15
Egg									
White	1 each	16	3.2	0.0	0.4	0	0.0	49	4
Whole	1 each	79	6.2	5.6	0.6	274	1.0	69	28
Yolk	1 each	63	2.8	5.6	0.0	272	0.9	8	26
Substitute	¼ cup	30	6.0	0.0	1.0	0	1.1	90	20
Eggplant, cooked without salt	½ cup	13	0.4	0.1	3.2	0	0.2	1	3
Extracts									
Almond	1 teaspoon	10	—	—	—	—	—	—	—
Coconut	1 teaspoon	6	—	—	—	—	—	—	—
Peppermint	1 teaspoon	22	—	—	—	—	—	—	—
Vanilla	1 teaspoon	12	—	—	—	—	—	—	—
Fennel, leaves, raw	½ cup	13	1.2	0.2	2.3	0	1.2	4	45
Figs									
Fresh	1 medium	37	0.4	0.2	9.9	0	0.2	1	18
Dried	1 each	48	0.6	0.2	12.2	0	0.4	2	27
Fish, cooked									
Catfish, farm-raised	3 ounces	195	15.4	11.3	6.8	69	1.2	238	37
Cod	3 ounces	89	19.4	0.7	0.0	47	0.4	66	12
Flounder	3 ounces	100	20.5	1.3	0.0	58	0.3	89	15
Grouper	3 ounces	100	21.1	1.1	0.0	40	1.0	45	18
Haddock	3 ounces	95	20.6	0.8	0.0	63	1.1	74	36
Halibut	3 ounces	119	22.7	2.5	0.0	35	0.9	59	51
Mackerel	3 ounces	134	20.1	5.4	0.0	62	0.6	56	11
Perch	3 ounces	100	21.1	1.0	0.0	98	1.0	67	87
Pompano	3 ounces	179	20.1	10.3	0.0	54	0.6	65	37
Snapper	3 ounces	109	22.4	1.5	0.0	40	0.2	48	34
Salmon	3 ounces	184	23.2	9.3	0.0	74	0.5	56	6
Sole	3 ounces	100	20.5	1.3	0.0	58	0.3	89	15
Swordfish	3 ounces	132	21.6	4.4	0.0	43	0.9	98	5
Trout	3 ounces	128	22.4	3.7	0.0	62	2.1	29	73
Tuna, canned in water	6½ ounces	251	49.1	4.5	0.0	77	1.1	722	—
Tuna, canned in oil	6½ ounces	343	48.9	14.9	0.0	57	1.2	730	7
Flour									
All-purpose, unsifted	1 cup	499	14.4	1.4	104.1	0	4.0	3	22
Bread, sifted	1 cup	420	13.6	1.3	85.8	0	3.3	2	18
Buckwheat, light, unsifted	1 cup	340	6.3	1.2	77.9	0	1.0	2	11
Cake, sifted	1 cup	349	7.2	0.8	76.2	0	0.5	2	16
Rye, light, sifted	1 cup	314	8.2	0.9	68.6	0	1.0	1	19
Whole wheat, unsifted	1 cup	400	16.0	2.4	85.2	0	3.8	4	49
Frankfurter									
All-meat	1 each	130	5.8	11.2	1.1	29	0.8	484	3
Turkey franks	1 each	63	3.8	5.3	0.1	—	0.3	299	33
Fruit bits, dried	1 ounce	93	1.3	0.0	20.0	0	0.5	24	—
Fruit cocktail, canned, packed in juice	½ cup	57	0.6	0.0	14.6	0	0.2	5	10
Garlic, raw	1 clove	4	0.2	0.0	1.0	0	0.1	1	5
Gelatin									
Flavored, prepared with water	½ cup	80	2.0	—	18.9	—	—	90	—
Unflavored	1 teaspoon	10	2.6	0.0	0.0	—	—	3	—
Grape juice	½ cup	77	0.7	0.1	18.9	0	0.3	4	11

Tr = Trace amount of nutrient   Dash (-) indicates insufficient data available

FOOD	APPROXIMATE MEASURE	FOOD ENERGY (CALORIES)	PROTEIN (GRAMS)	FAT (GRAMS)	CARBOHYDRATES (GRAMS)	CHOLESTEROL (MILLIGRAMS)	IRON (MILLIGRAMS)	SODIUM (MILLIGRAMS)	CALCIUM (MILLIGRAMS)
Grapefruit									
Juice, unsweetened	½ cup	47	0.6	0.1	11.1	0	2.5	1	9
Raw	1 medium	77	1.5	0.2	19.3	0	0.2	0	29
Grapes, green, seedless	1 cup	114	1.1	0.9	28.4	0	0.4	3	18
Grits, cooked	½ cup	73	1.6	0.2	15.7	0	0.8	0	0
Ham									
Cured, roasted, extra-lean	3 ounces	123	17.8	4.7	1.3	45	1.3	1023	7
Honey	1 tablespoon	64	0.1	0.0	17.5	0	0.1	1	1
Honeydew, raw, diced	1 cup	59	0.8	0.2	15.6	0	0.1	17	10
Horseradish, prepared	1 tablespoon	6	0.2	0.0	1.4	0	0.1	14	9
Ice cream, vanilla, regular	½ cup	134	2.3	7.2	15.9	30	0.0	58	88
Ice milk, vanilla	½ cup	92	2.6	2.8	14.5	9	0.1	52	88
Jams and Jellies									
Regular	1 tablespoon	51	0.0	0.0	13.2	0	0.3	3	4
Reduced-calorie	1 tablespoon	29	0.1	0.0	7.4	0	0.0	16	1
Jicama	1 cup	49	1.6	0.2	10.5	0	0.7	7	18
Kiwifruit	1 each	44	1.0	0.5	8.9	0	0.4	0	20
Lamb									
Leg, roasted	3 ounces	158	24.4	6.0	0.0	85	1.9	60	11
Loin, broiled	3 ounces	156	24.0	6.0	0.0	85	1.7	60	9
Chop	3 ounces	160	24.0	6.4	0.0	85	1.7	60	10
Ground, cooked	3 ounces	160	24.0	6.4	0.0	85	1.7	60	10
Lard	1 tablespoon	116	0.0	12.8	0.0	12	0.0	0	0
Leeks, bulb, raw	½ cup	32	0.8	0.2	7.3	0	1.0	10	31
Lemon									
Fresh	1 each	16	0.6	0.2	5.2	0	0.3	1	15
Juice	1 tablespoon	4	0.1	0.0	1.3	0	0.0	0	1
Lemonade, sweetened	1 cup	99	0.2	0.0	26.0	0	0.4	7	7
Lentils, cooked	½ cup	115	8.9	0.4	19.9	0	3.3	2	19
Lettuce									
Boston or Bibb, shredded	1 cup	7	0.7	0.1	1.3	0	0.2	3	—
Endive or escarole	1 cup	8	0.6	0.1	1.7	0	0.4	11	26
Iceberg, chopped	1 cup	7	0.5	0.1	1.1	0	0.3	5	10
Romaine, chopped	1 cup	9	0.9	0.1	1.3	0	0.6	4	20
Lime									
Fresh	1 each	20	0.4	0.1	6.8	0	0.4	1	21
Juice	1 tablespoon	4	0.1	0.0	1.4	0	0.0	0	1
Lobster, cooked, meat only	3 ounces	83	17.4	0.5	1.1	61	0.3	323	52
Luncheon meats									
Bologna	1 slice	74	2.5	6.9	0.4	13	0.2	241	2
Deviled ham	1 ounce	78	4.3	6.7	0.0	—	0.3	—	1
Salami	1 ounce	74	4.0	6.2	0.6	—	0.4	393	—
Turkey ham	1 ounce	35	5.6	1.4	0.0	16	0.8	196	3
Turkey pastrami	1 ounce	34	5.3	1.4	0.0	16	0.5	218	3
Lychees, raw	1 each	6	0.1	0.0	1.6	0	0.0	0	0
Mango, raw	½ cup	54	0.4	0.2	14.0	0	0.1	2	8

FOOD	APPROXIMATE MEASURE	FOOD ENERGY (CALORIES)	PROTEIN (GRAMS)	FAT (GRAMS)	CARBOHYDRATES (GRAMS)	CHOLESTEROL (MILLIGRAMS)	IRON (MILLIGRAMS)	SODIUM (MILLIGRAMS)	CALCIUM (MILLIGRAMS)
Margarine									
Regular	1 tablespoon	101	0.1	11.4	0.1	0	0.0	133	4
Reduced-calorie, stick	1 tablespoon	60	0.0	7.3	0.0	0	0.0	110	0
Salt-free	1 tablespoon	101	0.1	11.3	0.1	0	0.0	0	2
Mayonnaise									
Regular	1 tablespoon	99	0.2	10.9	0.4	8	0.1	78	2
Reduced-calorie	1 tablespoon	44	0.1	4.6	0.7	6	0.0	88	1
Milk									
Buttermilk, nonfat	1 cup	90	9.0	1.0	12.0	—	—	255	285
Chocolate, low-fat	1 cup	158	8.1	2.5	26.1	8	0.6	153	288
Condensed, sweetened	1 cup	982	24.2	26.3	166.5	104	0.5	389	869
Evaporated, skim, canned	1 cup	200	19.3	0.5	29.1	10	0.7	294	742
Low-fat, 2% fat	1 cup	122	8.1	4.7	11.7	20	0.1	122	298
Low-fat, 1% fat	1 cup	102	8.0	2.5	11.6	10	0.1	122	300
Nonfat dry	⅓ cup	145	14.5	0.3	20.8	8	0.1	214	503
Skim	1 cup	86	8.3	0.4	11.9	5	0.1	127	301
Whole	1 cup	156	8.0	8.9	11.3	34	0.1	120	290
Molasses, cane, light	1 tablespoon	52	0.0	0.0	13.3	0	0.9	3	34
Mushrooms									
Canned	¼ cup	13	0.1	0.1	2.5	0	0.0	1	1
Fresh	½ cup	9	0.7	0.1	1.6	0	0.4	1	2
Shitake, dried	1 each	14	0.3	0.0	2.6	0	0.1	0	0
Mussels, blue, cooked	3 ounces	146	20.2	3.8	6.3	48	5.7	314	28
Mustard									
Dijon	1 tablespoon	18	0.0	1.0	1.0	0	—	446	—
Prepared, yellow	1 tablespoon	12	0.7	0.7	1.0	0	0.3	196	13
Nectarine, fresh	1 each	67	1.3	0.6	16.1	0	0.2	0	7
Nuts									
Almonds, chopped	1 tablespoon	48	1.6	4.2	1.7	0	0.3	1	22
Hazelnuts, chopped	1 tablespoon	45	0.9	4.5	1.1	0	0.2	0	14
Peanuts, roasted, unsalted	1 tablespoon	53	2.4	4.5	1.7	0	0.2	1	8
Pecans, chopped	1 tablespoon	50	0.6	5.0	1.4	0	0.2	0	3
Pistachio nuts	1 tablespoon	46	1.6	3.9	2.0	0	0.5	0	11
Walnuts, black	1 tablespoon	47	1.9	4.4	0.9	0	0.2	0	5
Oats									
Cooked	1 cup	145	5.8	2.3	25.3	0	1.6	374	19
Rolled, dry	½ cup	154	6.4	2.5	26.8	0	1.7	—	21
Oil									
Vegetable	1 tablespoon	121	0.0	13.6	0.0	0	0.0	0	0
Olive	1 tablespoon	119	0.0	13.5	0.0	0	0.0	0	0
Sesame	1 teaspoon	40	0.0	4.5	0.0	0	0.0	0	0
Okra, cooked	½ cup	26	1.5	0.1	5.8	0	0.3	4	50
Olives									
Black	1 medium	5	0.0	0.4	0.3	0	0.1	35	4
Green, stuffed	½ cup	54	0.7	4.6	3.8	0	2.2	606	63
Onions									
Green	1 tablespoon	2	0.1	0.0	0.3	0	0.1	0	4
Cooked, yellow or white	½ cup	15	0.4	0.1	3.3	0	0.1	4	14
Raw, chopped	½ cup	29	1.0	0.2	6.2	0	0.3	2	21
Orange									
Fresh	1 medium	62	1.2	0.2	15.4	0	0.1	0	52
Juice	½ cup	56	0.8	0.1	13.4	0	0.1	1	11
Mandarin, canned, packed in juice	½ cup	46	0.7	0.0	12.0	0	0.4	6	14
Oysters, raw	1 cup	171	17.5	6.1	9.7	136	16.6	278	112

Tr = Trace amount of nutrient   Dash (-) indicates insufficient data available

FOOD	APPROXIMATE MEASURE	FOOD ENERGY (CALORIES)	PROTEIN (GRAMS)	FAT (GRAMS)	CARBOHYDRATES (GRAMS)	CHOLESTEROL (MILLIGRAMS)	IRON (MILLIGRAMS)	SODIUM (MILLIGRAMS)	CALCIUM (MILLIGRAMS)
Papayas, fresh, cubed	½ cup	27	0.4	0.1	6.9	0	0.1	2	17
Parsley, raw	1 tablespoon	1	0.1	0.0	0.3	0	0.2	1	5
Parsnip, cooked, diced	½ cup	63	1.0	0.2	15.1	0	0.4	8	29
Pasta, cooked									
Macaroni	½ cup	78	2.4	0.3	16.1	0	0.6	1	6
Medium egg noodles	½ cup	100	3.2	1.2	18.6	25	0.6	2	8
Lasagna noodles	½ cup	100	3.2	1.2	18.6	25	0.6	2	8
Rice noodles	½ cup	138	3.1	1.3	28.6	0	2.2	—	40
Spinach noodles	½ cup	100	3.8	1.0	18.9	0	1.8	22	46
Spaghetti	½ cup	96	3.2	0.3	19.6	0	0.7	1	7
Whole wheat pasta	½ cup	100	3.7	1.4	19.8	0	1.0	1	12
Peaches									
Fresh	1 medium	54	0.9	0.1	13.9	0	0.1	0	6
Canned, packed in juice	½ cup	56	0.8	0.0	14.7	0	0.3	5	8
Peanut butter									
Regular	1 tablespoon	95	4.6	8.3	2.6	0	0.3	79	5
No-salt-added	1 tablespoon	95	4.6	8.3	2.6	0	0.3	3	5
Pear									
Fresh	1 medium	97	0.6	0.7	24.9	0	0.4	0	18
Canned, packed in juice	½ cup	62	0.4	0.1	16.0	0	0.3	5	11
Juice	½ cup	59	0.0	0.0	14.2	—	—	6	—
Peas									
Black-eyed, cooked	½ cup	90	6.7	0.7	15.0	0	1.2	3	23
English, cooked	½ cup	62	4.1	0.2	11.4	0	1.2	70	19
Split, cooked	½ cup	116	8.2	0.4	20.7	0	1.3	2	14
Peppers									
Sweet, raw, green, red or yellow	1 medium	23	0.7	0.5	4.8	0	1.1	3	5
Sweet, chopped	½ cup	19	0.6	0.3	4.0	0	0.9	2	4
Jalapeno, green	1 each	4	0.2	0.0	0.9	0	0.1	1	2
Picante sauce	1 tablespoon	5	0.2	0.0	0.9	—	0.1	108	2
Pickle									
Dill, sliced	¼ cup	4	0.2	0.1	0.9	0	0.4	553	10
Relish, chopped, sour	1 tablespoon	3	0.1	0.1	0.4	0	0.2	207	4
Sweet, sliced	¼ cup	57	0.2	0.2	14.1	0	0.5	276	5
Pimiento, diced	1 tablespoon	5	0.2	0.1	1.1	0	0.3	5	1
Pie, baked, 9-inch diameter, cut into 8 slices									
Apple, fresh	1 slice	409	3.3	15.3	67.7	12	0.8	229	37
Chocolate meringue	1 slice	354	6.8	13.4	53.8	109	1.2	307	130
Egg custard	1 slice	248	7.3	11.6	28.6	149	0.9	229	129
Pecan	1 slice	478	5.8	20.3	71.1	141	2.4	324	51
Pumpkin	1 slice	181	4.0	6.8	27.0	61	1.1	210	78
Pineapple									
Fresh, diced	½ cup	38	0.3	0.3	9.6	0	0.3	1	5
Canned, packed in light syrup	½ cup	82	0.4	0.1	21.3	—	0.4	1	15
Canned, packed in juice	½ cup	81	0.6	0.1	21.0	—	0.6	1	22
Juice, unsweetened	½ cup	70	0.4	0.1	17.2	0	0.3	1	21
Plum, fresh	1 medium	35	0.5	0.4	8.3	0	0.1	0	3
Popcorn, hot-air popped	1 cup	23	0.8	0.3	4.6	0	0.2	0	1
Pork, cooked									
Roast	3 ounces	208	21.6	12.7	0.0	82	1.3	65	7
Tenderloin	3 ounces	141	24.5	4.1	0.0	79	1.3	57	8
Chop, center-loin	3 ounces	204	24.2	11.1	0.0	77	0.9	59	5
Spareribs	3 ounces	338	24.7	25.7	0.0	103	1.5	79	40
Sausage	1 link	44	2.4	3.7	0.1	10	0.1	155	4
Sausage patty	1 ounce	105	5.6	8.8	0.3	24	0.3	367	9
Potatoes									
Baked, with skin	1 each	218	4.4	0.2	50.4	0	2.7	16	20
Boiled, diced	½ cup	67	1.3	0.1	15.6	0	0.2	4	6

FOOD	APPROXIMATE MEASURE	FOOD ENERGY (CALORIES)	PROTEIN (GRAMS)	FAT (GRAMS)	CARBOHYDRATES (GRAMS)	CHOLESTEROL (MILLIGRAMS)	IRON (MILLIGRAMS)	SODIUM (MILLIGRAMS)	CALCIUM (MILLIGRAMS)
Potatoes *(continued)*									
Fried	½ cup	228	3.4	12.0	27.6	0	0.9	190	13
Potato chips									
Regular	10 each	105	1.3	7.1	10.4	0	0.2	94	5
No-salt-added	10 each	105	1.3	7.1	10.4	0	0.2	2	5
Pretzel sticks	10 each	106	2.1	0.0	23.3	—	1.4	772	9
Prunes									
Dried, pitted	5 large	127	1.1	1.4	30.9	—	1.1	23	21
Juice	½ cup	91	0.8	0.0	22.3	0	1.5	5	15
Pumpkin, canned	½ cup	42	1.3	0.3	9.9	0	1.7	6	32
Radish, fresh, sliced	½ cup	10	0.3	0.3	2.1	0	0.2	14	12
Raisins	1 tablespoon	27	0.3	0.0	7.2	0	0.2	1	4
Raspberries									
Black, fresh	½ cup	33	0.6	0.4	7.7	0	0.4	0	15
Red, fresh	½ cup	30	0.6	0.3	7.1	0	0.3	0	14
Rhubarb									
Diced, raw	½ cup	13	0.5	0.1	2.8	0	0.1	2	52
Cooked, with sugar	½ cup	157	0.5	0.1	42.1	0	0.3	1	196
Rice cake, plain	1 each	36	0.7	0.2	7.7	0	0.2	1	1
Rice, cooked without salt or fat									
Brown	½ cup	102	2.0	0.6	21.9	0	0.4	2	9
White, long-grain	½ cup	103	1.8	0.1	22.7	0	0.8	1	7
White, enriched	½ cup	93	1.7	0.1	20.3	0	0.7	313	17
Wild	½ cup	85	3.1	1.2	16.2	3	0.8	12	4
Roll									
Plain, brown-and-serve	1 each	84	2.2	1.9	14.1	2	0.5	144	13
Hard	1 each	156	4.9	1.6	29.8	2	1.1	313	24
Rutabaga, cooked, cubed	½ cup	29	0.9	0.2	6.6	0	0.4	15	36
Salad dressing									
Blue cheese	1 tablespoon	84	0.4	9.2	0.3	0	0.0	216	3
Blue cheese, low calorie	1 tablespoon	14	0.7	1.1	1.0	3	0.0	307	18
French	1 tablespoon	96	0.3	9.4	2.9	8	0.1	205	6
French, low calorie	1 tablespoon	22	0.0	0.9	3.5	1	0.1	128	2
Italian	1 tablespoon	84	0.1	9.1	0.6	0	0.0	172	1
Italian, no oil, low calorie	1 tablespoon	8	0.1	0.0	1.8	0	0.0	161	1
Thousand Island	1 tablespoon	59	0.1	5.6	2.4	—	0.1	109	2
Thousand Island, low calorie	1 tablespoon	24	0.1	1.6	2.5	2	0.1	153	2
Salt, iodized	1 teaspoon	0	0.0	0.0	0.0	0	0.0	2343	15
Scallops, raw, large	1 each	13	2.5	0.1	0.4	5	0.0	24	4
Sesame seed, dry, whole	1 teaspoon	17	0.5	1.5	0.7	0	0.4	0	29
Shallot, bulb, raw, chopped	½ cup	58	2.0	0.1	13.4	0	1.0	10	30
Sherbet, orange	½ cup	135	1.1	1.9	29.3	7	0.1	44	52
Shortening	1 tablespoon	94	0.0	10.6	0.0	—	—	—	—
Shrimp									
Fresh, peeled and deveined	½ pound	240	46.1	3.9	2.1	345	5.5	336	118
Canned, drained	½ cup	77	14.8	1.3	0.7	111	1.8	108	38
Soy sauce									
Regular	1 tablespoon	8	0.8	0.0	1.2	0	0.3	829	2
Low sodium	1 tablespoon	8	0.8	0.0	1.2	0	0.3	484	2
Soup, condensed, made with water									
Beef broth	1 cup	31	4.8	0.7	2.6	24	0.5	782	0
Chicken noodle	1 cup	75	4.0	2.4	9.3	7	0.7	1106	17
Cream of chicken	1 cup	117	2.9	7.3	9.0	10	0.6	986	34
Cream of mushroom	1 cup	129	2.3	9.0	9.0	2	0.5	1032	46

Tr = Trace amount of nutrient   Dash (-) indicates insufficient data available

FOOD	APPROXIMATE MEASURE	FOOD ENERGY (CALORIES)	PROTEIN (GRAMS)	FAT (GRAMS)	CARBOHYDRATES (GRAMS)	CHOLESTEROL (MILLIGRAMS)	IRON (MILLIGRAMS)	SODIUM (MILLIGRAMS)	CALCIUM (MILLIGRAMS)
Soup, condensed *(continued)*									
Tomato	1 cup	85	2.0	1.9	16.6	0	1.7	871	12
Vegetable, beef	1 cup	82	3.0	1.9	13.1	2	1.0	810	17
Spinach									
Fresh	1 cup	12	1.6	0.2	2.0	0	1.5	44	55
Cooked	½ cup	21	2.7	0.2	3.4	0	3.2	63	122
Canned, regular pack	½ cup	25	3.0	0.5	3.6	0	2.4	397	99
Squash, cooked									
Acorn	½ cup	57	1.1	0.1	14.9	0	1.0	4	45
Butternut	½ cup	41	0.8	0.1	10.7	0	0.6	4	42
Spaghetti	½ cup	22	0.5	0.2	5.0	0	0.3	14	16
Summer	½ cup	21	1.0	0.3	4.5	0	0.4	1	28
Strawberries, raw	1 cup	45	0.9	0.6	10.5	0	0.6	1	21
Sugar									
Granulated	1 tablespoon	48	0.0	0.0	12.4	0	0.0	0	0
Brown, packed	1 tablespoon	51	0.0	0.0	13.3	0	0.5	4	12
Powdered	1 tablespoon	29	0.0	0.0	7.5	0	0.0	0	0
Sunflower seeds	¼ cup	205	8.2	17.8	6.8	0	2.4	1	42
Sweet potatoes									
Whole, baked	½ cup	103	1.7	0.1	24.3	0	0.4	10	28
Mashed	½ cup	172	2.7	0.5	39.8	0	0.9	21	34
Syrup									
Chocolate-flavored	1 tablespoon	49	0.6	0.2	11.0	—	0.3	13	3
Maple, reduced-calorie	1 tablespoon	6	0.0	0.0	2.0	0	—	4	—
Pancake	1 tablespoon	50	0.0	0.0	12.8	0	0.2	2	20
Taco shell	1 each	52	0.7	2.8	5.9	—	0.4	62	—
Tangerine	1 each	38	0.5	0.1	9.6	0	0.1	1	12
Tapioca, dry	1 tablespoon	32	0.1	0.0	7.8	0	0.0	0	1
Tofu									
Firm	4 ounces	94	9.0	6.5	1.5	—	1.0	8	113
Soft	4 ounces	65	6.0	1.0	2.0	—	1.4	2	193
Tomato									
Fresh	1 each	27	1.2	0.3	6.1	0	0.6	11	10
Cooked	½ cup	30	1.3	0.3	6.8	0	0.7	13	10
Juice, regular	1 cup	41	1.8	0.1	10.3	0	1.4	881	22
Juice, no-salt-added	1 cup	41	1.8	0.1	10.3	0	1.4	24	22
Paste, regular	1 tablespoon	14	0.6	0.1	3.1	0	0.5	129	6
Paste, no-salt-added	1 tablespoon	14	0.6	0.1	3.1	0	0.5	11	6
Sauce, regular	½ cup	37	1.6	0.2	8.8	0	0.9	741	17
Sauce, no-salt-added	½ cup	42	1.2	0.0	9.7	—	—	27	—
Whole, canned, peeled	½ cup	25	1.2	0.2	5.1	—	0.6	155	38
Whole, canned, no-salt-added	½ cup	22	0.9	0.0	5.2	—	0.5	15	38
Tortilla									
Chips, plain	10 each	135	2.1	7.3	16.0	0	0.7	24	3
Corn, 6" diameter	1 each	67	2.1	1.1	12.8	0	1.4	53	42
Flour, 6" diameter	1 each	111	2.4	2.3	22.2	0	0.8	0	27
Turkey, skinned, boned, and roasted									
Dark meat	3 ounces	159	24.3	6.1	0.0	72	2.0	67	27
White meat	3 ounces	115	25.6	0.6	0.0	71	1.3	44	10
Turnip greens, cooked	½ cup	14	0.8	0.2	3.1	0	0.6	21	99
Turnips, cooked, cubed	½ cup	14	0.5	0.1	3.8	0	0.2	39	17
Veal									
Loin, broiled	3 ounces	199	22.4	11.3	0.0	86	2.7	68	9
Cutlet, pan-fried	3 ounces	155	28.2	3.9	0.0	111	0.8	69	—
Vegetable juice cocktail	1 cup	46	1.5	0.2	11.0	0	1.0	883	27

FOOD	APPROXIMATE MEASURE	FOOD ENERGY (CALORIES)	PROTEIN (GRAMS)	FAT (GRAMS)	CARBOHYDRATES (GRAMS)	CHOLESTEROL (MILLIGRAMS)	IRON (MILLIGRAMS)	SODIUM (MILLIGRAMS)	CALCIUM (MILLIGRAMS)
Venison									
Raw	4 ounces	143	23.8	4.5	0.0	74	1.7	102	11
Vinegar									
Distilled	1 tablespoon	2	0.0	0.0	0.8	0	0.0	0	0
Red wine	1 tablespoon	2	0.0	0.0	0.0	0	—	1	—
White wine	1 tablespoon	2	0.0	0.0	0.0	0	—	2	—
Tarragon	1 tablespoon	0	—	—	0.2	—	0.1	0	0
Water chestnuts, canned, sliced	½ cup	35	0.6	0.0	8.7	0	0.6	6	3
Watercress, fresh	½ cup	2	0.4	0.0	0.2	0	0.0	7	20
Watermelon, raw, diced	1 cup	51	1.0	0.7	11.5	0	0.3	3	13
Whipped topping, non-dairy, frozen	1 tablespoon	15	0.1	1.2	1.1	0	0.0	1	0
Worcestershire sauce									
Regular	1 tablespoon	12	0.3	0.0	2.7	0	0.0	147	15
Low sodium	1 tablespoon	12	0.0	0.0	3.0	0	—	57	—
Yeast, active, dry	1 package	20	2.6	0.1	2.7	0	1.1	4	3
Yogurt									
Plain, made from whole milk	1 cup	138	7.9	7.4	10.6	30	0.1	104	275
Plain, nonfat	1 cup	127	13.0	0.4	17.4	5	0.2	173	452
Plain, low-fat	1 cup	143	11.9	3.5	16.0	14	0.2	159	415
Fruit varieties, low-fat	1 cup	225	9.0	2.6	42.3	9	0.1	120	313
Frozen	½ cup	124	3.1	2.1	23.7	—	—	51	—
Zucchini									
Raw	½ cup	9	0.7	0.1	1.9	0	0.3	2	10
Cooked	½ cup	9	0.7	0.1	1.9	0	0.3	2	10

Sources of Data:

Adams, Catherine F. *NUTRITIVE VALUE OF AMERICAN FOODS.* U. S. Government Printing Office, 1975.

Computrition, Inc., Chatsworth, California. Primarily comprised of *The Composition of Foods: Raw, Processed, Prepared.* Handbooks - 8 series. United States Department of Agriculture, Human Nutrition Information Service, 1976-1986.

Recipe Index

Subject Index

Favorite Light Recipes

Record your favorite light recipes
below for quick and handy reference

Recipe	Source/Page	Calories